An Illustrated
Laboratory Text
in **ZOOLOGY**

AN Illustrated Laboratory

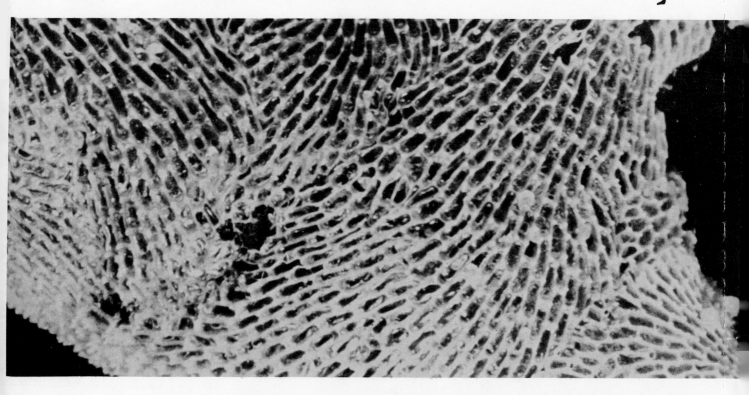

HOLT, RINEHART AND WINSTON, INC.

New York, Chicago, San Francisco, Toronto, London

Text IN
ZOOLOGY

ILLUSTRATIONS BY RICHARD A. BOOLOOTIAN
University of California, Los Angeles

TEXT BY DONALD HEYNEMAN
Hooper Foundation, University of California, San Francisco

Cover photograph and title page panel: BRYOZOA COLONIES ON KELP.
Courtesy of Servomechanisms, Inc. Research and Development Center, Goleta, California

To Our Children

Preface

To the Student

Students in Introductory Zoology often complain that the lecture and lab are two different courses. Actually, this is seldom true. The integration of seemingly diverse topics, however, such as the cell layers of an earthworm and the evolutionary importance of annelids, is often difficult. Nor is it easy to relate function, as discussed in lecture, with structure, as seen in the laboratory. An understanding of the pickled frog on your dissection tray is basic to an understanding of the interrelationships of all living things, and it is your responsibility to build a conceptual bridge between the two. To do so, you should realize that, however integrated, lectures and laboratory are *not* separate courses.

This book is a laboratory *text* designed to provide you with some of the tools necessary for building your bridge. To aid you in formulating the connection between the general and the specific, dissections and exercises are preceded by an outline and an introductory discussion of the animal group under study. When facts and details make sense to you, rather than being simply memory exercises, you will begin to appreciate the biological principles that underlie and govern the interrelated complex of all living things. This text will be successful if it can help you to go beyond the initial stage of memory to interest, and then finally to correlation and understanding.

Not all the material pertinent to a course in zoology can be laboratory oriented or presented in a book of this sort. Your general textbook will cover in greater detail topics that fall more logically into discussion areas. But wherever direct observation or experiment can yield information related to larger concepts or, as is often the case, basic to them, such relationships will be emphasized.

A total evaluation of an animal as it really exists in nature begins with observation in the natural habitat. These observations may then be tested and varied under the more controlled conditions of the research laboratory. Knowledge of the intricacies of animal organization and function develops in the physiological, biochemical, and biophysical laboratories. Finally, resynthesis of the whole complex is made through field observation—a return to the natural laboratory.

You will follow this sequence—from observation to study of structure and then of function, concluding with synthesis, renewed observation, and comparison.

Hazards abound in the process of learning biology. Wrong assumptions, wrong directions, and wrong conclusions plague biological science as they do all human endeavor, and we are far from a complete understanding of any level of biology. Let the student, therefore, recognize now something every biologist has learned, sometimes painfully: what we do *not* understand vastly exceeds what we do understand. Every breakthrough into a new realm of comprehension allows us to ask new questions that enormously expand the area of our newly recognized ignorance. Humility in science, as elsewhere, grows in direct proportion to knowledge. One mark of a keen student is the degree to which he recognizes what he does not know and what none of us knows.

This laboratory textbook is chiefly intended to introduce you to new information and to challenge, rather than dictate, your thinking. Never fall into the "It's in the book!" trap. If your dissection shows one location of a structure and the book states another, stick with your dissection. But then continue to expand your observations, studying other examples to see if your dissection is atypical or normal. Find out for yourself which is correct and, if possible, why the difference exists. Check other sources and retain a questioning, not a passive or accepting, attitude. It is true that keen minds working over many years have supplied the information recorded here. Yet some of their observations or conclusions may prove to be incomplete, misleading, or simply wrong. That is why every textbook must continually be revised and brought up to date. We would like you to think of this book, therefore, as a compilation of facts only as reliable as present knowledge permits. It is a guide to laboratory procedures and techniques designed to speed your efficiency and to simplify and clarify wherever possible the successive stops to zoological knowledge. It should help in your integration of this information into the larger framework of biological processes and relationships and serve as a challenge to those who want more information or wish to ask other, possibly more meaningful, questions.

To the Instructor

Courses in zoology can be taught in many ways. Most of them fall into one of two categories: a course of *principles*, dealing with a succession of key topics, and one with a *phylogenetic* orientation, dealing with the evolutionary succession of animal groups, the principles being developed and illustrated by different animal types. Both procedures have advocates and advantages. But both require a firm base in the animal itself, which necessitates a laboratory geared to a group-by-group approach, followed by consideration of major disciplines applicable to all living things, such as cell and tissue structure and function, embryology, and genetics. Such an approach is followed in this laboratory text. Evolution, the greatest synthesis in biology, is implicit and explicit throughout the book. Either lecture approach can be tied to the laboratory sequence employed here, or the sequence can be altered and followed selectively.

As with the animal groups it describes, the book itself has evolved and changed its scope and organization over the years. Its ideas and manner of presentation developed through the authors' teaching experience with the introductory course in zoology at UCLA. In turn, it reflects the teachings and writings of many others who have been influential in the authors' training. It would in fact be impossible to identify all of these sources, let alone acknowledge them with appropriate credit and thanks. Both for memorable teaching that brought into focus ideas on basic body types, and for critically reading the manuscript, however, thanks are expressed to Dr. Donald P. Abbott of the Hopkins Marine Station, Stanford University. Dr. George A. Bartholomew of the UCLA Zoology Department and Dr. Sears Crowell of Indiana University are also thanked for their detailed and constructive suggestions on the text. We particularly wish to express gratitude for the painstaking and complete evaluation and critical review given the text by Dr. Harry Hoogstraal of the United States Naval Medical Research Unit Number Three, Cairo, Egypt, U.A.R.

As noted above, this book has grown as its scope and purpose grew. It began in the mind of Richard Boolootian as a unique approach to a zoology laboratory guide: photographs, lots of them, to let the student see the real animal, not a diagrammatic abstraction. This was teamed with a text by Donald Heyneman to direct the student's work and ask questions. Finally, the text developed into a fuller review of the animal groups and of the biological concepts stemming from study of these groups. For both authors it has been a worthwhile and challenging labor of more than three years—an experience for which they are both grateful.

The authors share the responsibility for the ideas, methods, and organization of the book, encompassing as it does their joint teaching efforts and development of the course content. Specific responsibility for the original photography, all dissections and preparations photographed, and content of overlays lies with Richard Boolootian, while the text form, content, coverage, and arrangement is the work of Donald Heyneman.

R. A. B.
D. H.

Los Angeles, California
Cairo, Egypt
August, 1962

Contents

An Illustrated
Laboratory Text
in ZOOLOGY

Introduction

This book is designed to be an integral part of your introduction to structure, relationships, and way of life among animals. It, along with your zoology textbook, can supplement but never replace your examination of the animal itself, both living and preserved. In fact, nothing can ever substitute for the most important research tools you will ever have: your eyes and hands to see and sense the object, your mind to interpret and explain. Direct experience with the animal itself is the only real way to *know*. "Study nature, not books," said Louis Agassiz, as he threw a fish to his students at Harvard in the 1860's. That was the basic laboratory, and for the better students it was enough.

A laboratory textbook should help form a bridge between you and the animal, the two irreplaceable elements in a study of zoology. It is both a guide to the anatomy of representative animals and an aid to placing them in proper perspective within the wide range of animal types in nature. Organization of the text emphasizes these two phases of your work: first, *analysis*, study of structure by dissection and careful review of key parts of selected animals; second, *synthesis*, integration of this information into a larger scheme to help you appreciate relationships within the animal world. It must be strongly emphasized that if you approach the dissections in cookbook fashion, you will find them both useless and dull. The degree of your effort to relate specific organisms to their general group—that is, earthworm to the ANNELIDA, frog to the CHORDATA—will prove a measure of your appreciation of the purpose of this laboratory. Consciousness of this aim will increase your interest and pleasure in the work. We hardly need add that you will also do better in the course! Nothing focuses interest better than clear orientation, an understanding of what you are trying to do and why. Since clarification of animal structure and relationships also means a new concept of yourself, your attention and perception will be sharpened to an even greater degree.

Chapter Organization[1]

The chapter sequence is a *phylogenetic* or

---

[1] Some instructors prefer to start the study of zoology with the frog or some other vertebrate type, as the student then feels that he starts on familiar ground. He soon realizes, however, that the ground is far from familiar, even if he does start with man. Since the vertebrate and invertebrate portions fall into two rather distinct groups, often used as semester divisions, the arrangement can follow the particular lecture sequence preferred by the instructor. The phylogenetic succession, however, is the choice of the authors.

evolutionary one, from protozoa to vertebrates. Most of the major animal groups are covered insofar as laboratory time and availability of specimens permit. A more complete listing of animal groups, including many not considered in the text, will be found at the end of Chapter 2.

Included in each chapter is the following:

1—General introduction to the phylum; statement of the basic characteristics and points of interest of the animals included.
2—Systematic arrangement of the group as a whole and its major subdivisions.
3—Laboratory instructions for dissection or observation of the animal selected to represent the entire group or particular segment of the group.
4—Additional experiments or special projects to emphasize field or experimental possibilities available to students with more time or specialized interests.

Text

The textual matter is laboratory-oriented. It is to serve as a link between theories and generalizations considered chiefly in lectures, and structural detail you see only in the laboratory. Students often find it difficult to relate these two aspects of zoology, even to the point of treating them as different subjects. The more quickly you can dispel this view, the more easily you can remember the details and understand the principles underlying zoological concepts.

This laboratory textbook will therefore introduce basic material and review biological principles best demonstrated by each phylum, then guide you through the various laboratory procedures to be performed. Study it *in advance* of the scheduled laboratory on each topic. Again and again you will be asked to compare, correlate, integrate with the knowledge you already have acquired. Constant emphasis on relationship and comparative structure builds the conceptual framework to which the details of this book are tied, enabling us to look at nature as an integrated complex. Without it, the study of zoology is reduced to bewildering detail and terminology. Many ex-students recall their zoology laboratory exercises in terms of slimy snails, smelly frogs, and horrid dead cats. We hope that you can see it as the science of structure and process in every living animal, yourself included.

The most important of the integrating ideas and unifying principles to be considered is that of evolution. From a knowledge of evolution, we can determine the degree of relationship among similar forms, or the probability of common descent of organisms with similar patterns of structure and development. Our notion of relationship is based on traits shared by different species. For this reason we emphasize characteristics common to large numbers of organisms. Thus, we are able to conceive of a generalized animal, built from these traits, which we call a *basic body type*. This imaginary creature is a useful simplification, an "average" to represent a generalized type. It may, however, also resemble the primitive species, possibly fossil, thought to be ancestral to present-day specialized examples.

Groups of animals with traits in common are arranged by biologists into *taxa*—species, genera, families, or larger categories. The student learns by inductive methods to associate animals into these groups just as biologists have learned to do so over the past 200 years. Each category into which animals are placed can, in turn, be grouped systematically into a succession of more inclusive and therefore more generalized categories. This is the *taxonomic scheme*, hence: *taxonomy*, an organization of living things visualized as a *hierarchy of groups showing varying degrees of similarity*. These groupings lead to our ideas of *relationship*, and ultimately of *evolution*.

The best way for you to make sense of the huge assemblage of animal types and forms is to appreciate the convenience and value of taxonomic arrangement and to adopt it as a means to organize efficiently whatever body of facts you can encompass. So long as the relatively few basic types are clearly kept in mind, the information will remain well ordered, no matter how little or much it may be. It will, in other words, make sense. And most students find that their interest and knowledge increase markedly when they realize for themselves that it does make sense.

Examine the section on classification (Chap. 2) with considerable care. The terms and groups discussed will be referred to again and again to emphasize general relationships between the specific form you are studying and larger taxa to which that form belongs and which it therefore represents.

Photographs

A properly selected photograph is often second only to the animal itself in conveying the message of overall organization and specific structure. Within limits of depth of field, lighting, and other technical factors, a photograph is an exact illustration of a specific organism, a particular dissection, or a microscopic image, showing every detail just as you would see it. An outline drawing, on the other hand, is an abstraction, usually a composite of many examples. It is often a highly simplified or diagrammatic view of an extremely complex structure, such as a drawing of nervous or circulatory systems. Each illustrative technique has a definite place in zoology, each performs a useful, necessary function. The advantage of a drawing is that it can *select*, simplify, emphasize, and thereby explain by dropping unnecessary detail. The photographs used in this text, and their labels, should enable you to distinguish and name parts quickly, without need of greatly detailed descriptions. Given your own specimen and the labeled photograph for orientation, *you* must now make the important transition from specific to general. To determine by induction the construction, organization, or pattern within each group of animals from your specific example or a number of such examples is a basic method in science and one of the primary goals of this course.

Variation in structure among individuals of the same species (and variation in dissection assignments) precludes your using these photographs to replace your own specimens. You will discover that it is preferable to look at your specimen, compare it with a photograph of a similar but still different example, and then return to your *own* material for final study and drawing. In doing so, you will enjoy one of the greatest pleasures of science: independent observation and discovery.

Drawings

Most students hate to draw. They are convinced that they cannot draw, never could, and never will. Much of this fear is simply that they don't know what is expected and assume that nothing short of a perfect copy will do. Drawings in this course have *one* purpose: to force you to observe. You must observe so carefully that the outline of what you see can be transferred to paper. Looking at a slide or specimen sufficiently well to recognize the parts and get a general idea of shape and arrangement is one thing; but looking closely enough to *reproduce* these parts, even in barest outline, on a piece of paper (than which nothing seems vaster and emptier) is quite another. For example, try looking in a store window just carefully enough to recognize, while you continue watching, the types of materials represented and their relationship to one another. Then look again, knowing that *this* time you will be asked to name from memory or *sketch on paper* the brands

and products, showing their precise location. Quite a difference in the way you look the second time! This difference separates casual from critical observation.

The mechanics of drawing vary, but the rudiments are simple.

1—Decide precisely what you are going to show. Select a *typical* part or animal showing the required aspect to the fullest degree.

2—Select the appropriate scale or magnification. *Make your drawing large enough* to show full detail.

3—Divide your paper into quadrants with light pencil lines (#2 or soft pencil), then with the aid of these divisions sketch lightly the *outline* of your subject in order to produce the proper symmetry. For most students this is the hardest part, but with practice and use of guide lines or squares it can be mastered readily.

4—Replace your sketch lines with firm unbroken outlines, using a harder pencil (#3 or #4). *Do not shade. Do not use scratchy or feathery borderlines to achieve an artistic effect.* Your goal, remember, is to produce an accurate outline that shows correct proportion. You then can block in important structural details. You need not be artistic or photographic, but you must be selective since your drawing includes only those features you consider esential for the designated purpose.

5—Fill in structural detail, but no more than necessary. If your specimen is bilaterally symmetrical, details on one side are usually enough. If it is radially symmetrical, cellular detail can be confined to a small pie-shaped wedge.

6—*Labels* are extremely important. They must be accurate and neat without interfering with the general appearance. Confine them to the margins, *print* clearly, and connect them by light solid lines to the object or structure named. Arrange the labels so their lead lines never cross one another.

7—Complete the drawing assignment with a full title and magnification scale (*not* simply the scale of the microscopic image). State the view or angle illustrated, sex, or other pertinent details, and identification. It is often helpful to place the full classification in an upper corner of your page.

Emphasis on drawings is always on accuracy of observation, never on artistic talent as such. Confine the details and labels to what *your own specimen shows.* Other information may be added if desired, but *only* if the source is stated. Instructors have an uncanny talent for detecting whether a drawing or the parts included represents your own observation.

Questions

A number of questions are scattered in the text. They should cause you to think back over ground covered earlier or to retrace what you have just done, often from a different vantage point. Sometimes questions are introduced to anticipate what is yet to be done. The questions—and your answers—are an important part of the text and are not to be skipped. They will also tie in with lecture material and help you to integrate laboratory and theoretical aspects of the course.

Experiments

Emphasis during introductory laboratory periods must necessarily be on structure rather than function. Before we can learn about the *physiology* —or operation—of an organism, we must familiarize ourselves with its form—*anatomy*. Once the structural basis is learned, we can look more closely at the mechanics of operation. Later laboratory exercises will stress physiological and experimental approaches in the study of heart, muscle, and nerve, and more general physiological processes such as regeneration in planaria, embryology of the starfish, genetics of the fruitfly. Other experiments, involving application of structural information and dissection techniques, are suggested wherever appropriate or where more advanced studies can take off. Succeeding courses in zoology will stress functional, cellular, and biochemical aspects to an increasing degree. Still other studies will emphasize group interrelationships and activities of living communities of animals in nature. Such courses will give you a chance to see adaptation at work in the normal environment, and functioning of the intact, beautifully adapted *living* animal. Your ability to pursue these subjects are all based on thorough familiarity with the concepts and animal groups to be studied now.

CHAPTER 1

The

Microscope

I. INTRODUCTION No tool better typifies the biologist than his microscope. It is an instrument of wonder, a fascinating introduction to the world of the infinitely small. To the scientist, it is a great deal more, an extension of his most critical sense, his eyes, into a research tool that has made possible fundamental biological advances. Without the microscope, our notion of the elements of life would have remained archaic. For you the microscope will become a tool enabling you to see for yourself the structure of muscle, cell, protozoa, egg—many of the basic units of life. It is an instrument that must be respected and cared for, but *used,* and used properly. By the end of the semester you should be a sufficiently skilled microscopist to be able to wander freely in a world 10 to 1000 times beyond your ordinary range of vision, into the land of the mu (μ), a metric measure equal to one-thousandth of a millimeter.

Other optical instruments can utilize nonvisible portions of the light spectrum (ultraviolet, x-rays) and considerably extend the microscope's range into still smaller realms. Employment of these smaller wavelengths has substantially increased optical resolving power, visible in these cases only on photographic film. The most spectacular development in recent years is the *electron microscope,* employing streams of electrons that discriminate within thousandths of a mu. For example, viruses, the tiniest things we know that can be called alive (though this is still disputed), have been made visible for the first time from electron microscope studies. But these instruments are tools of the research specialist. We will utilize two basic types of light microscopes, better optically than most of those that were used to make the pioneering advances in histology and microanatomy, and the principal optical instruments employed by the biologist today.

First of these basic instruments is the *binocular dissecting microscope,* with a single lens system (Fig. 1-1); second, the *compound microscope,* with a double lens systems, either *monocular* or *binocular* (Fig. 1-2). The dissecting microscope offers several advantages: (1) direct magnification without reversal of the image; (2) stereoscopic vision; (3) a large working distance between the object and the lens, allowing dissection or manipulation of the object being observed; (4) use of either transmitted or reflected light. The degree of magnification, about 5 to 50 diameters, is, however, much less than that of the compound microscope, though sufficient for relatively noncritical study or for work requiring manual manipulation.

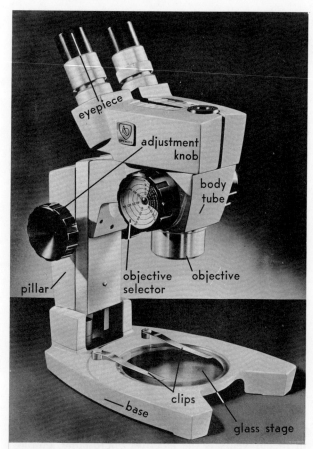

Fig. 1-1. Cycloptic dissecting microscope. (Photograph courtesy of the American Optical Company.)

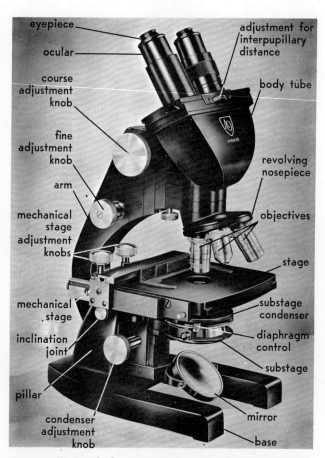

Fig. 1-2. Parts of the compound microscope. (Photograph courtesy of the American Optical Company.)

Microscopic studies of small, translucent animals, tissues, or cells utilize the compound microscope. The objective lens of this instrument creates a *primary image*, which is reversed in position (right to left and top to bottom) and then magnified again by the *ocular lens* to produce a *virtual image* seen by the eye. With the compound microscope, magnifications ranging from 100 to 1000 times are obtained, equivalent to seeing an object approximately 2 miles distant as if it were 10 feet away.

II. HANDLING AND SPECIAL CARE

Needless to say, optical instruments are expensive and fragile. With proper precautions, they should last for many years. Protection of lenses from shock and abrasion is especially important. Observe the following precautions:

1—Carry the instrument by the base and pillar, cradled vertically in both hands. Tipping it backwards may have disastrous results,

as the student whose oculars are sent crashing to the floor will quickly appreciate.

2—Set the instrument down carefully, especially on the hard surface of your laboratory bench.

3—Keep all exposed lens surfaces clean, but use fresh *lens paper* only. (Your handkerchief carries lint and highly abrasive dust and dirt particles that will scratch the polished, coated lens surfaces.) Never touch a lens with your fingers—the oil attracts dust, obscures vision, and is difficult to remove.

4—Check cleanliness of oculars by rotating them to see dust particles move. Make sure the mirror is clean. Be particularly cautious with the objectives, the most valuable part of the microscope.

5—Clean your instrument before each exercise. *Return it clean* to its case or shelf, with the *lowest power* objective in position over the stage and the coarse adjustment racked *down*. (Why?) Always double-check to be certain that no microscope slide remains on the stage and that the latter is carefully cleaned before returning the microscope to its case. These precautions are your complete responsibility—and one to which you will be held rigidly.

6—Do not remove the oculars from their tubes except briefly to clean them, as this permits dust to enter the instrument.

When you first inspect the microscope report to your instructor any scratches, oil, or other apparent misuse or damage to any part. This attention will ensure prompt repair or adjustment, and relieve you of considerable financial responsibility.

III. PARTS OF THE INSTRUMENT

A. Dissecting Microscope (binocular):

Locate, name, and review the function of each major part:

1—*Base*, with glass *stage* and slide-holding *clips*.
2—*Substage*, with mirror (may be absent from your microscope).
3—*Pillar*, supporting stand for the microscope *body*, housing of the lens system.
4—*Objective lenses*, contained in a *rotating* or *movable drum* or *pod*.

▶ How many lenses are there and of what magnifying power?

5—*Ocular lenses*, recessed in *ocular tubes* in upper portion of body.

▶ What is their magnifying power?
▶ How is this magnification expressed?

B. Compound Microscope (may be *monocular* or *binocular* with *vertical* or *inclined* oculars):

1—*Base*, or supporting stand.
2—*Pillar*, attached to base by *inclination joint*.
3—*Body tube*, the optical housing for the lenses. In newer binocular instruments, the body tube and oculars are inclined for more convenient viewing.
4—*Coarse-* and *fine-adjustment knobs*. Coarse for low-power work and initial focusing, fine for final adjustment and variation of *plane of focus* for viewing an object at different depths. These are your "steering wheels," the controls that bring the object into proper view—focus—so that it not only becomes sharp and clear, but can be viewed three-dimensionally as well.
5—*Substage condenser*, with *iris diaphragm*, controlled by a projecting handle

for management of light intensity and focus, a key control element for proper microscopy.
6—*Condenser elevation knob*, for control of condenser level, hence the plane of light focus and concentration of light reflected from the mirror onto the microscope stage and the object viewed. In instruments lacking a condenser, this function is performed by the concave mirror.
7—*Reflecting mirror*, with *concave (parabolic)* and *flat* surfaces.

▶ What is the purpose of each?

8—*Stage*, with *microscope clips*. Research instruments usually have a *graduated stage*, a special slide-holding device marked by graduations, with two *stage-adjustment knobs* for accurate movement of the slide.

▶ Of what value are the graduated markings?

Some instruments may be equipped with a *nongraduated stage* controlled by adjustment knobs.
9—*Ocular lens* or *lenses*. You may have two sets, for different magnifications (6× and 10×, or 10× and 15×). Usually, better results are obtained with a low-power ocular and high-power objective rather than the high-power ocular and lower-power objective, even though the actual magnification is the same. This is due to the correcting lenses built into the objective, the most optically critical part of the microscope.
10—*Objective lenses* are screwed into a rotating head, the revolving *nosepiece*. Observe that markings on these lenses state their magnifying power (10×, 43×, or 90×). The 90× objective is used only for oil immersion. The 10× is called the *low-power* objective (or *low-dry*); the 43× is the *high-power* (or *high-dry*) lens, in contrast to the 90× *oil immersion* lens. The latter is used with a drop of oil to form a liquid bridge between itself and the slide surface examined. For still more critical work, an oil bridge is also placed between the *lower* surface of the slide and the top lens of the condenser.

▶ Can you state the optical advantage of having light pass from the object viewed through oil rather than air before entering the lens and passing to your eye? Use of this lens will be restricted to special demonstrations or work demanding the optical limits of your instrument.

▶ Review with your instructor the function and basic optics of the lens system; be able to name and

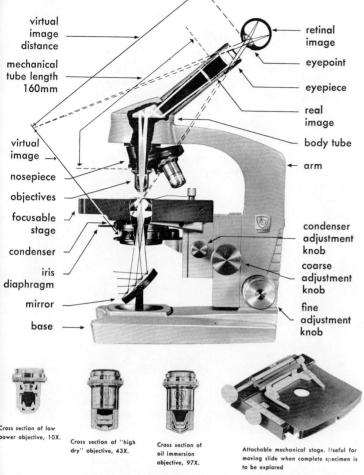

virtual image distance

mechanical tube length 160mm

virtual image →

nosepiece

objectives

focusable stage

condenser

iris diaphragm

mirror

base

retinal image

eyepoint

eyepiece

real image

body tube

arm

condenser adjustment knob

coarse adjustment knob

fine adjustment knob

Cross section of low power objective, 10X.

Cross section of "high dry" objective, 43X.

Cross section of oil immersion objective, 97X.

Attachable mechanical stage. Useful for moving slide when complete specimen is to be explored.

Fig. 1-3. Optical and mechanical features of a microscope, showing the path of light. (Photograph courtesy of the American Optical Company.)

describe each part of the instrument. Observe differences as well as similarities between your microscope and those illustrated here (Figs. 1-1 and 1-2). Know both *definition* and *significance* of each of the following terms:

resolving power	transmitted light
numerical aperture	reflected light
working distance	focusing
image reversal	parfocal
primary and virtual image	depth of field
focal plane	magnification

Be able to trace the path of light reflected by the mirror from its source, through condenser and object on the slide, into objective lens, optical tube, ocular lens (or lenses), to your eye, noting carefully the primary and virtual images produced (Fig. 1-3).

▶ At what points along this path can you control light intensity or change focus?

Remember that the chief purpose of your microscope is to enhance *detail,* not simply to give magnification. You can project an image on a huge screen, yet see nothing in greater clarity. The key is

resolving power, the ability of your lens system to separate two points. The closer the points, the greater the resolving power needed to see them distinctly as points, rather than one blur. Resolving power as a measure of quality of your instrument varies *inversely* with the wavelength of light used (the smaller the wavelength, the greater the resolving power), and *directly* with the ability of the condenser and objective lens to gather light, a measurement called the *numerical aperture.* Additional optical information should be sought in a booklet prepared by the American Optical Company, *The Effective Use and Proper Care of the Microscope,* or by the Bausch and Lomb Company, *The Use and Care of the Microscope.* (Copies are available on request.)

IV. PROCEDURE FOR PROPER USE OF THE MICROSCOPE

1—Position the instrument carefully at your desk, with pillar facing you. Incline the instrument to a comfortable position (unless, of course, your microscope has an inclined head). Do *not* incline the pillar if fresh material is to be used or you'll find the water and sample dripping into your lap.

2—Adjust the microscope lamp at least 6 inches behind the instrument, shielded so that light shines directly on the mirror, not on the stage or into your eyes.

3—Turn the *lowest* power objective into vertical position over the opening in the stage.

4—Adjust the mirror so that the light beam is reflected directly up through the center of the stage opening (check this by looking from the side). There should be a light bulb image in the center of your field of vision. Use the curved parabolic surface of the mirror *only* if there is no condenser in your microscope; with the condenser always use the *flat* surface of the mirror.

▶ Why?
▶ What is the purpose of the curved surface?
▶ Of the condenser?

5—Bring the substage condenser up to its highest position, then close down the iris diaphragm until the light is diffused evenly across the entire field of vision. It may be necessary to rack the condenser down to a somewhat lower position to reduce intensity of light for low-power work. *Remember to* *raise it again for high-power objectives* when greater light intensity is required.

NOTE

Always start with the lowest *power objective and the* coarse adjustment *since this offers a much larger field and allows more rapid orientation and preliminary focusing. The fine adjustment, in fact, need be used only with the high-dry lens. Avoid glare; reduce light intensity with the iris diaphragm or condenser, or by closing down the diaphragm on your lamp if such a control is present, or by moving the light source further back and readjusting the mirror. Do not simply change the mirror angle; this merely misdirects the light. You will discover that reduced light intensity adds considerable clarity and provides both greater degree of visual control and a more nearly three-dimensional image.*

Practice focusing, proper alignment, and changing intensity of light by examining a millimeter rule through various objectives, then a piece of lens paper placed on a slide in a drop of water, carefully covered by a coverslip. Practice placing the coverslip in position slowly to prevent entrapment of air bubbles. Focus critically on individual fibers under low and high power, using various intensities of illumination. Continue experimenting until you can confidently position, illuminate properly, and focus on a selected object or optical plane.

6—Now, after the above steps and practice procedures are completed, place a prepared slide on the stage. This will probably be a thin tissue slice, specially stained and cleared for microscopic study. It was mounted on the slide in an optically transparent fluid medium such as Canada balsam, then covered by a coverslip, under which the medium was allowed to harden. You may also be given a mounted intact animal ("whole mount") that is suitably stained and prepared for microscopic examination. If you have *living* material, such as a culture of protozoa, be careful not to place too much material on the slide. A drop or two on the center of the slide will easily fill the space under an 18 mm diameter coverslip. Place the coverslip *slowly* over the drop, lowering it gently in place to avoid trapping bubbles or forcing the organisms out from under the glass. Move the slide about on the stage until the area to be viewed lies directly in the beam of light coming up through the center of the stage opening.

▶ How was the light beam centered?

7—With the *low-power* objective in position (16 mm working distance), and while watching from one side, turn the coarse-adjustment knob so as to rack down to within ¼ inch of the object. Now view through the ocular while *keeping both eyes open* and turn the coarse adjustment towards you (rack *up*) until the object becomes fairly clear. Move the slide slowly with the stage-adjustment knobs or by hand until a field of interest passes under your vision.

8—Switch over to the *high-power* objective. It has only a *4 mm* working distance, so be certain your microscope is parfocal! Complete focusing with careful movement of fine-adjustment knob. Remember, too, that the limited working distance with the high-dry objective lens will not permit you to rack down more than a few millimeters before you crush the slide with your lens! Always remember to start with the objective slightly *below* the 4 mm distance so that you bring the object in view by racking *up* with the fine-adjustment knob. Racking down may force the objective into the coverslip, producing a smashed slide, damaged objective, and shattered student morale. Such careless focusing is the beginning microscopist's prime hazard—an expensive and inescapable sign of faulty technique.

More light will be needed with the high-dry than with the low-power objective. (*Why?*) Control light as before by the iris diaphragm, position of the condenser, or distance of light source. Switch back to low power. *Observe* that the *field* is sharply reduced, *light* reduced, and *working distance* reduced when magnification is *increased* (*Why?*) For this reason always orient yourself first under low power.

Proper control of light intensity is one of the keys to microscopic skill. Practice focusing using various slides or fields, and experiment with different controls of light intensity. Note results carefully to accustom yourself to the subtle but essential control methods at your disposal. Change the diaphragm opening, condenser level, and mirror position in order to appreciate the all-importance of proper light control. Often this will mean the difference between a successful laboratory exercise and a total failure, with eyestrain and headache thrown in.

V. LABORATORY EXERCISES

1—Letter e slide—With the compound microscope, examine a slide with the letter *e* marked on it. Note the position of the letter in your image. *Draw* it at low and high magnification to show its size relative to that of the field. State magnification employed. Do this by drawing a circle to represent the field and showing the *e* or that part of it that is visible within the circle. Now examine the same slide under each magnification of your *dissecting microscope.* Why is there no image reversal? Why is the working distance greater than with the compound instrument? Which instrument and which lens combination would you use for each of the following?

a. dissection of a mosquito
b. examination of frog blood
c. examination of a living tadpole
d. examination of the surface of your index finger (try it!)
e. examination of a hair
f. examination of a living amoeba

2—Specially prepared stained slides—Tissue, insect, or protozoa slides are all excellent for this practice. Review proper focusing procedure with each specimen and make drawings suggested by your instructor.

Practice focusing at low and high power to observe resulting differences in size of the field and in degree of visible detail. If you keep one hand on the fine-adjustment knob and constantly work it up and down, you will learn to see in depth and to appreciate various levels of focus until you can picture the specimen in a fully three-dimensional view. Remember that microscopic proficiency is essential throughout the entire course.

Whenever an illustration is requested, do it carefully, drawing an accurate outline with proper proportion and symmetry. Review the discussion of drawing procedure in the Introduction. You will soon see the difference between simply looking and observing well enough to reproduce what you see.

3—Slide preparation of scrapings from teeth or gums—Obtain material with a toothpick and place it in a drop of normal saline solution on a slide and add a coverslip. Neutral red or methylene blue will stain the cells, coloring the nucleus, cytoplasm, and various organelles to different intensities, allowing you to see these parts more clearly. *Do not overstain,* however. Add a drop of dilute stain under one corner of your coverslip, then draw it under the coverslip in a controlled fashion by using a bit of filter paper as a wick at the opposite corner of the coverslip. With some practice this technique will be found to be a most useful one.

4—Freshly prepared and stained sample of frog or human blood—You can make your own stained preparation in the following manner: with a blood smear prepared for you, or done yourself under your instructor's supervision, pour Wright's stain dropwise onto the slide until it covers the smear. Leave it for about 2 minutes, then add 2 ml distilled water. Leave this on for 4 or 5 minutes, then pour off and wash the slide quickly but carefully in distilled water. Add a coverslip and examine.

5—Preparation of frog skin—Compare with Fig. 15-3 and a bit of your own skin. As before, mount in saline and cover. Add a drop or two of vital dye at your discretion, using the procedure already learned.

6—Living ciliated cells—Place a bit of tissue from the roof of the mouth of a freshly killed frog in a drop of water on your slide. Cover without trapping air bubbles. Do you observe any direction of the beat of the cilia? Can you see any functional significance in this direction?

7—Living protozoa from a mixed culture—Place a drop on your slide, cover, and examine. How many different types of organisms can you find? Detailed study of these will be delayed until the next laboratory period, but don't spend thirty minutes staring at an air bubble!

8—Special exercise: measurement and computation of magnification in your drawing—Simple magnification is computed by taking the product of magnifications of objective and ocular lenses (for example, $10\times$ ocular and $43\times$ high-dry gives a visual magnification of 430 times what the naked eye can see at 10 inches. It is written $430\times$ or 430 diameters). It does not, however, give a direct reading in units of size nor tell accurately the magnification on your drawing. A simple way to determine this magnification is to lay a metric ruler alongside the right side of your instrument, about 10 inches from the objective lens and in the line of vision of one eye (the right) while you look through the eyepiece with your left eye (use the *right* eyepiece in case of a binocular microscope). For left-handed students the opposite arrangement is followed.

NOTES AND DRAWINGS

(Tear along line)

Practice this until you can train your eyes to juxtapose the two images and actually *read the diameter of the entire microscope field or the object you are observing through the microscope, measured against the ruler.* To determine the actual magnification of your *drawing* as opposed to that of the lens system (the virtual image), substitute in the following simple ratio: *lens magnification* (ocular times objective) is to *size of virtual image* (measured by the above procedure) as *magnification of drawing* is to actual *size of drawing*. Solving for the third element of this ratio will then give the final magnification.

Calibration of your microscope for *direct measurement* of object size in known units can be done with an *ocular disc* and a *stage micrometer* (actually a microruler) that enables you to measure accurately the total field of your microscope, or the size of any object viewed, at each power of the objective lens. The ocular disc fits into the ocular tube, the stage micrometer is placed on the microscope stage. Divisions seen through the ocular disc are then measured off against the divisions (in tenths and hundredths of a millimeter) on the stage micrometer. With each lens combination, a specific reading is obtained (that is, one ocular division might equal 11.5 stage divisions), from which ocular units can be determined in terms of the known units of the stage micrometer. This gives you a ruler in the ocular which can then be aligned with any object being studied to give a direct reading in *ocular units,* quickly converted to microns by use of the predetermined calibration. Review these steps carefully with your instructor and calibrate your microscope for several combinations of lenses or observe a demonstration of the process.

Measurement of cell (egg) volume by this technique makes a worthwhile special exercise. Can you think of any other applications of direct measurement of microscopic structures that might be made using the calibrated ocular disc?

CHAPTER 2

Classification and Phylogeny

I. INTRODUCTION

Classification, or *taxonomy*, has a dual purpose—to enable us to know what animal we are working with (to identify) and to organize and make sense of the arrangement (to systematize or classify). This means that each organism must have a name and that all names should be arranged to show varying degrees of similarity. Biologists agree that degrees of structural similarity indicate degrees of *relationship*. Hence, by arranging the most similar animals within groups, and these groups into larger groups that are more nearly alike, we construct a *classification* consisting of a series of categories, or *taxa*, like the table of organization of a large corporation or an army command. Ordinarily, 7 of these taxa are used. First and smallest grouping is the *species* (plural: *species*), the basic interbreeding unit (like man, the common amoeba, dog, black oak, robin). Then, distinct but similar species (like the domestic cat, mountain lion, African lion, and tiger) may be lumped together into the next higher category, called the *genus* (plural: *genera*), in this case the genus *Felis*. Similar genera are then united into a *family*, as Felidae, the cat family. (Note the ending *idae*, used for all animal family names.) Thousands of different families have been described, each consisting of one to many genera that show some measure of affinity. In like fashion, the taxonomist or systematist groups families that appear more nearly similar into a yet more inclusive category, the *order* (examples: the CARNIVORA, or meat eaters, the ANTHROPOIDEA, or man-monkey-ape group). Following this procedure, orders showing some degree of similarity are collected into a *class*. Thus, CARNIVORA, ANTHROPOIDEA, and all other animals that have hair and suckle their young are combined into the Class **MAMMALIA**. Other classes combine all birds, or all reptiles, all frogs and salamanders, all insects, and so on. Then the classes that show some still more general degree of similarity are placed in a huge assemblage of varied animals, the *phylum* (plural: *phyla*). The Phylum CHORDATA includes all fishes, amphibians, reptiles, birds, and mammals, plus some primitive organisms that lack vertebrae and are little known to beginning students but very important from an evolutionary (*phylogenetic*) standpoint. Finally, all phyla of the most general or fundamental similarity are placed within a single *kingdom*. **ANIMALIA**, the animal kingdom, is such a group, as opposed to **PLANTAE**, the plant kingdom.

Although our primary concern in this course must be larger assemblages, phyla and classes, we will utilize selected species as examples that serve to demonstrate characteristics of the entire group. When we look at a specimen it must be first and always a *species*, that is, have a specific identity, a name. Then it can be categorized as a member of each of the succession of larger, more inclusive groups.

▶ Beginning with an arbitrary assemblage of 24 species (labeled 1 to 24), prepare a diagrammatic chart to show how these 24 entities (species) *could* be arranged into successive taxa to form a hierarchy employing all 7 categories considered above. The arrangement you select is arbitrary, of course, but should demonstrate the simplest basic taxonomic principles.

▶ What do we mean by this statement: "Taxonomy arranges organisms into a series of categories of successively greater generality and inclusiveness"?

The scheme of classification now in use for all plants and animals, living and extinct, is traced back to the Swedish botanist Carl Linnaeus who established it early in the eighteenth century. In fact, 1759, the date of publication of the tenth edition of Linnaeus' great work *Systema Naturae*, marks the formal beginning of modern animal taxonomy. No name established prior to 1759 is considered valid. To be universally accepted, any name given to an animal after that date must conform to certain internationally accepted requirements. Once these conditions are met, the name is permanently enrolled in scientific literature and will not be removed unless a re-evaluation justifies the conclusion that the animal was indeed not distinct enough to warrant being named a new species.

Further refinements are used to break down the 7 basic categories into still more steps, giving greater flexibility to the system. For example, *subspecies, subgenera, suborders,* and *subclasses* denote subdivisions of species, genera, orders, and classes into additional systematic levels or taxa. *Superspecies, superfamilies, superclasses* also can be used. In fact, many such higher or lower groupings can be interpolated into the taxonomic scheme, a mark of its flexibility and usefulness. The system therefore serves to classify and arrange, to catalogue into more or less serviceable units.

Actually, biological classification is more than naming and recording. All the above and still other categories are needed to fill in our picture of living relationships extending too far back in time readily to be seen in adult morphology. As already stated, degree of similarity is considered to denote degree of relationship or recency of common origin. Thinking in terms of change throughout the long history of life, divergence from an ancestral group implies

evolution. Taxonomic arrangement is our chart of relationship, and hence of evolution. We attempt to construct a *natural classification* to represent true hereditary patterns. An *artificial classification*, such as lumping all swimming or flying animals in one group, would simply be a pigeon-holing file system. This evolutionary orderliness is the *sense* of taxonomy, the reason we emphasize larger categories and major patterns of relationship. Morphological similarities are the bedrock upon which both classification and our conception of evolutionary pattern is based.

The broadest taxonomic divisions, those between *phylum* and *kingdom*, are chiefly of theoretical importance. These are the so-called *supraphyletic* categories—*branch, grade, level,* and *superphylum*—which deal with the most fundamental of biological characteristics. They presumably best indicate distant heredity relationships and provide clues to the earliest branching points in the history of life. The significance of such features as type of body cavity (which determines the taxon *level*), basic body symmetry (the *grade*), or fundamental arrangement of cells and tissues (*branch*) cannot be studied in detail here. Recognize, however, that as one moves from the taxon *species* on up the ladder of categories, the nature of differences change. Above the phylum, these differences are particularly basic and therefore of special interest to scholars of the earliest stages of evolving life. The overall taxonomic system is one combining logic, convenience, and enormous usefulness.

Nomenclature, the mechanics of naming, remains to be considered. Very clear rules of the road ensure reasonable uniformity and wide international and interdisciplinary acceptance of names given to newly described organisms. These rules allow for creation of new names when undescribed species are discovered. They also allow a degree of flexibility towards errors or changes required when old names are found to be duplicated or single species twice-named. Rigorous standards are now required for a new name to qualify. Rules of nomenclature still must allow for disagreement among specialists and provide a scheme of priority to credit the first name given. In fact, an International Commission on Zoological Nomenclature empowered to decide disputed cases, of which there are quite a number, governs a complex legal code adhered to by scientists around the world. In addition, congresses of specialists convene from time to time to reconsider and revise the rules. Naming an animal is a demanding and specialized science, and formulating the guiding rules is an even more specialized and sometimes a tedious but nonetheless important responsibility. *Taxonomy* (the system as a whole) and *nomenclature* (the process of naming) underlie all biology, since each biological name becomes part of an integrated system, a code respected and recognized everywhere. Each name becomes of both theoretical significance and practical usefulness as it provides both a handle and a lead to the entire taxonomic arrangement, telling us the probable relationship of each animal.

Since there are two parts to each animal's name, genus and species, the system of nomenclature is often called *binomial*. A complete species name also includes the name of the person who first described and established it and the date this designation was published, thus: *Felis domesticus* Linnaeus, 1759. Note that the name of an organism, such as *Amoeba proteus* or *Homo sapiens*, always includes the *generic* name (with first letter capitalized) and *specific* name (first letter in small case). Both terms are *italicized* or underscored. Properly, then, reference to a "species" as the *name* of an animal includes its genus in addition to its species designation. This is necessary since identical species names, such as *domesticus, familiaris, americanus*, and so on, may be applied to a number of animals in different genera. The only way to sort out one and only one kind is

to use the genus in addition to the species. The generic name may be abbreviated to the first letter in a list or paragraph when there is no possibility of confusion. Observe that the term *species* is spelled the same in singular and plural; "specie" means gold or silver coin, *not* the name of an animal. Latin or Greek endings and forms are used, giving greater permanence and universality to the system, whether the scientist be Chinese, Eskimo, Hindustani, or an aspiring American college student. There is more of course, but this is enough to start with.

The following charts summarize, for present review and future reference, the major supraphyletic categories of animals, then the subdivisions within each phylum. You should add the names of the examples you study to the sections where they belong as a means of helping you to review the system and recognize the larger categories. Finally, on the last page of this chapter, the implied or hypothetical stages of complexity through which animals have passed in the course of evolution (as suggested by substantial biological evidence) is charted in a highly diagrammatic and necessarily conjectural fashion. Much of your course will be devoted to studying examples of this sequence and the nature of the evidence justifying the arrangement.

II. MAJOR OR SUPRAPHYLETIC CATEGORIES AND PHYLA

Kingdom **ARCHETISTA**—viruses, rickettsiae, pleuropneumonia-like organisms
Kingdom **MONERA**—blue-green algae, bacteria
[1]Kingdom **PROTISTA**—protozoa, algae (excepting blue-green and green algae), fungi, Phylum PROTOZOA (and others)
Kingdom **PLANTAE**—green algae, green flagellates, true higher plants
Kingdom **ANIMALIA**—typical multicellular animals

Branch **MESOZOA**	Phylum MESOZOA
Branch **PARAZOA**	Phylum PORIFERA
Branch **EUMETAZOA**	
Grade **RADIATA**	Phylum COELENTERATA
	Phylum CTENOPHORA
Grade **BILATERIA**	
Level **ACOELOMATA**	Phylum PLATYHELMINTHES
	Phylum RHYNCHOCOELA
Level **PSEUDOCOELOMATA**	Phylum ACANTHOCEPHALA
	Phylum ASCHELMINTHES
	[2]Class **NEMATODA**
	Class **NEMATOMORPHA** (or **GORDIACEA**)

[1] Arranged by many authorities in a Subkingdom **PROTOZOA** in the Kingdom **ANIMALIA**, with the remaining animals placed in a Subkingdom **METAZOA**.
[2] Classes listed here are treated by some zoologists as a superphylum of 6 phyla.

Class **Rotifera**
Class **Gastrotricha**
Class **Kinorhyncha** (or **Echinodera**)
Class **Priapulida**
Phylum ENTOPROCTA

Level **EUCOELOMATA**
Superphylum **SCHIZOCOELA**

Phylum BRYOZOA (ECTOPROCTA)
Phylum MOLLUSCA
Phylum ECHIUROIDEA
Phylum SIPUNCULOIDEA
Phylum ANNELIDA
Phylum ONYCOPHORA
Phylum ARTHROPODA

Superphylum **ENTEROCOELA**

Phylum ECHINODERMATA
Phylum POGONOPHORA
Phylum CHAETOGNATHA

Term "Protochordata" includes Hemichordates, Urochordates, and Cephalo-
chordates.

Phylum HEMICHORDATA
Phylum CHORDATA

Phylum PHORONIDA
    (relationship uncertain,
    probably with enterocoels)
Phylum BRACHIOPODA
    (relationship uncertain,
    possibly with enterocoels)

III. *PRIMARY SUBDIVISIONS OF THE PHYLA*

Underlined names should become thoroughly familiar to you. The others, somewhat less important for our purpose, should be reviewed, though you will not be required to know their distinguishing characteristics unless this is specifically suggested by your instructor. Additional taxa (*group, superclass,* *division, suborder*) are used when necessary and are designated in the preceding larger unit being separated (for example, "Phylum **Chordata** [chordates]. Separated into the following 2 *groups:* 1. . . . 2. . . .").

Animal groupings marked by an asterisk (*) are extinct.

PHYLUM   SUBPHYLUM   CLASS   SUBCLASS   ORDER

PROTOZOA (single-celled animals)
    [1] PLASMODROMA
        Mastigophora (flagellates; *Euglena*)
        Sarcodina (rhizopods; *Amoeba*)
        Sporozoa (sporozoans; *Plasmodium*)

---

[1] Current usage places the flagellates and rhizopods in one subphylum distinct from the sporozoans, which are placed in one or even two major groups of their own. This is done to indicate the distinctness of the Sporozoa and the evident relationship between flagellates and rhizopods. The older form is retained here to conform to most texts. The student should be aware, however, that ideas on basic relationships and evolutionary position of organisms are continually being modified as new studies reveal new information.

PHYLUM   SUBPHYLUM   CLASS   SUBCLASS   ORDER

CILIOPHORA

           CILIATA (ciliates; *Paramecium*)

           SUCTORIA (suctorians)

MESOZOA

PORIFERA (sponges)

           CALCAREA (or CALCISPONGIAE) (calcareous sponges)

           HEXACTINELLIDA (or HYALOSPONGIAE) (glass sponges)

           DEMOSPONGIAE (horny bath sponges)

COELENTERATA (or CNIDARIA) (hydroids, jellyfishes, corals, sea anemones, and others)

           HYDROZOA (hydrozoans)

                     HYDROIDA (hydroids; *Obelia, Hydra*)

                     TRACHYLINA (*Gonionemus*)

                     SIPHONOPHORA (Portuguese Man O'War or *Physalia*)

                     MILLEPORINA ⎫
                                         ⎬(hydrocorals)
                     STYLASTERINA ⎭

           SCYPHOZOA (jellyfishes)

           ANTHOZOA (sea anemones, corals)

                     ALCYONARIA (soft corals)

                     ZOANTHARIA (stony corals and sea anemones)

CTENOPHORA (comb jellies)

PLATYHELMINTHES (flatworms, flukes, tapeworms)

           TURBELLARIA (flatworms)

                     ACOELA (primitive flatworms)

                     RHABDOCOELA (saclike gut)

                     ALLOEOCOELA

                     TRICLADIDA (planarians)

                     POLYCLADIDA (marine flatworms)

           TREMATODA (flukes)

                     MONOGENEA (flukes with simple life cycles)

                     DIGENEA (flukes with complex life cycles)

           CESTODA (tapeworms)

                     CESTODARIA (tapeworms with no proglottids)

                     EUCESTODA (few to many proglottids)

RHYNCHOCOELA (ribbon worms)

ACANTHOCEPHALA (spiny-headed worms)

ASCHELMINTHES (pseudocoels)

           NEMATODA (nematodes, roundworms)

           NEMATOMORPHA (or GORDIACEA) (horsehair worms)

           ROTIFERA (rotifers)

           GASTROTRICHA (gastrotrichs)

           KINORHYNCHA (or ECHINODERA)

           PRIAPULIDA

ENTOPROCTA (nodding heads)

BRYOZOA (ECTOPROCTA) (moss animals)

PHORONIDA (*Phoronis*)

BRACHIOPODA (lamp shells; *Lingula*)

SIPUNCULOIDEA (peanut worms)

PHYLUM   SUBPHYLUM   CLASS   SUBCLASS   ORDER

ECHIUROIDEA (spoon worms)

MOLLUSCA (snails, clams, octopuses, and allies)

Monoplacophora (recently discovered segmented mollusks thought to be extinct for 300,000,000 years; *Neopolina*)

Amphineura (chitons, coat-of-mail shells)

Gastropoda (snails and allies)

Prosobranchiata (sea snails, limpets)

Opisthobranchiata (sea slugs)

Pulmonata (most fresh-water and land snails)

Scaphopoda (tooth shells)

Pelecypoda (clams, oysters)

Cephalopoda (squid, octopus)

ANNELIDA

Oligochaeta (earthworms)

Polychaeta (bristle worms, *Neanthes*)

Hirudinea (leeches)

Archiannelida (simple marine worms)

ONYCOPHORA (*Peripatus*, arthropod-annelid group containing characteristics of both)

ARTHROPODA (arthropods)

MANDIBULATA

Crustacea (crustaceans)

Branchiopoda (primitive crustacea with many leaflike appendages). Separated into following 4 *divisions:*

1. Anostraca (fairy shrimps, brine shrimps; *Artemia*)
2. Notostraca (branchiopods with shieldlike carapace)
3. Conchostraca (branchiopods with bivalved carapace)
4. Cladocera (water fleas; *Daphnia*)

Ostracoda (small, bean-shaped, bivalved crustaceans)

Copepoda (copepods; *Cyclops, Calanus*)

Cirripedia (barnacles)

Malacostraca (higher crustaceans). Separated into the following 5 *divisions:*

1. Leptostraca
2. Hoplocarida (mantis shrimps)
3. Syncarida
4. Peracarida

Mysidacea (abundant planktonic shrimps)

Cumacea

Tanaidacea

Isopoda (sow bugs; *Lygia*)

Amphipoda (beach fleas; *Gammarus*)

5. Eucarida

Euphausiacea (krill, planktonic shrimps)

Decapoda (crayfish, lobsters, crabs, and shrimps). Separated into the following 3 *suborders:*

1. Macrura (shrimps, lobsters)
2. Anomura (hermit crabs)
3. Brachyura (crabs)

PHYLUM   SUBPHYLUM   CLASS   SUBCLASS   ORDER

MYRIAPODA

  CHILOPODA (centipedes)
  DIPLOPODA (millipedes)
  SYMPHYLA
  PAUROPODA

INSECTA

  APTERYGOTA (primitive wingless insects)
   PROTURA
   COLLEMBOLA (springtails)
   THYSANURA (silverfish)
   DIPLURA (japygids)
  PTERYGOTA (winged insects). Separated into the following 2 *divisions:*
   1. **HEMIMETABOLA** (development by nymphal stages)
    ORTHOPTERA (grasshoppers, crickets)
    BLATTARIA (roaches)
    DERMAPTERA (earwigs)
    PLECOPTERA (stoneflies)
    ISOPTERA (termites)
    ODONATA (dragonflies)
    EMBIOPTERA (embiids)
    EPHEMEROPTERA (mayflies)
    MALLOPHAGA (biting lice)
    ANOPLURA (sucking lice)
    CORRODENTIA (book lice)
    THYSANOPTERA (thrips)
    HEMIPTERA (true bugs)
   2. **HOLOMETABOLA** (4-stage development with complete metamorphosis)
    HOMOPTERA (aphids, scale insects)
    MECOPTERA (scorpionflies)
    NEUROPTERA (lacewings)
    TRICHOPTERA (caddisflies)
    LEPIDOPTERA (butterflies, moths)
    DIPTERA (flies)
    SIPHONAPTERA (fleas)
    COLEOPTERA (beetles)
    STREPSIPTERA (stylopids)
    HYMENOPTERA (ants, wasps, bees)

CHELICERATA

  ARACHNIDA (spiders, scorpions, and allies)
   SCORPIONIDA (scorpions)
   PALPIGRADA
   PEDIPALPI (whip scorpions)
   PSEUDOSCORPIONIDA (false scorpions)
   SOLPUGIDA (sun spiders)
   PHALANGIDA (harvestmen or daddy longlegs)
   ARANEIDA (spiders)
   ACARINA (mites, ticks)

MEROSTOMATA

XIPHOSURA (horseshoe or king crabs; *Limulus*)

*EURYPTERIDA (extinct giant water scorpions)

PYCNOGONIDA (sea spiders)

TARDIGRADA (water bears)

*TRILOBITA (abundant in Palaeozoic seas)

PENTASTOMIDA (linguatulids—parasitic; possibly derived from mites)

POGONOPHORA

CHAETOGNATHA (arrow worms)

ECHINODERMATA (echinoderms)

ELEUTHEROZOA

ASTEROIDEA (sea stars)

OPHIUROIDEA (brittle stars)

ECHINOIDEA (sea urchins, sand dollars)

HOLOTHUROIDEA (sea cucumbers)

PELMATAZOA

CRINOIDEA (sea lilies) (Also includes several related classes known only as fossils)

HEMICHORDATA (acorn worms)

CHORDATA (chordates). Separated into the following 2 *groups:*

1. ACRANIA

TUNICATA (or UROCHORDATA) (tunicates)

LARVACEA (planktonic, neotenic forms)

ASIDIACEA (sea squirts)

THALLIACEA (planktonic, chain tunicates)

CEPHALOCHORDATA (amphioxus, lancelets; *Branchiostoma*)

2. CRANIATA

VERTEBRATA (vertebrates). Separated into the following 2 *superclasses:*

1. PISCES (fishes)

AGNATHA (jawless fishes)

*OSTRACODERMI (primitive jawless armored fishes)

CYCLOSTOMATA (lampreys and hagfish, living jawless fishes)

*PLACODERMI (early jawed fishes)

CHONDRICHTHYES (cartilaginous fishes, sharks, rays, chimaeras)

SELACHII (sharks, rays)

HOLOCEPHALI (chimaeras)

OSTEICHTHYES

PALAEOPTERYGII (sturgeons, spoonbills, and allies)—4 orders

NEOPTERYGII (ganoid and teleost fishes)—31 orders

CHOANICHTHYES (lungfish, lobe-finned fishes)—2 orders

2. TETRAPODA (four-legged animals)

AMPHIBIA (amphibians)

STEGOCEPHALIA—4 orders, including:

*LABYRINTHODONTI (ancient giant salamanders)

GYMNOPHIONA (or APODA) (caecilians; legless amphibians)

CAUDATA (salamanders, newts)

PROTEIDA (*Necturus*)

MUTABILIA (true salamanders)

MEANTES (*Siren*)

PHYLUM   SUBPHYLUM   CLASS   SUBCLASS   ORDER

SALIENTIA (or ANURA) (frogs and toads)—5 orders, including:
    PROCOELA (true toads; *Bufo*)
    DIPLASIOCOELA (true frogs; *Rana*)

REPTILIA (snakes, lizards, turtles, alligators)
    CHELONIA (turtles)
    RHYNCHOCEPHALIA (*Sphenodon*)
    SQUAMATA (lizards, snakes)
    CROCODILIA (alligators, crocodiles)
    *COTYLOSAURS (primitive reptiles)
    *ICHTHYOSAURS (short-necked fishlike marine reptiles)
    *PLESIOSAURS (long-necked fishlike marine reptiles)
    *MOSASAURS (lizardlike marine reptiles)
    *THECODONTS (early running reptiles)
    *PTEROSAURS (flying reptiles)
    *DINOSAURS—2 orders
    *MAMMALLIKE reptiles—2 orders

AVES (birds)
    *ARCHAEORNITHYES (ancient birds; *Archaeopteryx*)
    NEORNITHYES (true birds)—30 orders
    Samples:
    PELECANIFORMES (pelicans)
    ANSERIFORMES (ducks)
    FALCONIFORMES (falcons and hawks)
    GALLIFORMES (chickens, fowl)
    COLUMBIFORMES (pigeons)
    PASSERIFORMES (perching birds)

MAMMALIA (mammals)
    PROTOTHERIA (monotremes, platypus)
    *ALLOTHERIA (multituberculates)
    THERIA (marsupials and placentals). Separated into the following 3 *divisions:*
      1. *PANTOTHERIA
      2. METATHERIA (marsupials; kangaroos, wallabies)
      3. EUTHERIA (placental mammals)
        INSECTIVORA (shrews, moles)
        CHIROPTERA (bats)
        DERMOPTERA (flying lemurs)
        PRIMATES (lemurs, monkeys, apes, man)
        EDENTATA (sloths)
        LAGOMORPHA (hares, rabbits)
        RODENTIA (rodents)
        CETACEA (whales, dolphins, porpoises)
        CARNIVORA (cats, dogs, and the like)
        PROBOSCIDEA (elephants)
        HYRACOIDEA (hyraxes)
        SIRENIA (manatees, dugongs)
        PERISSODACTYLA (odd-toed hoofed herbivores; horses)
        ARTIODACTYLA (even-toed hoofed herbivores; pigs, camels, deer, goats, sheep, cattle)

IV. EVOLUTION CHART

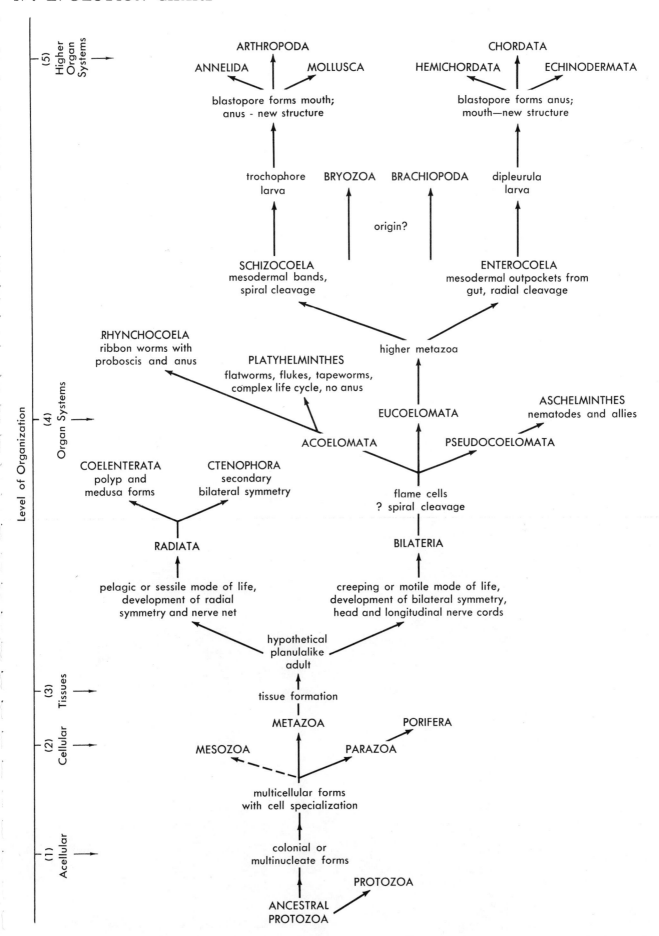

CHAPTER 3

Phylum

Protozoa

I. INTRODUCTION

The first sight of a *Paramecium* (Fig. 3-6) racing across the microscope field or of an *Amoeba* (Fig. 3-2) extruding its granule-filled endoplasm is a sight few biologists ever forget. The complex microworld of tiny organisms is every bit as interesting as the macroworld of our familiar daily experience. To realize the abundance, variety, and complexity of minute creatures is to extend one's knowledge into a new dimension. Once we recognize the role that protozoa play in human life and in the economy of nature, we can also appreciate their importance in contemporary biological research. We then look at these single-celled organisms with increased respect and wonder.

Protozoa are not confined to "simple" *Amoeba, Paramecium,* and other textbook examples. The group includes millions of tons of organic matter, found wherever living things exist. Members of this phylum range from organisms causing disease, as malaria or African sleeping sickness, to marine organisms of incredible beauty, complexity, and abundance (Figs. 3-3 and 3-4) whose remains form hundreds of thousands of square miles of ocean bottom, sometimes a mile or more deep. A single straw placed in a jar of water will yield a culture of myriads of protozoa whose species composition will change from day to day, a spectacular assemblage of every conceivable type and form of one-celled animal or plant.

We start reviewing the animal world with the Phylum PROTOZOA, one-celled or acellular animals. A protozoan is a complete organism in one intact, undivided unit. It seems incongruous to some experts to call the organism a "cell," since the protozoan cell performs essentially what it takes us two and a half trillon cells to accomplish. If a cell is, properly speaking, only a *part* of a living whole, then the PROTOZOA clearly are exceptions, for they combine all the business of living in a single unit. Hence many biologists prefer to call members of the phylum *acellular* rather than *unicellular*. All agree, nonetheless, that PROTOZOA are far from simple (Fig. 3-7). These animals carry out essential life processes in an incredibly small but complex unit that is just beginning to be appreciated through electron microscopy and other modern research methods. Protozoans are proving, too, to be invaluable means for investigating such processes as reproduction and cell division (Figs. 3-8 and 3-9), movement of substances through cell membranes, and various physical and biochemical problems in physiology, genetics, ecology, and evolution. Results from protozoan research are often as pertinent to understanding biological processes and functions of higher animals as to understanding the amoeba or *Paramecium*.

In this laboratory we can review only a few organisms, hence we emphasize the PROTOZOA as a vast and varied assemblage found wherever living things can survive.

▶ List some uses of protozoa in theoretical biology and research.

▶ Why should research on protozoa be of value to understanding human processes and functions?

▶ Why is the term "simple one-celled animal" misleading or false?

▶ Compare the term *unicellular* with *acellular*. What does each imply?

II. CLASSIFICATION

Taxonomic arrangement or classification of the protozoa reflects their importance in general biology. Since one-celled organisms are thought to be at the evolutionary base of life, they include members whose affinities may be with the plant kingdom or the animal kingdom or perhaps with both.[1]

Most opinions accept the following arrangement of the protozoa:

Phylum PROTOZOA
  Subphylum PLASMODROMA
    Class 1. MASTIGOPHORA—flagellates (Fig. 3-1)
      Subclass A. PHYTOMASTIGINA—plantlike flagellates
      Subclass B. DINOFLAGELLATA—dinoflagellates
      Subclass C. ZOOMASTIGINA—animallike flagellates
    Class 2. SARCODINA—rhizopods or amoebae (Figs. 3-2, 3-3, and 3-4)
    Class 3. SPOROZOA—sporozoans (Fig. 3-5), malaria, and allies
  Subphylum CILIOPHORA
    Class 1. CILIATA—ciliates (Figs. 3-6 to 3-9)

[1] Some workers have placed the protozoa in a separate Kingdom, **PROTISTA**, apart from all multicellular animals and plants. They divide the **PROTISTA** into several very large groups or subkingdoms, **PROTOZOA** being one of these. In this classification, the Subkingdom **PROTOZOA** would have its own phyla. Most scientists, however, place protozoa in a phylum within the Kingdom **ANIMALIA** with major subdivisions then being classes, subclasses, orders, and so on. Do not be disturbed by such differing opinions, which merely reflect changing ideas and the dynamic state of science. No expert and certainly no textbook can, at the present time, present more than an opinion or a consolidation of many viewpoints.

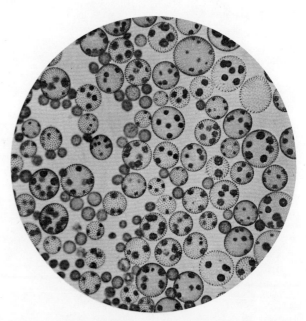

Fig. 3-1. *Volvox*, ×47.6. (Copyright by General Biological Supply House Inc., Chicago.)

Class 2. SUCTORIA—suctorians (Fig. 3-10)

You should learn the major groups of protozoa (whether they are considered phyla or classes) and know both the overall classification and specific groups of each laboratory example we shall study.

With the aid of your textbook, place each of the following species in its appropriate larger grouping in the above classification: *Amoeba proteus, Paramecium caudatum, Paramecium bursaria, Euglena viridis, Plasmodium vivax, Trypanosoma gambiense, Entamoeba histolytica.*

III. LABORATORY INSTRUCTIONS

A. Amoeba proteus (Fig. 3-2) (Which class does this organism represent?)

1—Structure—Examine a stained slide of *Amoeba*. Note the general outline and structures often difficult to distinguish in living amoebae, such as *ectoplasm, endoplasm, food vacuoles, nucleus, pseudopodium,* and *contractile vacuole.*

Vary light intensity with the iris diaphragm and condenser and observe the result. Learn to achieve a three-dimensional effect by constantly altering the fine focus, enabling you to see different layers of the animal. This will give you the "feel" of the organism's shape.

Now examine a drop of material containing living amoebae. Near the drop, place bits of filter paper or glass chips to support the coverslip and prevent crushing the specimens as fluid evaporates. Be careful not to wash the organisms out from under the coverslip while placing it over your preparation.

First search the field under low power. The protozoa will appear gray or bluish and show fine granulations. Vary the light and examine your specimen under high power.

Focus continually with the fine adjustment to determine the shape and thickness of the amoeba.

Watch carefully—look for granular movement (protoplasmic streaming). Find pseudopod formation (temporary protoplasmic protrusions for moving or for enveloping food) and retraction of a pseudopod and replacement by other pseudopodia.

▶ How does the amoeba move? (Even experts argue over this. Discuss it with your instructor.)

Draw various stages of motility in four or five outlines made one or two minutes apart. Show the *actual sequence* of movement of your own specimen.

▶ Can you trace protoplasmic streaming during formation of a pseudopod?

Watch for food capture or presence of living paramecia or other organisms trapped and held in *food vacuoles* within the amoeba.

▶ Are the prey still moving about in the vacuole? What finally kills them?

Look for the large, clear, bubblelike *contractile vacuole* usually seen in the trailing portion of the animal. Watch it fill and suddenly empty.

Draw a large specimen and include as many of the following structures as you can find (in your *specimen*, not your text): *nucleus, contractile vacuole, food vacuoles, granules.* Observe the *ectoplasm* with *plasmalemma* (outermost membrane enclosing a thin clear zone). The bulk of the amoeba is endoplasm divided into a gelatinous *plasmagel* underlying the ectoplasm, and a central liquid *plasmasol*, marked by protoplasmic streaming.

▶ Can you see changes in the plasmasol and plasmagel?

▶ How are they related to motility?

2—Observations—Watch the tip of a pseudopod and the posterior or trailing portion of endoplasm for changes in its consistency. These changes, apparently fundamental as-

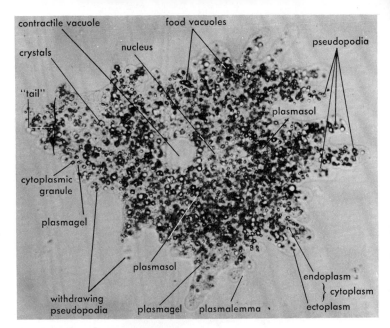

Fig. 3-2. *Amoeba proteus.*

pects of cytoplasm of all cells, are a clue to basic properties of living matter.

Record your observations by sketches and notes and try to develop some conception of the intricate structure, movements, feeding, and other habits of this allegedly simple animal.

Try to observe food capture, then food vacuole formation, and eventually egestion of undigestible portions of the prey. This is best seen in a starved culture to which paramecia have recently been added.

Time the pumping of the contractile vacuole.

▶ What is the function of this vacuole?

▶ What is implied by a high rate of pumping? A slow rate?

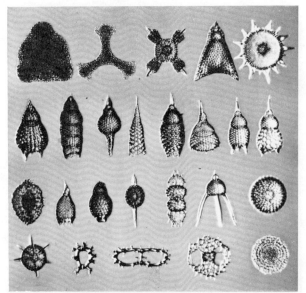

Fig. 3-3. Assorted *Radiolaria*, ×80. (Copyright by General Biological Supply House Inc., Chicago.)

Fig. 3-4. Assorted *Foraminifera*, ×80. (Copyright by General Biological Supply House Inc., Chicago.)

▶ Why do many marine rhizopods lack contractile vacuoles?

Check response by the amoeba to a light tap on the coverslip and watch it change shape. Try to observe one floating or slowly sinking.

▶ What shape is it?

▶ What happens to the shape after contact with glass?

▶ What is the normal habitat of *Amoeba proteus*?

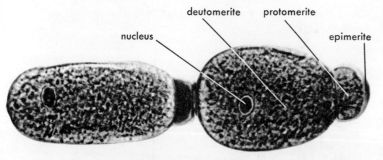

Fig. 3-5. Two gregarines in syzygy.

Fig. 3-6. *P. caudatum*, phase-contrast photo, ×470.

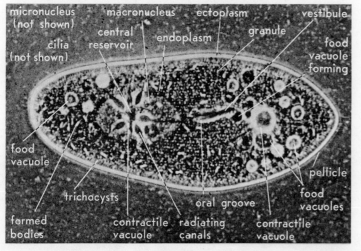

▶ What rhizopods are found in the ocean?

▶ Which ones inhabit the human intestine?

▶ Which occur in the human mouth?

▶ How are amoebae utilized in oil geology?

B. Euglena viridis (What class is represented by this form?)

Examine microscopically a drop from a culture of living *Euglena*. Watch them carefully under reduced illumination, at both low and high power. Notice the slow *directed* movement.

▶ Can you observe crawling, wormlike movements? Focus critically.

▶ Can you see the *flagellum* whipping about near the narrow anterior end?

▶ Can you find the red *stigma* or eyespot?

Notice the flexibility as some specimens coil about and appear to twist, extend, and contract. Continue observation under varying light, changing the fine adjustment to develop your three-dimensional sense. Discern the striated appearance of the outer *pellicle*, then locate internal structures. After 20 to 30 minutes of careful observation, aided by sketches and notes, carefully make a large drawing to show the normal or expanded profile. Illustrate the *gullet, flagellum, stigma, chloroplastids, pyrenoid granules, nucleus,* and *contractile vacuoles* grouped near the stigma. Add notes on motility or habits observed. Include with your sketch the magnification of the drawing (not just the lens system) and classification of the organism.

Improved differentiation of certain structures is possible with a light iodine stain (which colors the starch or paramylum in special storage granules). Methyl violet may help distinguish the flagellum as will other stains called *vital dyes*, which stain the living specimen.

▶ In what fashion does *Euglena* divide?

Study stained demonstration slides of the division process if they are available. *Euglena* is sometimes found in tremendous concentrations coloring pond water green and forming a surface scum.

▶ How do these protozoa later resist drying out or freezing over of ponds?

▶ How does *Euglena* react to light?

▶ Is *Euglena* a plant? Why? What, then, would you call euglenoids like *Astasia*, which lack chloroplastids?

▶ What would you call a *Euglena* grown in the

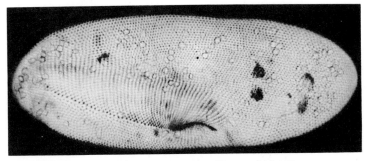

Fig. 3-7. Ciliature pattern of *Paramecium*. (Copyright by General Biological Supply House Inc., Chicago.)

dark, lacking chloroplastids, which feeds on dissolved nutrients in the medium?

► Can you see why it might be questioned whether *Euglena* is a plant or an animal?

C. Volvox (Fig. 3-1)

Volvox is a *colonial* flagellate. Each unit is a biflagellated protozoan rather like the individual flagellate *Chlamydomonas*. In fact, *Volvox* is considered the end of a series of evolutionary transitions. These lead from *Chlamydomonas* (one-celled, but four-celled at certain stages of its life cycle), through similar green flagellates consisting of flat plates of cells (*Gonium*) or of small spheres (*Pandorina*), through a larger spherical grouping (*Eudorina*), and finally to *Volvox*, which may consist of several thousand cells. If it were not for these intervening forms, it might be questioned whether *Volvox* is a colonial or a multicellular animal or plant. This developmental series is considered by some to indicate a possible sequence of stages in the origin of true plants.

Volvox clearly represents a high level of protozoan complexity with controlled movement, intercellular communicating fibers, and functional specialization involving reproductive and vegetative (feeding and locomotory) cells.

► Justify the inclusion of *Volvox* within the PROTOZOA, despite the fact that to some degree it acts like a *cellular* organism.

► Does *Volvox* also show cell specialization?

Study living specimens if available, or stained preparations. Identify *daughter colonies.*

► How are flagella oriented on these colonies?

► What happens to daughter colonies immediately after they pass out of the mother *Volvox*?

Draw a typical *Volvox* showing in detail a few cells with their interconnecting strands and outlining others. Show colonies and, if possible, germ cells. Identify and label the cellular detail you can actually discern in your specimen.

If slides are available, study and compare *Volvox* with slides of *Chlamydomonas*, *Gonium sociale* (4 cells per plate colony), *G. pectorale* (16 cells), *Pandorina* (16 cells), *Eudorina* (colonies spherical and of distinct sexes), *Pleodorina* (32 or 128 cells with differentiation between germ or reproductive cells and somatic or vegetative cells).

Compare the life history of *Chlamydomonas* with those of *Pleodorina* and *Volvox*, emphasizing development of specialization in reproductive cells.

D. Paramecium (Figs. 3-6 to 3-9) (representing which class?)

Few organisms have been peered at by more inquisitive eyes than *Paramecium*. Not only are countless student hours spent examining this "slipper animalcule," but biologists of many disciplines and research interests look at *Paramecium* with equal interest.

1—Observations—Obtain a drop from a healthy *Paramecium* culture. Examine it with the naked eye to locate the reflecting specks of fast-moving organisms. Look at them under your dissecting microscope at various magnifications. Try to follow their general activity. Then cover and examine again under low power of your compound microscope. Observe motility, shape, and orientation. (Locate relatively motionless organisms near the edge of the fluid or crowded together with bits of debris.)

► What is the symmetry of *Paramecium*?

► Which end is anterior? Can it back up or must it always go in one direction?

► Is movement controlled?

► How does it feed? (Place a strong light near one end of the microscope stage.)

► How do paramecia orient themselves?

► How do they react to tapping?

► How do they react to a few salt grains at one end of the slide? What would you conclude from this reaction? Watch them move about in bits of debris on the slide.

► What restricts their change of shape as they squeeze into crevices?

As the fluid gradually dries, find a quiet individual, then switch over to high-dry (43×). One way to slow the organisms is to use methocel—a clear, highly viscous liquid, *methyl cellulose.*[2]

[2] To make 100 cc of solution, add 10 grams methocel to 45 cc of boiling water, soak 20 minutes, then add 45 cc cold water, and cool until clear. Place a small ring of this fluid in the center of your slide; inside the ring add a drop of culture fluid containing the organisms. Add cover *slowly* and examine. Locate an organism trapped in the sticky material.

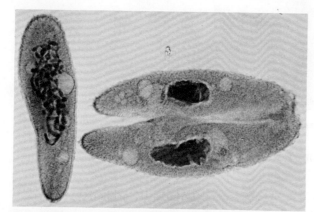

Fig. 3-8. *Paramecium* conjugation (pairing), ×420. (Copyright by General Biological Supply House Inc., Chicago.)

Fig. 3-9. Paramecium exconjugant, ×630. (Copyright by General Biological Supply House Inc., Chicago.)

2—Structure—Carefully work out the detailed structures of *Paramecium* to locate those described below.

Draw your specimen, at least 6 inches in length, oriented with anterior end near the top of the page. Look at several paramecia to make certain the example you select is typical. Examine and draw the feeding apparatus, showing *oral groove, vestibule* (depression leading to the mouth), *mouth,* and *gullet (or pharynx)* (Fig. 3-7). The end of the gullet is a small *esophageal sac* surrounded by fine fibers. The *food vacuole* formed here is released into the cytoplasm where it proceeds along a spiraling path, during which time the contents undergo digestion. Find and draw *cilia, pellicle, macronucleus, food vacuoles, granules,* and the stellate *contractile vacuoles.*

Fig. 3-10. An isolated suctorian from an amphipod appendage, ×200.

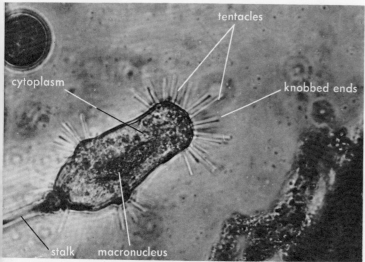

tentacles

cytoplasm

knobbed ends

stalk   macronucleus

Watch as contractile vacuoles fill by *radial canals,* empty into the *central reservoir,* and quickly discharge externally through a permanent pore.

► How many discharges can you count per minute? Compare this with other counts by your classmates.

► How would a small amount of sea water affect the count?

3—Special procedures—Certain structures show up well only when specific dyes are used. Add a droplet of dye to one side of your preparation, then draw it under the coverslip by sucking up water from the opposite side with a bit of filter paper or blotter. (Do not try to stain methocel preparations.)

a. *methyl green* will stain the *macronucleus.*

► Does this indicate a chemical difference between the macronucleus and cytoplasm?

b. *fountain pen ink.* Parker's "Quink" is an excellent excitant to cause paramecia to eject rodlike or hairlike *trichocysts,* said to be protective in function. Other stains, such as iodine or methyl green, may also be used to demonstrate trichocysts.

c. *congo red.* Stain a suspension of yeast cells and feed a drop to paramecia. When protozoans ingest the dyed yeast, digestive process can be followed inside the food vacuole, as congo red is an *indicator dye* that will gradually turn blue as the yeast particles become more acid. Watch carefully to observe swallowing and food vacuole formation. Then follow the winding course as vacuoles move through the endoplasm.

► How is this color change related to digestion?

► Is this process similar in paramecia and vertebrates?

Outline a *Paramecium* and trace the path of a food vacuole within it, noting color changes en route.

4—Asexual reproduction—If permanent stained slides are available, study *division stages* and nuclear changes during division.

► What is the plane of division?

► Why is this type of division considered an *asexual* process?

► Describe the precise steps before and during transverse binary fission.

► What happens to the macronucleus? To the micronuclei?

NOTES AND DRAWINGS

(Tear along line)

Try to find division stages that will enable you to follow the organism through successive stages of division.

Sketch three or four division stages including elongation and breakup of the macronucleus, dividing micronuclei, and gradual separation of daughter cells.

5—Sexual reproduction or conjugation (Figs. 3-8 and 3-9)—Conjugation can be studied in fixed stained preparations or in living material, but the latter gives a far better concept of this remarkable process. If appropriate *mating types* are available, obtain a drop of the freshly mixed *clones* and watch the stages of *clumping, pairing* (Fig. 3-8), and finally *exconjugant formation* (Fig. 3-9), followed in several hours by *asexual fission* of each exconjugant. Search for characteristic nuclear changes in stained preparations. Review the nuclear steps in conjugation, the genetic significance of which will be considered later in the course.

▶ How can the process of conjugation be compared with metazoan sexual processes?

6—Additional studies—The study of protozoa is truly a study of life in miniature. Experiments in genetics, ecology, and physiology can all be undertaken if proper facilities are available. Such special projects as mating type determination, culturing of protozoa, reactivity to various stimuli, vital staining and bleaching of *Euglena,* and keying and identifying pond or ocean samples are interesting and challenging studies. A simple but dramatic demonstration of biological succession requires only microscopic examination of samples taken daily from a freshly collected jar of pond water or from a hay infusion (a few wisps of hay or broom straw in tap water). From these, you can determine quantitatively the sharp daily fluctuation of populations and the different species that appear, "bloom," and disappear under changed conditions or after invasion by a predator.

Information on distribution, variety, and identification of protozoa can be found in such books as:

Jahn and Jahn, *How to Know the Protozoa,* William Brown Co. 1949.

Kudo, R. R., *Protozoology,* Thomas, Springfield, Ill. 1954.

Ward and Whipple (ed. Edmondson), *Freshwater Biology,* Wiley, N.Y.

Hyman, L., *The Invertebrates,* Vol. 1, McGraw-Hill, N.Y. 1940.

CHAPTER 4

Phylum
Porifera

I. INTRODUCTION

There is nothing like a sponge—to paraphrase Rodgers and Hammerstein. Nothing looks like a sponge, nothing acts like a sponge, nothing eats like a sponge. In fact, nothing *is* like a sponge. Find another living thing that feeds through a thousand outside pores, whose cells can be completely dissociated and then can wander together again to make many small new organisms. And find in nature another example of such fragile beauty as the Venus flowerbasket (Fig. 4-1), literally made of glass. These and other features make sponges unique. From the standpoint of *structure* (body organization and spicule skeleton), *manner of feeding* (collar cells for food handling, water pumping), and *reproduction* (amphiblastula, gemmules, regenerative reorganization), truly there is nothing like a sponge.

Hence, we divide the multicellular animals into three branches: sponges, the **PARAZOA** (near animals), and non-sponges, or **EUMETAZOA** (true animals). A third branch, **MESOZOA** (mid-animals), is a poorly known group whose relationship to the rest of the animal kingdom is still much disputed among the experts.

The Branch **PARAZOA** has just one phylum, the PORIFERA. Branch and phylum description are therefore alike. The difference between sponges and all other animals (which we might term nonsponges) is so clearly defined that it involves more basic characteristics than those dividing invertebrates from vertebrates. Your bath sponge thus becomes a most distinctive as well as utilitarian animal.

II. CLASSIFICATION

Kingdom **ANIMALIA**
Branch **PARAZOA**
Phylum **PORIFERA**
Definition: aquatic organisms attached to a substrate, permeated by pores through which water passes into inner flagellated chambers where feeding occurs.

Endoskeleton (internal skeleton) consists of discrete spicules made of calcium carbonate, glass, or spongin. A very ancient group with many fossils, PORIFERA contains about 5000 species, mostly marine. One family is found in fresh water. Reproduction is either sexual or asexual and involves an unusual larval form, the *amphiblastula*. Asexual reproduction is by budding, fragmentation and regeneration, and *gemmule* formation. The latter, found only in fresh-water forms, is a specialized, enclosed

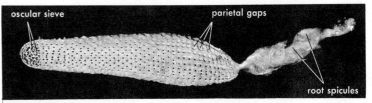

group of sponge cells forming a cystlike resistant body.

Three classes are generally recognized:

1—CALCAREA—with calcareous straight, or 3- or 4-branched spicules.

2—HEXACTINELLIDA—so-called glass sponges, with silica spicules bearing 6 rays.

3—DEMOSPONGIAE—spicules of spongin (as in common bath sponges), of glass, or lacking.

Much of the taxonomy of sponges is based on details of spicule structure (Fig. 4-2) since these are the only hard parts available for study. Despite its seemingly arbitrary nature, the system works and agrees remarkably well with another method based largely on the steroid biochemistry of sponges. In this, as in many such instances, results of newer and older methods of classification coincide, adding to our confidence in the scheme of classification based upon descriptive or morphological criteria. Morphological designations of species and larger groups are probably still our best means of identification and best overall measure of relationship, though physiological and ecological criteria are being employed whenever possible, and, as will be seen later, embryological characteristics are especially helpful in determining supraphyletic relationships.

III. LABORATORY INSTRUCTIONS

A. Scypha coronata (= *Grantia coronata*)

1—Observations on living specimens—If you are fortunate enough to be able to watch a living sponge in a laboratory or in its natural environment, try adding some powdered carmine or India ink to the water to demonstrate water currents through the animal.

Trace the direction of water flow.

▶ Which speed of flow is greater, into or out of the sponge?

▶ Why is it advantageous to the sponge to have the *excurrent* flow as rapid as possible?

Observe under the dissecting microscope: shape, color, mode of attachment, spicules projecting from the surface, excurrent pore (*osculum*), incurrent pores (*ostia*).

Draw as many of these structures as you can make out in your own specimen.

2—Preserved specimens—Repeat the above microscopic observations on preserved material. If living specimens are not available, make a sketch of general morphology of a preserved specimen.

Fig. 4-1. *Euplectella,* the Venus flowerbasket. Specimen 11.4 inches long.

3—Dried specimen (Fig. 4-3)—Examine a dried sponge. With a razor or scalpel make a careful cross section and longitudinal cut to show internal organization. Examine critically under a dissecting microscope and attempt to work out the canal system. Note that many *flagellated chambers* are directed towards the large central cavity or *spongocoel*. This organization, intermediate in complexity among sponge types, is of the *syconoid* form.

Locate the central cavity or spongocoel leading to the osculum and receiving water from each flagellated chamber of collar cells (*choanocytes*). *Excurrent canals* carry used water from flagellated chambers into the spongocoel via small openings, *apopyles.*

▶ How does water get into the flagellated chamber?

Draw a section of sponge wall to show the route by which water passes from ostium to flagellated chamber, then via an excurrent canal and apopyle into the spongocoel.

Place a bit of tissue in a glass dish, add bleach, examine the residue when bubbling ceases.

Fig. 4-2. Assorted monaxon and triaxon spicules of *Scypha coronata,* ×125. (Copyright by General Biological Supply House Inc., Chicago.)

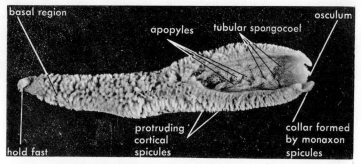

Fig. 4-3. *Scypha coronata* with upper end cut to exhibit spongocoel and internal details. Specimen 42 mm long.

▶ What has happened?

▶ What remains? Examine a drop of the residue under high power.

Draw several spicules. In another dish add some 10% KOH to the sponge tissue and compare the results.

4—Stained sections on slides—The best way to observe structural detail is with well-stained, special preparations. Even then normal cell appearance is seldom achieved because of distortion and shrinking. Living sponge cells viewed under the *phase microscope* make a remarkable demonstration—a sight even few biologists are fortunate enough to see.

Study your section and compare it with charts, models, or photographs (Fig. 4-4). Locate *choanocytes* and *amoebocytes*, the two basic cell types. The latter give rise to other cell types, such as the reproductive cells. Look for masses of *spermatozoa* or developed *ova*. Other specialized cells are *scleroblasts*, which secrete spicules, and dermal cells, or *pinacocytes*, which line the outer surface, incurrent canals, and entry pores.

Draw these cells in normal location as you work them out from your slide. Label the cell types you can actually find.

▶ How are spicules normally arranged? (Compare your slide with demonstration slide showing normal spicules.)

▶ What is the function of the collar cell?

▶ What is the function of the amoebocyte?

▶ How is the water current maintained?

▶ Where does sexual reproduction occur?

Review in your textbook the structure and stages of development of the amphiblastula larva.

B. Other Sponges

Examine dried or preserved specimens of as many sponge types as are available. Consult museum collections and various textbooks for illustration of living sponges to appreciate their variety and beauty.

32

1—Leucosolenia—shows the highly simplified *asconoid* type, in which the spongocoel is at the same time a single large flagellated chamber.

2—Venus flowerbasket (*Euplectella*)

▶ What class does this complexly beautiful glass sponge represent?

3—Horny or bath sponges

▶ What is the skeletal material of these sponges?

Members of this class constitute the most complex of sponges, the *leuconoid* type, with the most extensive network of chambers and ducts of any sponges. How does this basic organization compare with the *asconoid* and *syconoid* types? Leuconoid sponges are the most efficient in terms of water conduction, having a far greater total feeding surface. More convolutions and more flagellated chambers allow both a greater water-holding capacity and a relatively more rapid exit of used waste water out the osculum. Therefore, food-laden water enters a vast number of ostia, moves slowly as it enters, and spreads over a great number of flagellated chambers. Since

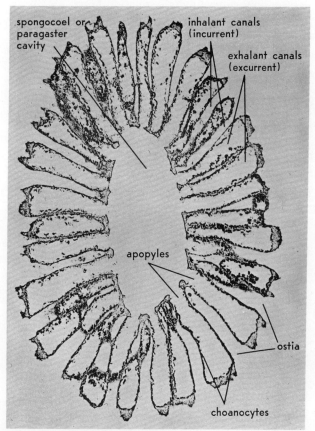

Fig. 4-4. Cross section of *Scypha*.

NOTES AND DRAWINGS

(Tear along line)

all chambers end in a very small number of spongocoels and oscula, water is compressed out at a rapid rate. Compare the simple and complex sponge with an elementary hydrodynamic problem. Water passes into 10 feeder pipes, each 1 inch in diameter, which merge and exit through a 10-inch pipe. In the more complex system, water passes from one hundred 1-inch feeder pipes out a 1-inch exit.

► *Compare* rate of water movement in the feeder systems (flagellated chambers) and in the exit pipes (osculum).

► In which system does the water remain longest in the feeding area (allowing choanocytes more time to work) and in which is the water ejected farther (preventing contamination of the feeding zone)?

This relative efficiency of water conduction apparently has enabled far more species of leuconoid than asconoid or syconoid types to survive and to occupy a greater variety of habitats.

Review the three basic sponge types, their relative degrees of complexity, and the ecological importance of these differences.

► What special characteristics enable *fresh-water* sponges to survive in their habitat?

► In what respect is fresh water more demanding and challenging to an invertebrate's survival than sea water?

Study a *Spongilla* if available. It belongs to a subclass of the **DEMOSPONGIAE** and contains spicules of silica plus binding threads of spongin. Usually it encrusts submerged sticks or stones.

Study a sectional drawing of a *gemmule.*

► Is it a sexual or asexual form of reproduction?

► Of what advantage is a gemmule to the sponge groups possessing it?

► Why do you suppose that gemmules are found only in fresh-water sponges?

Return to the definition of the phylum and the basic sponge organization. Justify separation of sponges from all other animals.

► Why is this phylum considered just above the protozoan level of multicellular organization, barely reaching the *tissue* stage of structural complexity?

► Explain why sponges are considered to be an evolutionary "dead end" (not ancestral to any other groups) despite their primitive and simple organization.

CHAPTER 5

Phylum

Coelenterata

or Cnidaria

I. INTRODUCTION

Jellyfish, hydra, corals, anemones, and related animals impress most of us as pretty low forms of life. Yet an entire course on basic zoological principles could be taught using COELENTERATA as the sole source of material. This is evidence of the enormous structural variety and wide range of adaptations in these aquatic predators, all built upon a common *basic body type*. Among points of biological interest these animals illustrate are the following:

1—Tissue level of body organization— Lacking organs, coelenterates consist of two well-defined layers, *epiderm* and *gastroderm*, with a third variably thick layer of *mesoderm* sandwiched between. Owing to its jellylike structure, this middle layer is often termed *mesoglea*, although in the Class ANTHOZOA (example: *Metridium*) the mesoderm layer is a true cellular tissue with considerable structural complexity. In *Hydra*, however, it is only a thin lining between the other two tissue layers.

2—Polymorphism (different body forms) —This phenomenon is illustrated both by distinct developmental forms (life-cycle stages) and by striking differences between individual members or units of a colony. In the jellyfish *Aurelia*, for example, the attached or *polyp* stage (in this group called the *scyphistoma*) develops by forming segments or buds that separate and become free-floating young *medusae* (specialized term: *ephyrae*). These develop into sexually mature adults. Another type of polymorphism is seen in colonial animals, such as *Physalia*, the Portuguese Man O'War, whose member individuals are so different that they look like separate parts or organs of a single animal.

3—Life cycles—Coelenterate growth and development involve a sequence of body forms, such as the polyp and medusa as noted above for *Aurelia*. Varying degrees of emphasis of one or the other stage produce many different patterns. In a somewhat typical type, both polyp and medusa are equally well developed (*Obelia*). In one instance the medusa stage is entirely eliminated (*Hydra* and *Metridium*); at the other extreme, the polyp stage is reduced (as in *Aurelia*) or absent (*Pelagia*). Some species have a sequence of polyps or of medusae produced by budding. Certain environmental factors may even influence the sequence of forms.

4—Evolution—COELENTERATA are generally considered an evolutionary link connecting **PROTOZOA** with more complex **METAZOA**. It is therefore an important group phylogenetically, one which contributed much to our understanding of the overall sweep of biological change. Review in your text the various (and conflicting) views on the origin of the higher metazoans.

Other characteristic coelenterate features include:

5—Symmetry—Radial symmetry in this phylum and biradial symmetry in the Phylum CTENOPHORA suggested the taxonomic term **RADIATA** (for what taxon?).
6—Nematocysts—Presence and variety of stinging capsules, probably more than any other single criterion, characterize the Phylum COELENTERATA.
7—Nervous system—The nervous system consists of *nonpolar cells* arranged in a nerve net, a critical morphological advance over sponges and protozoans, though far simpler than in any of the structurally more complex groups.
8—Reef formation—Remains of corals and other anthozoans contribute in large measure to formation of many miles of tropical coastline, fringing reefs, and atolls. The Great Barrier Reef of Australia is a 1500-mile-long example.
9—Characteristics of embryology, regeneration, and growth—Fundamental contributions to these topics have resulted from studies on *Hydra* and other coelenterates.

II. CLASSIFICATION

The 10,000 or more coelenterate species are placed in 3 large assemblages or classes, each based on overall body form.

Phylum COELENTERATA (or CNIDARIA):

Aquatic, mostly marine organisms at the tissue level of organization; lacking definitive organ systems, head, or anus. Symmetry radial or biradial. Tentacles surround the mouth, which leads to a saclike digestive cavity (enteron), with or without branches. Body form a sessile, single, or colonial polyp, or a floating medusa. Stinging cells of many types characteristic of both polyp and medusa stages.

Class 1. HYDROZOA, hydroids:

The gastrovascular cavity is undivided and lacks nematocysts; a noncellular mesoglea is present. Most hydroids possess a small medusa with a velum

but lack a stomadeum. Orders, with examples of genera, are the following: (1) HYDROIDEA (examples: *Hydra*,[1] *Obelia*), (2) TRACHYLINA (*Gonionemus*), (3) SIPHONOPHORA (*Physalia*), (4) MILLEPORINA (hydrocorals), and (5) STYLASTERINA (hydrocorals).

Class 2. SCYPHOZOA, true jellyfishes:

The free-swimming medusae are bell shaped, with 4-part radial symmetry, a thick and gelatinous mesoglea, and no velum or stomadeum. The mouth has gastric tentacles about it, a pouched gastrovascular cavity, and sense organs (tentaculocysts) on the edge of the bell. These sense organs are said to be the nearest approach to a true organ existing in the phylum. Gonads are located in the gastric cavity. The polyp phase is reduced to a segmented scyphistoma (see, for example, *Aurelia*).

Class 3. ANTHOZOA, the corals, sea anemones, and related forms:

These are mostly sessile coelenterates, with a flat oral disc from which hollow tentacles extend. The mouth leads to a gullet or stomadeum, then to an enteron divided into chambers by vertical septa bearing nematocysts, gonads, and, in some cases, special digestive tentacles (acontia). Mesoglea is well developed, forming a true connective tissue. The heavy calcareous epidermal skeleton secreted by corals produces oceanic reefs.

Subclass 1. ALCYONARIA (8 septa with lateral projections; 8 tentacles). Includes the organ-pipe coral, soft corals, horny corals, sea fans (*Gorgonia*), sea pen (*Pennatula*), and sea pansy (*Renilla*).

Subclass 2. ZOANTHARIA (6 to many tentacles, never 8). Includes the sea anemones (*Metridium*, *Anthopleura*), stony corals, black corals.

We will study the following representative forms of each class:

HYDROZOA—*Hydra, Obelia, Gonionemus*
SCYPHOZOA—*Aurelia*
ANTHOZOA—*Metridium*

Remember that these samples are selected from among many and hence provide no more than a suggestion of the wide variety of adaptive variations in each class. Observe each critically to compare it with others studied in order to obtain a balanced view of the whole phylum. "Take home" knowledge should include:

1—Basic coelenterate organization.
2—Particular characteristics of each type, in-

[1] The common name, hydra, is often used when referring to experimental work with various species of the genus *Hydra* or with similar genera, such as *Chlorohydra* and *Pelmatohydra*.

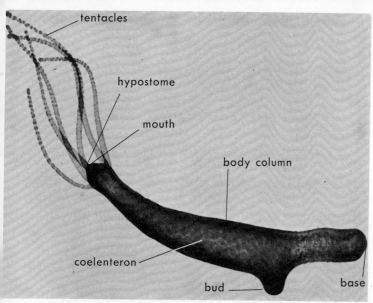

tentacles

hypostome

mouth

body column

coelenteron

bud

base

Fig. 5-1. *Hydra,* whole mount.

cluding overall form and specific structures, cell types, and degree of mesogleal development.

3—Habitats in which the animal is normally found, and its life cycle. Wherever possible, add observations of living activities including such things as motility, feeding reactions, response to selected stimuli, and study of regeneration and growth.

You should be able to recognize how structural variation from the general body type permits adaptation of these structures and habits to specific environments.

III. LABORATORY INSTRUCTIONS

A. Class 1. HYDROZOA—*Hydra* (Fig. 5-1)
   Order 1. HYDROIDEA

Hydra is an easily available example for study of coelenterate organization, including its basic cell types and response to external stress. Remember, however, that this organism is not a "typical" coelenterate. It is a fresh-water solitary polyp, without a free-swimming medusoid phase and with a greatly reduced mesoderm layer.

1—Gross structure of the living specimen —Study a living hydra in a shallow dish. Add enough pond water to allow it free movement. Observe general body form under hand lens or dissecting microscope. Locate *tentacles, nematocyst batteries, hypostome, mouth, base,* and (if present) a *bud* and/or *ovary* or *testis.* Observe the outer epiderm and inner gastroderm in your specimen. *Draw* a general view showing these structures.

2—Reactions of the living specimen—Observe reactions to:

a. Light tapping and rotation of the dish.
b. Touch. Lightly probe your specimen with a needle while observing it under the dissecting microscope.
c. *Dilute* acid, base, or salt solution.
d. Varying local intensity of light.
e. Presence of other hydra individuals.
f. Motility, including "tumbling" and "inchworm" movements (use a fresh specimen).
g. Nematocyst firing. Place specimen in a drop or two of water on a slide, cover, and observe under the compound microscope. Locate the batteries of intact nematocysts, each in a *cnidoblast* cell. The nematocysts are found in rings or masses on the tentacles. Then tap the coverslip lightly or place a drop of safranin solution or fountain pen ink under the coverslip. Observe discharge of nematocysts, seen as rapid eversion of nematocyst threads.

Locate and *draw* at least two different types of discharged cells.

h. Feeding reaction. Using fresh specimens starved about 48 hours, observe grappling, stinging, and engulfing reactions. For food use very small *Daphnia,* copepods, or brine shrimp, bits of earthworm or *Tubifex* worm, or tiny scraps of almost any meat. Put the food particles close to the hydra being careful not to cause withdrawal of the tentacles. Accurately record your observations during the feeding process.

Since no single preparation will show all these activities to maximum advantage, share your observations with those of other students.

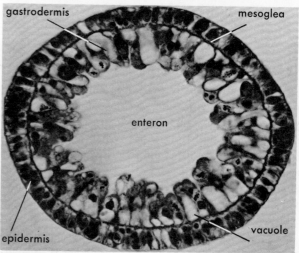

gastrodermis

mesoglea

enteron

epidermis

vacuole

Fig. 5-2. *Hydra,* cross section through body column, ×500. (Copyright by General Biological Supply House Inc., Chicago.)

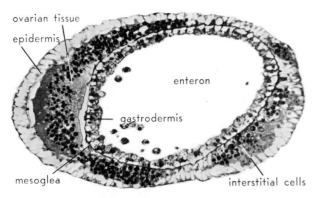

Fig. 5-3. *Hydra,* cross section through ovarium.

3—Histology (cross section) (Fig. 5-2)— From a prepared slide, observe and draw the cellular detail of a selected section (draw details in a wedge-shaped portion, outline the rest). Find: *epiderm,* with *epithelio-muscular cells,* and *interstitial cells, gastroderm* with *epithelio-muscular cells, gland cells, flagellated cells,* and *food vacuoles* in some gastrodermal cells.

▶ What additional structures would be visible if the section were through the hypostome? Through the gonad (Fig. 5-3)?

Diagram a longitudinal section cut from the hypostome and a tentacle down to the base of the animal. (Work out the structure from other sections you have studied.)

4—Questions

▶ How does hydra shorten? Lengthen?

▶ What type of symmetry does it show?

▶ What type of digestion is found? (Compare with a sponge and with a predaceous protozoan.)

▶ How is waste material egested?

▶ What is the life cycle?

▶ How is hydra adapted to a fresh-water environment?

▶ What other characteristics enable it to survive in its normal habitat?

5—Special projects

a. Observe the distribution and habitats of hydra in nature. Select a particular pond or series of sites and keep careful records of collections and observations at regular intervals.

b. Culture hydra in the laboratory from field collections. Study life cycle, feeding, growth.

c. Study regeneration of the hypostome, tentacles, or foot of hydra after removal of these parts.

d. Observe development of the sexual organs and of growth stages during bud formation (asexual reproduction). Make slide preparations of various stages.

B. Class 1. HYDROZOA
Order 1. HYDROIDEA; *Obelia* (Fig. 5-6)—a colonial hydroid

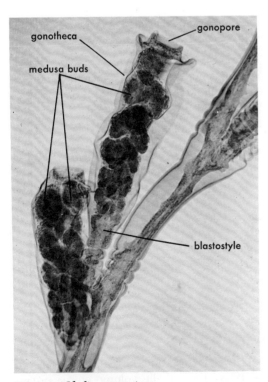

Fig. 5-4. *Obelia* gonangium.

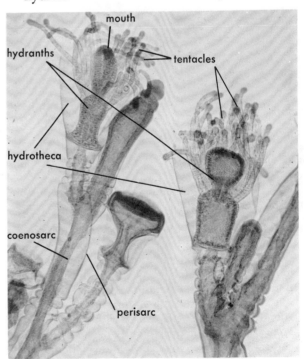

Fig. 5-5. *Obelia* hydranth.

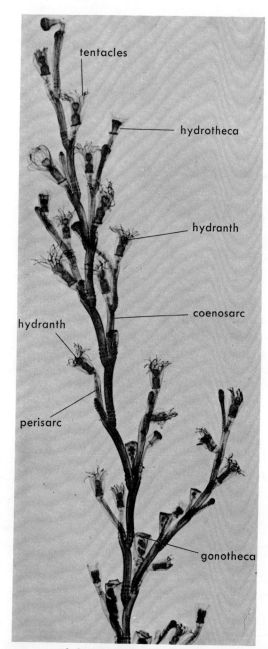

Fig. 5-6. *Obelia* colony.

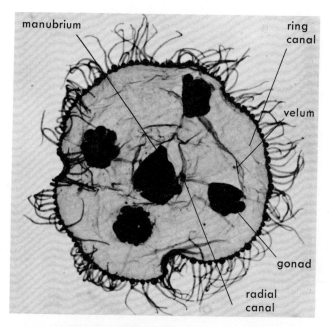

Fig. 5-7. Medusa of *Obelia*.

Sketch the general arrangement of a colony.

Draw each of the two types of polyp within this polymorphic colony.

Compare the function of the various units of the colony.

► How does the individual hydra perform these same functions?

► Is anything equivalent to the coenosarc, perisarc, hydratheca, or gonotheca found in hydra?

2—Medusa—Study a medusa of *Obelia* (Fig. 5-7), or some other hydroid, and locate the *bell* and the *manubrium* hanging from the *subumbrella* (ventral surface).

► Where is the *mouth*?

From the mouth, food passes to the *enteron* and into the *radial canals* and *ring canal*. These structures are lined by gastrodermal cells in which *intracellular digestion* occurs. Digested food products are passed to *amoebocytes* (wandering cells), which transport them to other body cells.

Between the tentacles are balancing organs, the *statocysts* (Fig. 5-7), containing a tiny "stone" (*statolith*).

► How do these organs work?

► Why are they of such importance to survival of medusae?

The mesoglea is thick in all medusae. In fact, it comprises much of the volume of the organism.

► In what way does *Obelia* represent a more "typical" coelenterate than hydra?

1—Colony (Fig. 5-6)—Examine an intact colony under a hand lens, then look for greater detail by placing a small portion of the colony in water in a watch glass or by studying a mounted, stained preparation. Using a dissecting microscope, study a *hydranth* (Fig. 5-5). Identify *tentacles, cnidoblasts* with their *nematocysts, hydrotheca,* ringed *perisarc,* and central *coenosarc.* Find a well-developed *gonangium* and locate the *gonotheca* (Fig. 5-4), *blastostyle,* and *medusa buds.*

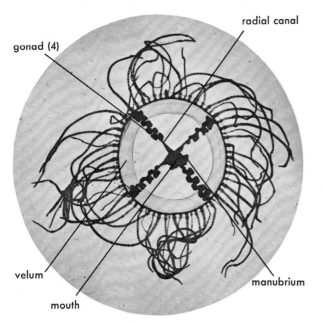

Fig. 5-8. *Gonionemus*, oral view, ×3. (Copyright by General Biological Supply House Inc., Chicago.)

► What is its function?

Gonads containing ripe sperm or eggs are located in the 4 dark central structures near the manubrium base.

► How do sex cells escape from the parent animal?

3—Life cycle—Describe the steps in the *Obelia* life cycle.

C. Class 1. HYDROZOA

Order 2. TRACHYLINA; *Gonionemus* (Fig. 5-8)

1—Anatomy—Study the anatomy of a specimen under water and try to observe structures already described for the medusa of *Obelia*. Do not dissect this specimen as it is to be returned to the instructor. The *velum* will be particularly clear, as well as the large gonads.
Draw an oral view of *Gonionemus*.

► What is the normal habitat of *Gonionemus*?
► On what does it ordinarily feed?

2—Comparative material—If available, observe museum specimens of other scphomedusae, such as the jellyfish *Pelagia*, *Cyanea*, or *Dactylometra*. Perhaps the most intriguing coelenterate of any yet described is *Physalia*, the Portuguese Man O'War (Order SIPHO-NOPHORA). This is a colonial organism in which individual zooids are so specialized and integrated within the colony that they appear to be parts of a single animal. It probably rep-

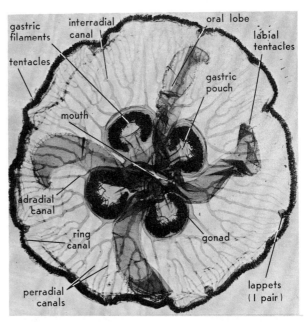

Fig. 5-9. *Aurelia*, adult.

resents both the highest known degree of polymorphism and the highest evolutionary development in which specialization of *whole individuals* rather than *cells* or subunits of a single organism are involved. Consider bee, ant, or termite colonies. Since the members are polymorphic and interdependent, should the hive or anthill be considered a loosely aggregated colony?

► How do the zooids of *Physalia* develop?
► How do we know that they actually *are* separate individuals and not all one animal?

D. Class 2. SCYPHOZOA—*Aurelia* (Fig. 5-9)

1—Anatomy—Study the anatomy of an *Aurelia* medusa without dissecting it (return it intact later).

► Is a velum present?

Differentiate the SCYPHOZOA from the Medusae of HYDROZOA.
Locate oral lobes, labial tentacles, gastric or *enteric pouches* with *gastric filaments* inside them, *radial* and other canals (*interradial* and *adradial*), 8 pairs of *lappets* at the edge of the bell, and *balancing organs*.

► Can you find an *eyespot* in each of these organs?

Draw a ventral view of *Aurelia*, giving details in one quadrant only.

► How do jellyfish swim? Feed? Digest their food?

Fig. 5-10. *Scyphistoma.*

Fig. 5-11. *Strobila.*

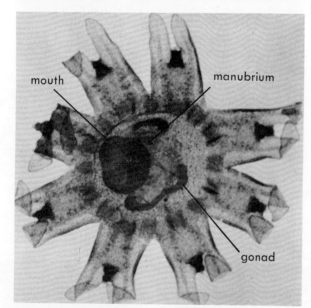

Fig. 5-12. *Ephyra.*

2—Life cycle—Describe the complete life cycle (Figs. 5-10 to 5-12).

▶ Basically, how does it differ from that of *Hydra*? From *Obelia*?

E. **Class 3. ANTHOZOA**—*Metridium* (Figs. 5-13 to 5-16)

1—Anatomy—On an intact specimen (Fig. 5-13) find the *oral disc, mouth, tentacles, body column,* and *pedal disc.*

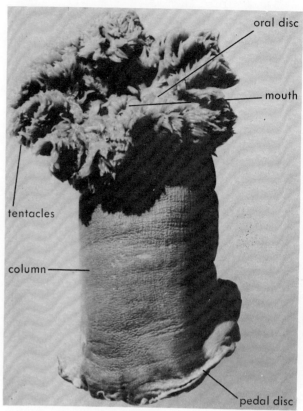

Fig. 5-13. *Metridium,* expanded.

2—Sections—Split a specimen lengthwise, from mouth to pedal disc. Locate the above structures, and, in addition, the *gullet* with its *siphonoglyph* (one or two?), and the *enteron* lined by *septa* (or *mesenteries*) (Fig. 5-14).

At the edge of the septa are thick,

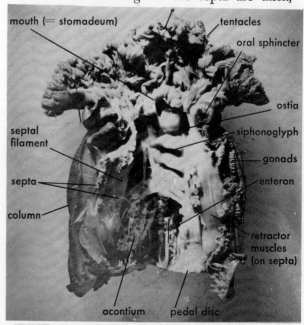

Fig. 5-14. *Metridium,* dorso-ventral section.

NOTES AND DRAWINGS

(Tear along line)

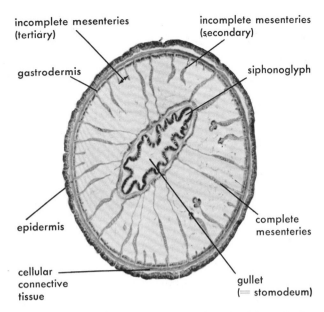

incomplete mesenteries (tertiary)

incomplete mesenteries (secondary)

gastrodermis

siphonoglyph

epidermis

cellular connective tissue

gullet (= stomodeum)

complete mesenteries

Fig. 5-15. *Metridium,* cross section through siphonoglyph.

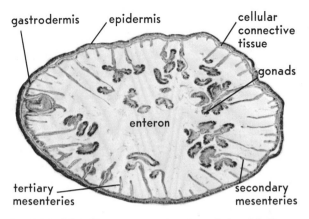

gastrodermis

epidermis

cellular connective tissue

gonads

enteron

tertiary mesenteries

secondary mesenteries

Fig. 5-16. *Metridium,* cross section through basal half.

convoluted *septal filaments* ending in the *acontia.* The *gonads* resemble clusters. of beads on the septa.

Have your dissection and knowledge of these parts checked by your instructor.

► Where are body muscles found?

► How does lengthening of the body column occur? Shortening? Withdrawal of tentacles?

► How does the sea anemone avoid drying out when exposed to air and sunlight at very low tides? Describe feeding and digestion in this animal.

► What is the probable function of the various radial septa?

► What is the life cycle of *Metridium*? Of corals?

Prepare and study several cross sections of *Metridium* (Figs. 5-15 and 5-16) to

determine the different types of septal divisions. Find the *retractor muscles* on the septa.

► Where is the mesoglea?

► What is its function in these animals?

F. Review Questions on COELENTERATA

► How can we state that *Hydra* and *Metridium* show the same basic body type despite the obvious differences in their structure?

► Compare the life cycle of *Hydra, Obelia, Aurelia,* and *Metridium.*

► Which is the most highly developed (most complex) coelenterate you have studied?

► Why do we speak of the coelenterate life cycle as a single developmental sequence, despite the fact that two phases (and also two types) of reproduction are involved? Why is the medusa considered to be the adult form?

► Compare: individual, aggregation, colony. Compare the types of colony represented by *Volvox, Obelia,* and *Physalia.* How do they differ?

Flatworms, or platyhelminths (*platy*, flat; *helminth*, worm), form 3 classes, the free-living (that is, nonparasitic), ciliated TURBELLARIA and 2 classes of highly specialized parasites, the TREMATODA (flukes) and CESTODA (tapeworms). Flatworm is a term usually restricted to the Class TURBELLARIA, whereas flukes and tapeworms, along with certain other groups of parasitic worms, are commonly called helminths.

The Phylum PLATYHELMINTHES demonstrates remarkable adaptive adjustment to free-living intertidal or fresh-water existence on one hand and to parasitism on the other. This phylum also demonstrates (1) *the organ level of complexity*, (2) *bilateral symmetry*, and (3) *the simplest form of body organization built largely of mesoderm*. These are three such critical steps in the evolutionary sequence toward more complex organisms that we shall have to consider their more widely extending implications before we review PLATYHELMINTHES separately.

I. INTRODUCTION TO HIGHER ANIMALS (GRADE BILATERIA)

Certain characteristics of free-living flatworms suggest that the Phylum PLATYHELMINTHES is ancestral to the so-called higher animal phyla,[1] and hence to all animals more complex than a jellyfish or sea anemone. Increased specialization of mesoderm with development of efficient organs is the most marked and significant distinction between flatworms and jellyfish or sponges. TURBELLARIA are the simplest animals yet discovered with a brain and central nervous system, a well-organized excretory system, and a complex reproductive system. Most body functions of flatworms are performed by specialized tissues or organs—a significant evolutionary advance over even the most complex coelenterates, in which organs are absent and individual, nonspecialized cells often share several body activities.

During the ages, distinct advantages have obviously accrued to the first flatworms with bilateral symmetry, improved sensory perception, increased muscular coordination, more rapid movement, and

CHAPTER 6

Phylum

Platyhelminthes

---

[1] The stages of complexity of body structures described in this section should suggest to the student why members of this and the following phyla are referred to as "higher animals."

greater efficiency in processing food, excreting wastes, and controlling metabolic processes.

Associated with greater structural complexity is a way of life employing *directed motility*, active seeking of prey. This is a distinctly different pattern of behavior from that of coelenterates, which sting prey accidentally encountered in their non-directed swimming, floating, or sessile existence.

Much of our time in this course will be devoted to comparing structural and functional evolutionary changes in this and in succeeding animal phyla and relating them with pattern of living and habitat. Our purpose in doing so is threefold. *First*, to review the various manifestations of animal structure and function. *Second*, to see how these are increasingly more efficient and better adjusted (adapted) to the environment, including competition from other animals. *Third*, to account for these adaptive changes in a scientifically valid manner.[2]

Structural complexity permits functional specialization. Both are associated with increased adaptation or improved methods of coping with environmental stress that we consider characteristic of higher animals.

To understand the structural organization that makes further complexity possible, we must concentrate on *mesoderm*, the tissue from which most body structures of higher animals are derived. Recall that sponges have no such tissue, only wandering *amoebocytes*. Coelenterates have *mesoglea* of varying thickness from a thin jellylike layer to a true connective tissue. In platyhelminths, mesoderm fills the body cavity (space between body wall and gut) and is therefore called *parenchyma*. This body filling consists of a mass of cells lacking clearly defined cell walls. In more complex animals, mesoderm is clearly defined, forming tissues and organs of

---

[2] *Caution.* Adaptation is nearly universal in nature. Everywhere we see examples of it. Some adaptations are incredible, some so widespread and obvious we scarcely notice them. However, because an animal is perfectly adjusted to its environment, do not assume that the environment *caused* such a change. The camouflaging spots of a leopard are not explained by its *needing* them. This caution may seem to be unnecessary, yet the need for it will appear time and time again. Often we assume a simple cause and effect relationship between the environment and adaptation, between "need" and structure, though it may sometimes be disguised by minute detail or lofty jargon. But do not permit preconceived notions or automatic assumptions to mask your search for scientific understanding of such evolutionary processes as variation in nature, differential reproduction, and natural selection. These subjects comprise much of the theoretical material to be considered in the course. The laboratory will demonstrate and lectures will explain these processes.

highly specific structure and function. Associated with this increase in complexity is the development of a *coelom*, a body cavity *lined with mesoderm*.

Two intermediate stages of mesoderm organization within the body cavity occur in different animals. PLATYHELMINTHES, as noted, possess a parenchymatous (mesoderm-filled but not mesoderm-lined) body cavity. This is considered the most primitive type, called an *acoelom* (without coelom). Further integration of organ systems is found in the Phylum ASCHELMINTHES (see Chapter 7), with the body cavity *partially* lined with mesoderm. This type of mesoderm development is termed a *pseudocoelom* (false coelom).

In animals possessing a true coelom, body structures lying between the body covering (*epiderm*) and intestine (*gastroderm*) are enclosed by mesodermal sheets called *mesenteries* or *peritoneum*. One sheet underlies the body wall (hence: *somatic peritoneum*), another encloses the gut (hence: *splanchnic peritoneum*). The two sheets merge along the dorsal wall to form the *dorsal mesentery,* and in some instances form a *ventral mesentery* as well. Additional linings of mesentery enclose each organ, so that in all animals having a coelom, the organs are literally suspended within the body cavity by their mesodermal lining.

Each of these types of mesoderm organization characterizes large groups of animals of increasing structural complexity and integration. Mesoderm development is therefore used for taxonomic groupings as 3 *levels* within the Grade **BILATERIA** (see Chapter 2).

Level 1. **ACOELOMATA**   lacking coelom
Level 2. **PSEUDOCOELOMATA** partial coelom
Level 3. **EUCOELOMATA**   true coelom

II. INTRODUCTION TO PLATYHELMINTHES

The acoelomate structure of flatworms permits a greater degree of tissue specialization than is possible in lower animals. Hence, we find flatworms to be at the *organ level* of complexity. Instead of a nerve net, they possess a central nervous system with ganglia and nerve trunks. Well-developed sheets of opposing longitudinal and circular muscles underlie the outer epidermal layer of the body and control the body shape. The excretory system, particularly characteristic of flatworms, consists of flame cells or protonephridia—special ciliated cells that collect body fluids and pump them into a complex series of ducts and channels. Fluids pass afterwards to an excretory bladder and out one or more excretory pores. Flexible and coordinated motility is well developed in free-living TURBELLARIA, as they possess cilia on their ventral body surface and secrete a coat of mucus on which they can easily glide. They can pass smoothly over a razor's edge in the laboratory (try it) or over the sharpest rocks or softest mud in their aquatic habitat. Some seek animal prey, others vegetation, usually algae.

In their protected habitat inside the body of a vertebrate host, flukes and tapeworms have lost both cilia and epiderm (although some immature stages retain these structures) and are covered by a tough, nonciliated *cuticle*. In these internal parasites, motility seems to have been sacrificed for the capacity to adhere in the gut and to resist digestion by the host. Structural adaptations include hooks, spines, suckers, flaps of tissue, or combinations of these, to provide a mechanism for "staying put," usually in the intestine of vertebrates. Accompanying these structural changes are numerous physiological adaptations as well as adjustments of life cycle and reproductive. powers to the exigencies of parasitism.

The digestive system among PLATYHELMINTHES is extremely variable. In fact, variations of this system determine the taxonomic orders of free-living flatworms. The intestine of most flukes (TREMATODA) branches into two blind sacs, or *ceca*, while tapeworms (CESTODA) have lost the system entirely and obtain food by absorption through the cuticle. Dissolved materials pass directly into the interior parenchyma.

The reproductive system is perhaps the most impressive of all specialized structures in flatworms. Well developed in TURBELLARIA, it is extraordinarily complex in the flukes and tapeworms, which have essentially become reproductive machines. Since the chance of a parasite to transfer its progeny from one host to another is remote at best, high reproductive capacity is obviously an adaptive mechanism for survival. Combined with this adaptation in certain trematodes are sometimes highly bizarre, complex life cycles involving intermediate hosts, specialized larvae, and both sexual and asexual reproduction.

In tapeworms, sexual reproduction follows mutual exchange of sperm between segments of different worms or different segments of the same worm. As is generally true of platyhelminths, most tapeworms and flukes are *hermaphroditic (monoecious)*—both sexes occurring in the same individual. Another form of reproduction in tape-

worms—*asexual* (not involving sexual organs)—occurs in *larvae* of certain taenia-like cestodes. In these instances, the larvae develop in bladderlike cysts within the tissues of a certain host, but *many* rather than one larva bud from special germinative tissue in each cyst. This type of larval asexual reproduction is called *polyembryony* (many larvae).

A different kind of asexual reproduction occurs in nearly all adult tapeworms. The body consists of a chain of segments budded out from a growth area near the scolex ("head"). These segments contain 1 or 2 complete sexual systems. Segmentation, therefore, is a duplication of sexual organs and perhaps of individuals, if one can call a segment a separate individual. In some heavy-bodied cestodes, the segments actually do break off and crawl about in the host intestine like separate worms.

► Would you therefore call segmentation a form of asexual reproduction?

► Would this make the tapeworm an attached series of individuals forming a *colony*? The answer revolves around one's definition of *individual* in terms of its independence from the group to which it belongs. Notice how the distinction between *reproduction* and *growth* may be modified or lost in considering the above question.

In some flukes (Order DIGENEA—a name denoting 2 hosts in the life cycle), larvae bud off within themselves individual germinal cells or clusters of cells that give rise to successive generations of structurally different larval forms, all from a single initial egg. The resulting larvae develop, escape from the "parent" larva into the tissues of the host (usually a snail), and proceed to form new larvae. The sequence of larval forms differs so markedly that each is given a special name: *miracidium, sporocyst, redia,* and *cercaria* (a nonreproductive motile form). This process is another form of larval asexual reproduction and polyembryony. In all digenetic flukes the general reproductive pattern is quite similar, but the specific host and manner of development is characteristic of each species. Sexual reproduction occurs in the final host of these flukes, in which the worms mature (become adults), copulate, and produce eggs. Elucidation of trematode life cycles offers biological detective work of extreme interest and the research needed is scarcely begun.

Another group of TREMATODA, the Order MONOGENEA (single-host life cycles), lacks polyembryony and develops directly on its specific host, usually a fish or other aquatic vertebrate.

Of necessity, most of your time will be spent on fixed stained specimens mounted on slides. Take advantage of any living material available to you and be assured that the actually moving worms will arouse your interest. Remember, however, that the stained specimens are *animals,* not just so much colored material on glass. Once very much alive, they should represent to you millions of still living organisms, some perhaps in your own body, certainly in the bodies of multitudes of other human beings. Those who have the opportunity to study and search for living examples of these parasites find that the common feeling of revulsion towards such a way of life is replaced by keen interest and continual surprise at the variety and habits of living organisms. Special projects, such as observation of regeneration in planaria or necropsy of hosts for parasitic worms, may particularly intrigue you.

III. CLASSIFICATION

Phylum PLATYHELMINTHES, flatworms:

Soft-bodied, flattened, usually elongate worms, covered by epiderm or cuticle, and unsegmented (except CESTODA). Digestive tract incomplete (no anus) or entirely lacking (CESTODA). Excretory system of flame cells (or protonephridia) leading to ducts and to one or more excretory pores. Body cavity acoelomate, the space filled with parenchyma. Nervous system consists of an anterior ganglia or nerve ring and 1 to 3 pairs of longitudinal nerve cords. No skeletal, circulatory, or respiratory organs. Usually hermaphroditic, with complex sexual apparatus; fertilization internal with yolky, shelled, microscopic eggs. Development direct in TURBELLARIA and MONOGENEA; indirect, with highly distinctive larval stages in CESTODA and DIGENEA. Polyembryony in DIGENEA and some cestodes. Free-living or commensal (TURBELLARIA) and parasitic (TREMATODA and CESTODA).

Class 1. TURBELLARIA, free-living flatworms:

Ciliated epiderm with rhabdites and mucous glands; mouth ventral. Usually pigmented and with eyespots. Orders, based on type of digestive tract, are the following:

(1) ACOELA[3] (no digestive tract) (2) RHABDOCOELA (single digestive tube, usually saclike) (3) ALLOECOELA (straight tube or with short branches) (4) TRICLADIDA (3-branched, usually with secondary short branches, as,

---

[3] Do not confuse ACOELA with acoelomate or acoelom, descriptive terms for the type of body cavity in all platyhelminths.

for example, in *Dugesia*) (5) POLYCLADIDA (many-branched; mostly marine forms).

Class 2. TREMATODA, flukes:

All parasitic; with cuticle; suckers and/or hooks for attachment; mouth usually anterior, leading into a 2-branched digestive tract; ovary single and testes usually paired.

Order 1. MONOGENEA—usually a single host, development direct (without distinct larval stages); large posterior sucker with or without hooks, anchors, or spines; parasitic on gills, mouth, pharynx, or anus of aquatic vertebrates.
Order 2. ASPIDOBOTHRIA—entire ventral surface forming a specialized sucker divided into small divisions.
Order 3. DIGENEA—more than one host, the first a mollusc and the final host a vertebrate; two suckers; no hooks; polyembryony only in molluscan host. (*Clonorchis, Fasciola.*)

Class 3. CESTODA, tapeworms:

Parasites of vertebrates, usually intestinal; most segmented, with each segment (proglottid) lined with cuticle, bearing 1 or 2 complete, hermaphroditic reproductive systems; anterior scolex (plural: scoleces) with suckers and/or hooks for attachment. No digestive system or sense organs; life cycle complex. No larval multiplication except in a few exceptional forms, such as *Echinococcus* and other relatives of *Taenia* with asexual multiplication of scoleces in a larval cyst. (*Taenia, Diphyllobothrium, Hymenolepis.*)

IV. LABORATORY INSTRUCTIONS

A. Class 1. TURBELLARIA

Free-living flatworms will be represented by the fresh-water planarian, *Dugesia tigrina* (Fig. 6-1), or some related form. It is an active, predaceous,

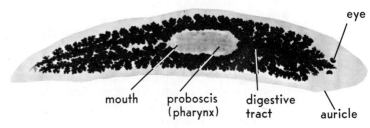

Fig. 6-1. *Dugesia,* whole mount, stained to show intestine.

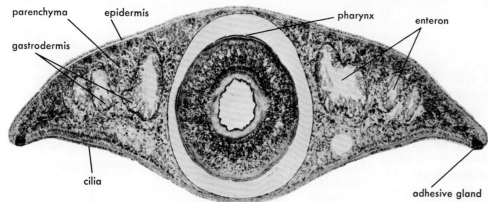

parenchyma   epidermis   pharynx   enteron

gastrodermis

cilia

adhesive gland

Fig. 6-2. *Dugesia*, cross section through pharynx.

responsive animal, extremely sensitive to chemicals, pH, light change, electrical fields, gravity, food, and similar stimuli.

1—Living responses—Carefully record observations on a living specimen in pond water in a clean syracuse dish or watch glass. Follow its movements with a hand lens or dissecting microscope. Note motility and reaction to such factors as food (bits of liver), jostling, strong light, and flipping the worm upside down with a needle. Check reactions to a drop of weak acid or base, to 1 percent salt solution, or other chemicals. (Remember that it may respond by disintegrating.)

2—External anatomy—Observe the entire organism, its bilateral symmetry and major axes. Locate the *dorsal* and *ventral* surfaces, *anterior* and *posterior* ends. Note lobelike *auricles* (lateral extensions of the head), *pharynx* and *pharynx sheath, mouth,* and *intestine.* The *genital pore,* a small spot posterior to the mouth on the midventral surface, can be seen if the specimen happens to be lightly colored.

3—Detailed structure—Place specimen on a slide in a drop or two of water, cover with another slide or strong coverslip, press slightly, and observe under the high-dry lens of your compound microscope. Look for detailed structure of the *eyes, cilia, pigment granules,* and particularly for *flame cells,* detected by a faint flickering of the cilia inside the cell. The latter will be the reward of a persistent and diligent search, plus a certain amount of drying and compression of the specimen. After the specimen disintegrates (and it will), locate separated groups of cells and study their structure. Active movement of ciliated cells of the ventral epidermis may be studied in this way.

4—Histology (cross section) (Fig. 6-2)—Study a stained cross section of a turbellarian. Use it as a means to picture a three-dimensional view of the animal you have previously seen in surface view. Locate *rhabdites, gland cells,* and *cilia* in the *epidermis.* Find the *pharynx* (or *proboscis*), *pharynx sheath, intestine* (how many branches?), and endodermal *gastroderm*

with gland and storage cells. Next observe the "body filling" of parenchyma cells. Look for the two ventral nerve cords near the midventral line. Below the epiderm find the *circular, transverse,* and *longitudinal muscle layers.*

Make a large *drawing* of your section, giving cellular detail for a pie-shaped portion only. Show only structures you can find in your own slide.

For a more complete understanding of this class, study other species from charts, diagrams, and text illustrations. Note variations and appearance of other orders. Check structure of the reproductive system particularly, as it is extremely difficult to discern in *Dugesia.* Details of this system can be seen satisfactorily only in appropriate cross sections or in serial sections—which is one reason why there are so few experts on taxonomy of TURBELLARIA.

5—Special projects

a. Search for planarians in fresh-water ponds, under leaves or stones, or on the lower surface of rocks turned over in the intertidal zone of a rocky coastal area. Try to locate representatives of each order of TURBELLARIA. Bring living planarians back to the laboratory in fairly large jars of the original water in which they were found. *Keep them cool and do not overcrowd* with other specimens or with organic material. Identify them and record observations on feeding, reproduction, and responses to various stimuli. Special experiments can be developed to test reaction to such stimuli as an electric field, varying light intensity, chemicals or drugs, and various types of food. Keep careful notes on rhythms of activity, on feeding preferences, combativeness, mating, or rates of activity of undisturbed animals. Such observations may prove to be original and valuable scientific contributions.

b. Study *regeneration* or replacement of body parts. Plan your experiment in advance after reading your text and references suggested there. Careful preparation and follow-through during the experiment will pay off in results—regeneration instead of disintegration. Use a sharp scalpel or razor blade to cut selected large specimens after they are first placed on a cube of ice, on moistened paper toweling, or on a new white blotter. Maintain your operated specimens in a covered container kept filled to a uniform level with clean pond or aged water, and do not feed them during the experiment. Place worm fragments in separate labeled containers (petri dishes or small jars). If partial cuts are made to test formation of multiple heads, *these must be recut periodically* to prevent healing over. Examine the worms at regular intervals during a two-week period; draw their outlines periodically to show zones of regeneration, and prepare a report of your experiments and final results.

▶ Is regeneration a form of reproduction?

▶ What types of reproduction are found in Turbellaria?

B. Class 2. Trematoda—flukes

This class includes many hundreds of parasitic species, ranging from a half millimeter to elongate, coiled forms a meter in length. Generally, they are leaf-shaped (hence: fluke) and characterized by a complex hermaphroditic reproductive system and, in the Order Digenea, by a weirdly complex life cycle.

Two species of flukes, both in the Order Digenea, are used in most introductory laboratories —the human liver fluke, *Clonorchis* (or, properly, *Opisthorchis*) *sinensis* (Fig. 6-3), and the sheep liver fluke, *Fasciola hepatica* (Fig. 6-4). The latter is atypical in that all major organ systems have multiple branches, making it difficult to study. *Clonorchis*, a more representative fluke, is easier to study structurally. However, many other species might also be used. Examination of lungs, intestine, and bladder of a few freshly killed frogs will dramatically demonstrate the availability of flukes in nature.

1—Adult structure (*Clonorchis*, stained whole mount)—On a stained specimen find the *suckers* (anterior *oral sucker* surrounding the mouth, and *ventral sucker* or *acetabulum*), then the *pharynx* and intestinal branches (*ceca*). Work out the reproductive system carefully with the aid of Figure 6-3. The male system consist of 2 *testes, sperm ducts, seminal vesicle, cirrus* or *penis* often enclosed in a *cirrus pouch*, and *genital pore* (common exit of both reproductive systems). The female organs, somewhat more complex, consist of an

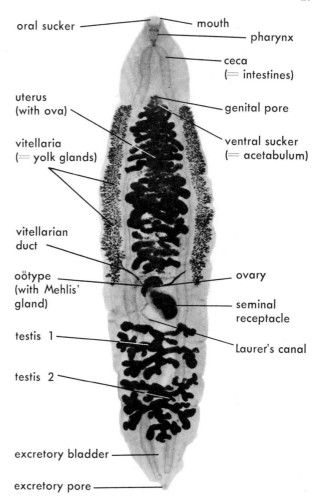

Fig. 6-3. *Clonorchis,* whole mount, stained to show reproductive system.

ovary connected by an egg tube or *oviduct* to a fertilization and yolk accretion chamber, the *oötype*. Connected to the oötype is a *seminal receptacle* (for storing sperm received during copulation), and a *vitelline duct* bearing yolk material from the yolk or vitelline glands. Fertilization occurs in the oötype, after which yolk is rapidly pressed onto the egg in a veritable stamping-mill process, in some forms producing a finished egg every few seconds. The oötype is usually surrounded by a rather diffuse *Mehlis' gland*, often difficult to see. Review the structures and function of organs surrounding and feeding into the oötype. From the oötype, the newly fertilized, yolk-laden egg moves into the coiled *uterus*, a large structure characteristic of digenetic flukes. Here, egg shells are hardened and darkened by a chemical tanning process, and eggs are stored until they pass out the genital pore.

Next, locate the terminal *excretory pore* and, if not obscured, the excretory bladder.

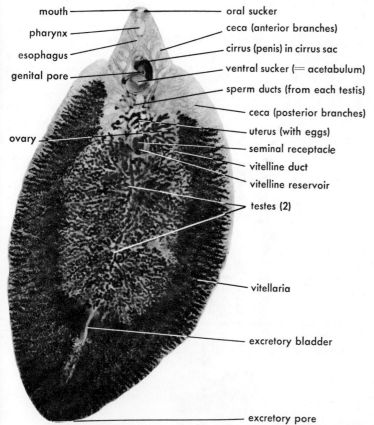

mouth
pharynx
esophagus
genital pore
ovary

oral sucker
ceca (anterior branches)
cirrus (penis) in cirrus sac
ventral sucker (= acetabulum)
sperm ducts (from each testis)
ceca (posterior branches)
uterus (with eggs)
seminal receptacle
vitelline duct
vitelline reservoir
testes (2)
vitellaria
excretory bladder
excretory pore

Fig. 6-4. *Fasciola hepatica,* whole mount, stained to show internal structure.

► Why are flame cells not visible in your specimen?

Review fluke structures and work out the entire reproductive system so that you can follow the process of sperm and egg formation, copulation, fertilization, yolk accretion, and egg passage from ovary to genital pore.

► What happens to eggs after they pass out the genital pore?

2—Larval structure—If available, study living or stained preparations of larval stages: *miracidia, sporocyst, redia, cercaria,* and *metacercaria.*

► In which of these stages does asexual reproduction take place? By what process?

3—Special projects

a. Collect fresh-water snails such as *Helisoma, Gyraulus, Physa, Lymnaea,* or mudflat brackish-water snails like *Cerithidea,* and examine them for larval stages of flukes. Crush or break open the snail shells in pond water in a syracuse dish so that you can remove the visceral whorl and search it for parasites. Any infection will usually be readily apparent, as larval flukes, when present, are generally abundant. Under the dissecting microscope, look for wriggling, tailed cercariae, saclike sporocysts, or the larger rediae,

which may be colored and are often distinguished by an oral sucker and a darkly pigmented gut. Find the *germ balls* and later developmental forms inside the sporocysts and rediae. Developing cercariae should be particularly easy to discern. Identify as many different types of larvae as you can, especially types of cercariae (representing different species infecting the snail). Review several life cycles in your text, and consult a parasitology textbook for additional examples. Clarify in your mind the sequence of stages and multiplication involved.

b. Autopsy (necropsy) of nearly any vertebrate will yield parasites. Frogs, salamanders, fish, snakes, carnivorous or fish-eating birds, bats, and rodents are all excellent hosts. Nothing creates an appreciation of parasitism more quickly than the sight of a living fluke, tapeworm, or nematode—especially when you find it yourself in an animal you have collected.

C. Class 3. CESTODA—tapeworms

Tapeworms are always good for a recoil—especially those guaranteed by casual eyewitnesses to measure "79 feet long." Most tapeworm parasites of animals are only several inches long, though they are just as interesting and a good deal easier to study. Human tapeworms of the genera *Taenia* or *Diphyllobothrium* are, however, comparative giants. They actually may grow to as long as 50 feet, although 10 to 14 foot lengths are more common. Refer to your text for the life cycle of these and other cestodes.

1—Structure of adult *Taenia* or *Dipylidium* (double-pored dog tapeworm)—Observe the gross anatomy of your preparation.

► Can you identify the worm from the structure of the segment or portion on your slide?

If available, the small anterior end or *scolex* (Fig. 6-5) should be examined. Under the microscope, examine the *suckers* (how many?) and the anterior projection or *rostellum.* In some species this structure will be lined with one or more rows of *hooks.*

► What is the function of the scolex?
► Where is the mouth?

Study a mature segment (Fig. 6-6) showing the male and female reproductive systems essentially intact. (These systems will be destroyed or distorted by pressure of eggs

Fig. 6-5 (center). *Taenia pisiformis.* scolex.

Fig. 6-6 (left). *Taenia pisiformis,* mature segments.

Fig. 6-7 (right). *Taenia pisiformis,* gravid or ripe segments.

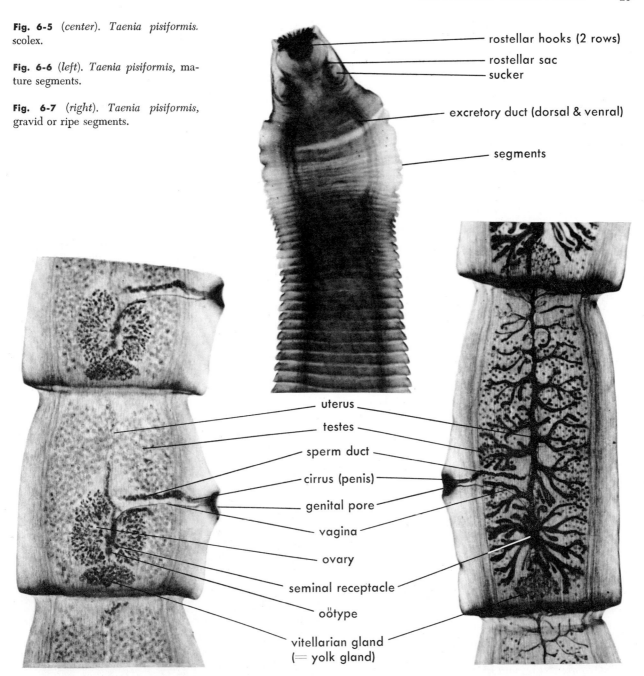

rostellar hooks (2 rows)

rostellar sac

sucker

excretory duct (dorsal & venral)

segments

uterus

testes

sperm duct

cirrus (penis)

genital pore

vagina

ovary

seminal receptacle

oötype

vitellarian gland
(= yolk gland)

in the *ripe* or *gravid* segment.) Trace out the male structures, including the scattered *testes, sperm ducts, seminal vesicle, cirrus pouch,* and *genital pore.* The female system in the same segment will show the *vagina* (passing from the genital pore to the *seminal receptacle* just above the center of the divided *ovary*). It is seen as a fine, downcurving line. As in flukes, eggs from the ovary pass down an *oviduct* and into the *oötype.* Sperm, having entered the system through the vagina after copulation, pass from their storage point in

the seminal receptacle through the oviduct and into the oötype where fertilization occurs. Eggs are then quickly coated with yolk and shell material pressed over them by contraction of the oötype. This material comes from the compact *vitelline gland* located below the ovary. In other groups of tapeworms, the vitelline gland may be distinct follicles either scattered throughout the segment or in discrete marginal bands (these criteria are means for distinguishing *orders* of tapeworms). Finished eggs are quickly pushed along into the uterus, where they gradually fill and expand it into a shape characteristic for each species.

▶ How does the uterus of *Taenia* compare with that of *Clonorchis*?

▶ What traits distinguish scolex, immature, mature, and gravid segments of *Taenia* from *Dipylidium*?

Draw the mature segment, label the parts, and be prepared to tell the function of each organ.

▶ How do eggs escape from the uterus?

▶ How do they get into the intermediate host?

▶ How do larvae reach a final host?

Now study a ripe or gravid segment of *Taenia* (Fig. 6-7), in which reproductive organs are practically obliterated by egg-filled branches of the uterus. Under high power, examine some eggs mounted in water under a coverslip. Try to distinguish the 6-hooked larva, the *hexacanth,* inside the shell. This larva emerges from the shell after accidental ingestion of feces of the final host by the *intermediate host.* The released larva then penetrates the intestinal wall, invades the body tissues and forms a *cysticercus.*

▶ What are the intermediate hosts of *Taenia solium* and *Taenia saginata*?

▶ What host tissues are invaded?

Another larval form, the *cysticercoid,* occurs in the life cycle of tapeworms that utilize an *invertebrate* intermediate host, usually an insect. *Hymenolepis diminuta* in grain beetles and in rats is a common example.

2—Larval structure—Study a slide of a stained *Taenia* cysticercus (sometimes called a bladderworm). It is found, as we know, in the flesh of an appropriate vertebrate intermediate host. Locate the *bladder, neck, scolex,* and if possible the *rostellum* with a double row of hooks that characterizes *Taenia solium. Taenia saginata* has a similar cysticercus but lacks the hooked rostellum.

3—Special projects

a. Examine intestines of rabbits, cats, or dogs (from animals destroyed at the local pound), sheep (from a slaughterhouse), bass, trout, pike, or other predaceous fish. From appropriate references provided by your instructor (or better, through your own library efforts), find the techniques for processing the tapeworms you find. Prepare your own stained, mounted, and labeled slides.

b. Set up an experimental tapeworm life cycle, using available tapeworm ova or larvae. If a naturally infected rabbit can be obtained, feed cysts from this animal in a bit of meat to an experimental cat. The final host (cat) need not be sacrificed unless adult worm specimens are desired. Eggs can be recovered from the cat feces and fed back to uninfected rabbits or rats in order to complete the cycle. A simpler life cycle, employing grain beetles (Genus *Tribolium*), laboratory rats, and the rat tapeworm, *Hymenolepis diminuta,* can also be studied. Because of ease of transmission under controlled conditions, *Hymenolepis* is used in many laboratories for a number of research projects designed to study tapeworm development or physiology.

D. GENERAL QUESTIONS

1—What are the probable morphological stages in the transition from free-living to parasitic flatworms?

2—What special planarian structures are lacking in parasitic groups? How is this absence correlated with function? What structures characteristic of flukes and tapeworms are absent in free-living flatworms?

3—Is a tapeworm a colony or an individual? Compare this answer with those involving *Volvox* and *Physalia.*

4—What primary adaptations would you consider necessary for parasitism in general? Would you include physiological as well as structural modifications? If so, which ones?

5—Are helminth parasites degenerate organisms? If not, what do you feel would be a more appropriate term?

6—How would you explain the fact that *Clonorchis,* with its relatively small adult size, has a reproductive capacity comparable with that of *Taenia,* with its larger adult size and far greater egg-producing capacity?

NOTES AND DRAWINGS

(Tear along line)

CHAPTER 7

Phylum

Aschelminthes

I. INTRODUCTION

ASCHELMINTHES as a phylum is an assemblage of 6 different classes,[1] dominated by the Class NEMATODA—the nematodes, which are threadworms (*nema*, thread) or roundworms. These ubiquitous small worms dwarf in numbers all other groups of multicellular animals except insects and mites.

The *pseudocoelom*, a primary structural advance over the body cavity of flatworms, is one important characteristic shared by all aschelminths. The *cuticle* together with its underlying *hypodermis* and muscle layer forms an outer, mesoderm-lined wall of the body cavity. The intestine, lacking a mesoderm covering, forms the inner margin of the body cavity. Filled with fluid and tubes of the reproductive system, the pseudocoel is seen very clearly in nematodes. This incomplete or false coelom, as previously reviewed, represents an evolutionary step between ACOELOMATA (which phyla?), in which the body cavity is filled with undifferentiated mesodermal cells, and EUCOELOMATA (all the so-called higher phyla), in which the body cavity is lined by mesoderm underlying the outer body wall and overlying the intestine. Advantages of the complete coelom will be described in later chapters.

► Can you suggest an advantage of the pseudocoelom over the acoelom?

A second major advance in ASCHELMINTHES is a *complete digestive system:* mouth, intestine, and anus. Cellular specialization in this system allows ingested food to be processed along a one-way passage and unassimilated matter to be ejected posteriorly, rather than to be returned and passed out the oral opening, as in TURBELLARIA or TREMATODA.

► What advantages in terms of digesting and processing food come with development of a one-track alimentary canal?

The rugged body wall, or cuticle, is not only an extraordinarily effective protection against harmful external substances (or intestinal substances in the case of internal parasites) but also serves as an exoskeleton (external skeleton), allowing an extensive area for muscle attachment.

An unusual aschelminth trait is *parthenogenesis* (development of an unfertilized egg). In the

---

[1] These 6 classes are combined into one phylum because of certain common features. As observed in the footnote on p. 14, some authorities consider each of these classes as a separate phylum.

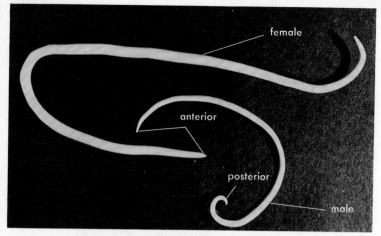

Fig. 7-1. *Ascaris lumbricoides.*

classes NEMATODA, ROTIFERA, and GASTROTRICHA, males may be lacking and successive generations of females are produced parthenogenetically. In a subsequent generation, normal sexual reproduction may occur, the product often being a resistant or over-wintering stage. In other cases, no males have ever been discovered.

Still another remarkable characteristic of the phylum is constancy of cell numbers *(eutely),* in which a precise and relatively small number of cells, remaining unvaried throughout the animal's life, comprise both specific organs and the entire animal. The number, constant not only for the species but also for the taxonomic group, can be used as part of its morphological definition (for example, the central nervous system in *Ascaris* and many other nematodes consists of 162 cells).

II. CLASSIFICATION

Classes combined in the Phylum ASCHEL-MINTHES include:

Class 1. NEMATODA—roundworms or thread-worms (defined below).

Class 2. NEMATOMORPHA (or GORDIACEA)—"horsehair worms" somewhat nematodelike; larvae parasitic in insects, adults emerge in fresh water to reproduce and spend a brief free-living life.

Class 3. ROTIFERA—rotifers, microscopic "wheeled animals" (look for them in your pond-water protozoan cultures); free-swimming, sessile, and tube-building forms known.

Class 4. GASTROTRICHA—microscopic aquatic animals, with spiny cuticular skin and ventral cilia.

Class 5. KINORHYNCHA (or ECHINODERA)—minute, marine mud-dwelling worms, similar to gastrotrichs and rotifers.

Class 6. PRIAPULIDA—burrowing marine worms, heavy bodied, with a large, spined anterior proboscis.

52

A. Class Nematoda

Characteristics of NEMATODA include an elongate, pointed body, round in cross section (hence, roundworms), and a tough, impermeable cuticular exoskeleton.[2] A complete digestive system, separate sexes, a tubular reproductive system, and a pair of "lateral lines," containing nerve trunks and excretory tubes, are additional nematode features.

Biologically, nematodes are the most important and successful aschelminths (sometimes called "ashcan-helminths" by their close and irreverent observers). Most of us are familiar with these worms only as internal parasites of humans and animals, but nematodes are chiefly free-living and microscopic. They occupy a great number and variety of habitats in soil, mud, and fresh or salt water. Soil nematodes, plant parasites of the first magnitude, cause millions of dollars in agricultural damage annually. Others, such as marine forms, represent various manifestations of the nematode basic body type and therefore are interesting biologically simply because they are there. As parasites, nematodes infect more hosts in greater variety and number than do any other helminth groups. Humans, for example, are parasitized by pinworms, *Trichinella, Trichuris, Strongyloides, Ascaris, Dracunculus* (guinea worm), numerous filarial worms, and several species of hookworms. Infection rates with some worms may run close to 100 percent in certain areas. Sanitation-conscious Americans still have one of the highest rates of trichinosis in the world. Probably every reader of these words has been infected by pinworms at least once in his lifetime.

III. LABORATORY INSTRUCTIONS

A. Ascaris lumbricoides[3]

1—External anatomy (Fig. 7-1)—Observe a preserved specimen of *Ascaris.* Find the *head* with three lips surrounding the *mouth* (examine from the anterior end, looking directly

---

[2] If free-living existence preceded parasitic, as is generally assumed, one can see how the resistant cuticle would serve the parasitic nematode as well as it did its free-living ancestor.

[3] *Ascaris* is not a typical nematode; it is merely large and easily available, and therefore commonly used in beginning zoology laboratories. Like *Taenia* and *Fasciola, Ascaris* is a giant, with most of its bulk filled with a tremendously elongated, coiled reproductive system capable of producing 200,000 eggs daily.

down on the head in good light using a strong hand lens). The specimen can be examined under a dissecting microscope after cutting off the head as close as possible to the lips and mounting it on a slide for an *en face* view. This type of mounting is often used in nematode identification. The largest lip is the *dorsal;* the other two are the *ventrolateral* lips.

The male, considerably smaller than the female, is identified by its hooked or recurved tail, which sometimes shows paired copulatory *spicules* (Fig. 7-2) protruding from the *cloaca* (combined digestive and genital opening). Locate the *lateral lines* (paler in color than the rest of the cuticle) and the smaller *dorsal* and *ventral lines,* which mark the *dorsal* and *ventral nerve trunks.* Through the cuticle of a female worm one can usually see numerous fine coils of the reproductive system that surround the intestine and fill most of the pseudocoel. The female genital pore can usually be seen one-third of the way back from the head on the midventral surface.

2—Internal anatomy—Pin your specimen dorsal side up, on a wax-bottom dissecting pan, preferably a dark one for good contrast. Cover the worm with water. Make a straight dorsal slit, fold and pin cuticle back (be careful not to damage the internal organs).

Examine first the *digestive system.* Carefully tease loose the coiled ovaries and oviducts to expose the intestine. Trace the alimentary canal from *mouth* to *esophagus* (*pharynx*), *intestine, rectum,* and *anus* (Fig. 7-3). Note the relatively simple straight-tube construction of the gut.

The *muscular system* consists of large elongate cells forming specialized, neuro-contractile units on the dorsal and ventral body walls. Projections from these cells enter the nerve cords enclosed in the lateral lines. Locate muscle cells under the cuticle. Remove several and examine them microscopically. Careful dissection around the pharynx may disclose the *nerve ring* (circumpharyngeal ganglion) lying at an angle around the gut about halfway back from the head to the end of the pharynx.

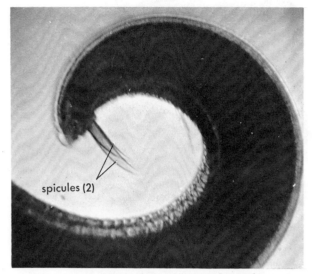

Fig. 7-2. *Ascaris,* male tail showing paired spicules.

The *excretory system* consists of paired *excretory tubes,* one in each lateral line. These connect to a specialized pair of extremely large excretory cells in the pharyngeal region. Collected fluid drains out a nearby *excretory pore.* The pore may not be visible in your dissection, but you should be able to locate the excretory tubes and possibly the excretory cells as well.

The *male reproductive system* is a single, long, highly differentiated tube. The thin, terminal portion (blind end) is the *testis.* Sperm move from it into a *sperm duct,* which then becomes a larger *seminal vesicle.* During copulation, stored sperm are discharged via an *ejaculatory duct* out the *cloaca* (combined digestive-reproductive opening). A pair of spicules protruding from the male pore presumably aids copulatory action, although their precise function is unknown. Trace out and identify the male sexual structures.

The *female reproductive system,* far larger than that of the male, is responsible for the great difference in size between the two sexes. Notice, however, that the basic tubular organization of the two systems is essentially the same. Trace the female system from its external opening—the *genital pore*—to the *vagina*—a short heavy tube formed by the fusion

Fig. 7-3. *Ascaris,* internal anatomy.

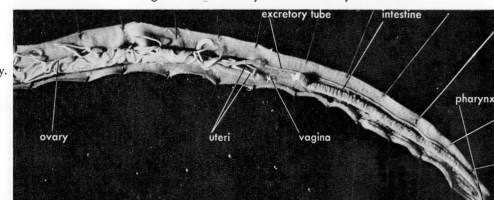

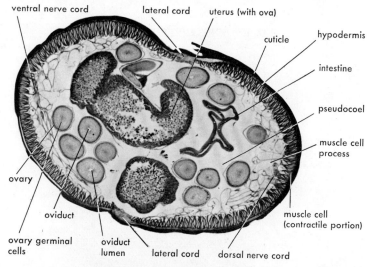

ventral nerve cord   lateral cord   uterus (with ova)

cuticle

hypodermis

intestine

pseudocoel

muscle cell
process

ovary

oviduct

muscle cell
(contractile portion)

ovary germinal
cells

oviduct
lumen   lateral cord   dorsal nerve cord

Fig. 7-4. *Ascaris,* cross section through uteri.

of two large tubes, the *uteri,* each of which
connects to an *oviduct.* The oviducts each end
in a greatly elongated, fine tube, the *ovary.*
Ovaries, coiled about the rest of the reproductive system and intestine, form a large portion
of the worm's bulk. It may be difficult to visualize the entire system as simply two long
tubes joined at the vagina. Tease one tube out
to prove this to yourself.

Eggs formed in the end of each ovary
are forced by pressure from masses of younger
eggs behind them to move down the reproductive tube into oviducts and uteri. Near the
point where the oviduct bends back on itself,
enlarges, and becomes the egg-storing uterus,
is a swollen portion, the *seminal receptacle.*
During the female's lifetime, millions of eggs
pass down the tube, enter the seminal receptacle, and are fertilized by sperm stored there
from a previous copulation. Fertilized, fully
formed, heavy shelled eggs that fill the uteri
are periodically forced through the vagina and
out the genital pore. The eggs become enmeshed in the host's intestinal contents and
are passed in feces to the soil, where development continues. Within the highly resistant
eggshells the larvae develop, grow, and molt
within their cuticle to form the next larval
stage. Strictly speaking, the egg is now no
longer an egg, but an eggshell-enclosed infective larva. Infection of the vertebrate host
(pig or man in the case of *Ascaris
lumbricoides*) occurs after accidental ingestion of the embry-
onated eggs. Resistance and durability of
these eggs, due chiefly to the thick-walled
shell, are attested by the fact that *Ascaris* ova
may have even developed within the uteri of
the pickled worm in your dissection tray. So
long as the female worms have been killed in
cold rather than in hot formalin, and the fixative concentration does not exceed 5 percent,
larvae will develop and the eggs remain viable

for years. (Though you would be well advised
not to chew your fingernails during this exercise, common-sense care and cleanliness is all
that is needed to avoid becoming an involuntary host.)

▶ What does this phenomenon suggest about
survival of *Ascaris* eggs in nature?

Draw your dissected specimen to
show the digestive, reproductive, muscular,
and excretory systems, and other observable
morphological features.

Carefully pipette onto a slide a small
drop containing eggs from the vagina, then
alongside it a drop from the uterus, one from
the oviduct, and another from the ovary.
Small sections cut from these parts of the reproductive tract will serve as well. Examine
the egg samples microscopically.

▶ What differences do you notice in size, form,
and state of development of eggs from each site?

▶ What would you conclude from these differences?

3—Histology: cross section of *Ascaris* (Fig.
7-4)—Study a stained *Ascaris* cross section.
Observe the ducts and tubes you previously
saw in surface view. Locate the *cuticle, neuro-
muscular cells,* projections from these cells,
and their connection to lateral, dorsal, or ventral nerves.

B. *Trichinella spiralis* (Figs. 7-5 and 7-6)

Study a section of trichina-infected
pork or other meat. Locate a cyst and observe
it under high power. Note the coiled larvae,
the surrounding cyst wall and host tissues, and

Fig. 7-5. *Trichinella spiralis* larva encysted in muscle tissue,
×228. (Copyright by General Biological Supply House Inc.,
Chicago.)

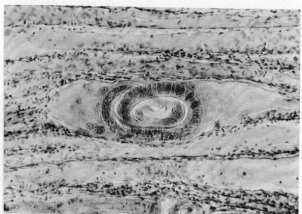

perhaps evidence of calcification—a host tissue reaction that eventually kills the larva.

▶ What is the life cycle of this parasite?

▶ Why do we say that man, the *final* host, is also the *intermediate* host?

▶ Why is man a "dead-end" for completion of the life cycle?

▶ Compare the life cycles of *Trichinella* with those of *Ascaris*, hookworm (*Ancylostoma*), and pinworm (*Enterobius*).

C. Free-living nematodes

1—Observations—Study examples of living nonparasitic nematodes. Genera commonly available include the soil nematodes *Rhabditis* and *Cephalobus*, and the "vinegar eel," *Turbatrix aceti*. Place a few worms on a slide in water or in 5% methylcellulose to slow their rapid thrashing movement.

Observe direction and orientation of movement. The alignment and location of muscle cells along the body wall of nematodes indicate that movement is possible only in one plane. The worms on your slide lie on their sides, so the observed lateral movement is actually a *dorso-ventral* swimming action. Press the coverslip down to stop movement and study detailed structure of lips and head, pharynx (note the valvular bulb), intestine, and anus. Observe the clarity and relative simplicity of the reproductive system compared with that of *Ascaris*.

▶ Do you see evidence of *ovoviviparity* (hatching of eggs inside the uterus)?

▶ Are special sensory structures visible about the head?

▶ What are the chief morphological differences between *Ascaris* or other parasitic nematodes and free-living roundworms?

2—Special projects

a. Make a microscopic study of free-living or plant-parasitic nematodes from soil, plant, or water samples. Study various samples by direct microscopic examination. To obtain larger numbers of worms, simple concentration and culture techniques can be employed. One common procedure (described in most parasitology texts) is the use of the Baerman Funnel, in which worms swim out of a soil sample through a fine screen or cloth into a funnel containing warm water. A pinchclamp controls the release of worms in the bottom of the funnel. Another suitable method is the use of a tier of successively finer wire

Fig. 7-6. *Trichinella spiralis* larva digested out of cyst, ×300.

mesh strainers that allow only nematodes and smaller organisms to pass into the sample chamber. More dramatic and illuminating is the use of a simple culture method.

Pour salt agar (0.5 percent NaCl, 1.5 percent agar, and distilled water) into a sterile petri dish to a depth of about 4 mm. Allow it to harden and place small bits of selected soil on the surface. Incubate at room temperature for periods varying from two or three days to a week or more, depending on the richness of the culture desired. If the soil contains nematodes, you will soon observe swarms of larvae in all stages of development on the surface and tunneling into the agar. Samples can be removed for detailed study at any time. *Rhabditis* will be one of the most common forms. If you try culturing worms from various types of soil you will be convinced of the truth of the often-stated abundance of soil nematodes.

Try adding a piece of earthworm tissue to another agar plate. A flourishing culture derived from nematode larvae living within the earthworm should appear in three or four days. Observe and record the life cycle changes and relative abundance of various stages of nematodes in your culture over a fixed period of time. Estimate population size of the colony and rates of growth and development (see p. 63).

▶ What further observations can you suggest making?

A variety of cultures from different soil or water habitats will assure you of many nematode species with a wide assortment of interesting structures and adaptations. You will also find this a relatively little known but potentially rich area of zoological research.

D. General questions

1—What structural characteristics of free-living nematodes permit or increase the likelihood of successful parasitism (for example, what "preadaptations" to parasitism may such nematodes have)?

2—What traits found in parasitic nematodes are absent in free-living forms, and vice versa?

3—Name some of the traits or structures that help to account for the abundance, wide distribution, and ecological versatility of nematodes.

4—Compare adaptations to parasitism in protozoa, trematodes, tapeworms, and nematodes.

5—What general characteristics unite the 6 classes of ASCHELMINTHES into a single phylum?

NOTES AND DRAWINGS

(Tear along line)

(Tear along line)

I. INTRODUCTION

The Phylum ANNELIDA includes some 8000 species of segmented worms. In it are earthworms (Class OLIGOCHAETA), marine bristleworms (Class POLYCHAETA) with numerous forms and much variation, leeches (Class HIRUDINEA), and a small group of tiny marine annelids (Class ARCHIANNELIDA) thought to be primitive, as implied by the class name.

If forced to choose, most zoologists would probably select an annelid, perhaps a marine polychaete worm, as the most nearly "typical animal." It represents an evolutionary stage midway in complexity between the most primitive metazoan and the vertebrate level of organization. It is the simplest of *eucoelomate* animals (those possessing a true coelom lined with sheets of mesoderm, one round the gut and the other beneath the body wall). Yet it possesses important *organ systems* characteristic of all so-called higher organisms.

Earthworms, the representatives of this phylum usually selected for classroom study, are abundantly distributed in moist soil and easily available to every student. Although demonstrating the *annelid basic body type*, earthworms possess distinctive adaptations enabling them to thrive in an environment of moist soil and decaying organic matter.

CHAPTER 8

Phylum
Annelida

II. CLASSIFICATION

Phylum ANNELIDA:

Segmented worms characterized by a ringlike series of similar segments containing paired setae, nephridia, ventral ganglia, and other duplicated structures; a complete digestive tract, large coelom, thin nonchitinous cuticle, closed circulatory system. Widely distributed, mostly marine, but also in fresh water and soil. About 8,000 species.

Class 1. OLIGOCHAETA, earthworms and allies (Figs. 8-1 to 8-10):

External and internal segmentation, head and parapodia reduced or lacking, few setae per somite. Gonads in anterior section, monoecious (hermaphroditic), clitellum secretes egg cocoon, development direct (no distinct larval form). Chiefly in moist soil and fresh water. Soil forms with complex alimentary canal adapted for ingestion of soil and digestion of organic matter.

Class 2. POLYCHAETA, bristleworms, sandworms, clamworms, sedentary worms (Figs. 8-11 to 8-13):

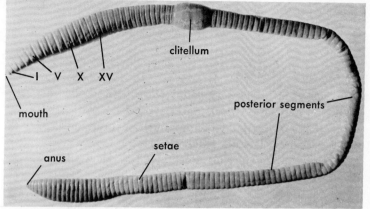

Fig. 8-1. *Lumbricus terrestris,* the earthworm, dorsolateral view.

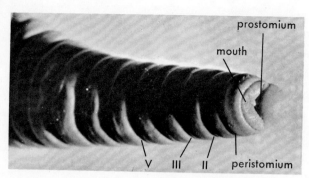

Fig. 8-2. *Lumbricus,* anterior end, ventral view.

Numerous somites with internal and external segmentation; well-developed parapodia with many setae. Head with tentacles, no clitellum. Usually dioecious (sexes in separate individuals), gonads appear only at certain periods, trochophore larva found. Chiefly marine, both active predators and tube-builders or attached forms feeding by tentacles. About 4000 species.

Class 3. HIRUDINEA, leeches:

Large posterior sucker, often a smaller one at anterior end. Heavy-bodied, coelom filled with connective or muscle tissue. Thirty-four somites but with many external divisions *(annuli).* No tentacles or parapodia; setae usually also lacking. Hermaphroditic, cocoons formed, no larvae. Active predators or bloodsucking parasites. About 300 species.

Class 4. ARCHIANNELIDA:

Small, relatively little known marine forms. Segmentation mostly internal, with epidermal cilia, without setae or parapodia, separate-sexed, trochophore larva well developed. Thought by some experts to be primitive prototypes from which other annelids evolved, by others to be degenerate forms that have recently lost such structures as parapodia.

III. LABORATORY INSTRUCTIONS

A. Class Oligochaeta—*Lumbricus terrestris*[1]

1—Observations—If a living worm is available, observe its general appearance, segmentation, epidermal texture, and surface color dorsally and ventrally. Find the anterior and posterior ends—mouth and anus. Study methods of locomotion. Note its reactions to stimuli such as moisture, mild acetic acid, dilute salt

solution, and touch. Place the worm in a dish and study it under a dissecting microscope. Find the dorsal blood vessel (note the direction of blood flow); locate the small lateral bristles or setae and watch their movements. If possible, observe a number of worms over several days. Accurately record your observations on methods of feeding, production of castings, copulation, and cocoon formation.

▶ Can you suggest a series of experiments to test more fully the habits and reaction patterns of earthworms?

2—External anatomy (Fig. 8-1)—For anatomical study use a specially prepared specimen, one killed and fixed in formalin, which hardens tissues. An anesthetized living worm may also be used (immersed in water or placed on wet toweling saturated with chloroform).

Note the *general body form, segmentation, clitellum, mouth, prostomium,* and *anus* (Fig. 8-1). Observe the shape of the mouth and anal openings (Figs. 8-2 and 8-3); count the segments from I[2] (prostomium plus peristomium) through the clitellum. On the anterior ventral surface, locate the *male gonopore* on XV, and the openings of the female *oviducts* on XIV (Fig. 8-4). Between these openings and the clitellum, find the ventral or *genital ridges,* marked by *genital setae.* Compare genital setae with *lateral* setae. By careful use of a hand lens, try to find the ventral openings of the *seminal receptacles* between IX and X, and X and XI.

Draw a ventral outline showing only the structures visible.

3—Internal anatomy

a. General layout. Carefully place your specimen dorsal side up in your dissecting pan. Add enough tap water to submerge the worm. Make a shallow dorsal incision a few segments posterior

---

[1] Should you be given specimens of other earthworm genera, such as *Eisenia* or *Helodrilus,* look for minor differences in arrangement and size of genitalia and the other organs compared with those of the common *Lumbricus terrestris.*

[2] Roman numerals are customarily used to indicate earthworm segments.

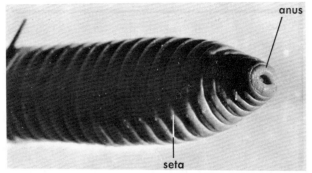

Fig. 8-3. *Lumbricus,* posterior end, ventral view.

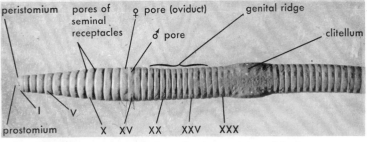

Fig. 8-4. *Lumbricus,* ventral view, showing position of body openings.[3]

to the clitellum. Then cautiously make a continuous shallow cut just to the *right* of the median dorsal wall, continuing to the anterior end of the worm. Do not cut deeper than the thickness of the outer body wall, or the scissors will injure organs lying below the thin epidermis. Carefully separate the flaps by inserting a scalpel under the cut edges. Keep the blade as close as possible to the body wall. Cut away adhering tissues and septal walls, moving anteriorly until the full length is cleared along each side. Pin back the exposed flaps; place pins firmly, pointed obliquely away from the specimen. Observe the general layout of *pharynx, esophagus, hearts* and *dorsal blood vessel, genitalia* (mostly *seminal vesicles*), *crop* and *gizzard* (Fig. 8-5), and crosswalls that mark internal segmentation. These form *septae* with paired *nephridia* running through them. By placing pins in segments V, X, XV, XX, and so on, to serve as markers, it will be unnecessary to make repeated counts of segments in relation to the particular structure being studied. Keep your dissection clean by using an eyedropper to wash away collected debris.

b. *Reproductive system.* First observe the exposed organs, the most conspicuous of which in the male are 3 pairs of sperm reservoirs where spermatozoa mature—the *seminal vesicles* (Fig. 8-5). These are large lobed structures overlying the esophagus in IX, XI, and XII; the *posterior,* usually the largest, forms a folded, bilobed sac. The *middle* and *anterior* vesicles are considerably smaller. Occasionally one vesicle may be larger than its partner, owing to degree of filling with seminal material. These vesicles all join basally IX and X), where they form 4 ventral *testes sacs* (X and XI), which enclose *sperm funnels* and the minute *testes.*

During copulation the funnels discharge spermatozoa from the seminal vesicles, through *sperm ducts* into a single *vas deferens,* at XII.

Sperm then pass out the male pores previously seen in XV, cross over to the *seminal grooves* of the other worm in copula, and enter its *seminal receptacles* through pores between IX and X, and X and XI. Note that *both* worms receive sperm, this being a process of mutual cross fertilization between hermaphroditic organisms. Most of the structures can be seen by carefully pushing the seminal vesicles aside with a blunt probe, or by removing them from one side as in Figure 8-8. To locate testes and sperm funnels will require careful searching under a dissecting microscope and teasing away the testes sacs. Finding these organs is a worthwhile technical challenge and will give you a sense of achievement by working out the functional relations of each structure within the entire system.

The female system consists of paired *ovaries* (XIII), *egg funnels* (XIII), and *oviducts* (XIV), ending in the female openings seen in XIV. These tiny structures are best observed with hand lens or dissecting microscope after careful removal of the seminal vesicles (Fig. 8-8). The *seminal receptacles* (or *spermathecae*)—2 pairs of small, lobular whitish sacs in IX and X—lie lateral to or under the anterior and the middle seminal vesicles.

Study your text and charts of copulation and cocoon formation; carefully work out the functioning of the entire reproductive system, and learn the highly specialized habits associated with it. A model of the earthworm, if available, will prove most helpful.

► How do the specialized reproductive organs aid survival of this animal in its terrestrial environment?

Remember, however, that the large majority of annelids are marine and lack such terrestrial or fresh-water adaptations as cocoon formation.

c. *Circulatory system.* Use an anesthetized living worm. Much of this system cannot be seen in gross dissection, but you should be able to locate the following: *dorsal hearts*—5 pairs (VII-XI)

---

[3] The symbols ♂ and ♀ are used to indicate male and female, respectively.

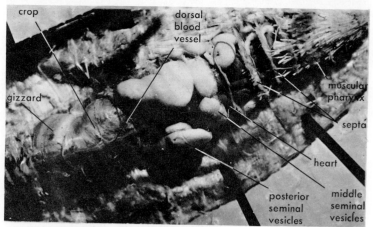

crop

dorsal
blood
vessel

gizzard

muscular
pharynx

septa

heart

posterior
seminal
vesicles

middle
seminal
vesicles

Fig. 8-5. Anterior view of worm, showing general arrangement of organs.

(Fig. 8-6); *dorsal blood vessel* (above digestive tract, Fig. 8-6); *ventral* or *subintestinal vessel* (look under intestine); and *body wall vessels.*

Review models or charts of *Lumbricus* for the circulatory pattern, a *closed* pathway running from the dorsal vessel, out the hearts, posteriorly down the ventral vessel, into body wall capillaries, back via *lateral-neural vessels* to the *subneural vessel,* and finally returning to the dorsal blood vessel through numerous *parietal vessels.*

Diagram this circulatory pathway, showing direction of flow and names of primary vessels. Locate as many vessels as possible in your own specimen.

d. *Digestive system.* The digestive system, which consists of *mouth* and *buccal cavity* (I-II), *pharynx* (II-V), *esophagus* (VI-XIV), *crop* (XV-XVI), *gizzard* (XVII-XVIII), *intestine,* and *anus*—is a continuous, highly specialized, food-handling tube. The animal can be visualized as a tube within a tube, that is, an intestine within the outer body wall. The intestine, however, is actually enclosed by the inner wall of the coelom, the *splanchnic mesoderm* or *peritoneum,* just as the inner lining of the body wall is *somatic mesoderm* or *peritoneum.* The space between these two mesoderm layers is the true *coelom,* con-

Fig. 8-6. As Fig. 8-5, with reproductive organs dissected away to show 5 pairs of hearts.

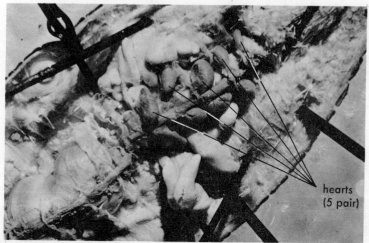

hearts
(5 pair)

taining reproductive, excretory, and other organ systems. Marked specialization of the digestive tract in *Lumbricus* is an adaptation for passing large quantities of soil and detritus. Food is extracted as ingested soil is passed through the mouth and buccal cavity, the well-developed, muscular pharynx, and the esophagus—a passageway leading to the storage and digestive area. In X and XI, the esophagus may have three paired glandular swellings (*calciferous glands*) of uncertain function. Immediately posterior is the thin-walled crop for storage, and a thick, muscular grinding gizzard, followed by a long intestine for food digestion and absorption. Specialized areas and cells (*chloragogue cells*) along the outer intestinal wall appear to have a storage or excretory function. The *typhlosole,* by forming a fold extending into the lumen of the intestine, greatly increases the intestinal surface area (Fig. 8-12). The alimentary canal ends at the anus, through which soil and unused food material is egested. Piled up fecal *castings* are often seen on lawns. These castings represent a substantial amount of tunneling and turnover of soil, an important contribution to aeration and loosening of millions of tons of surface soil. Charles Darwin gave a fascinating account of this in a book on the earthworm's role as a primary factor in enriching the soil (*The Formation of Vegetable Mould, Through the Action of Worms,* 1881).

Draw an outline of the dissected worm; show the complete alimentary canal with specialized portions in their correct locations.

e. *Central nervous system* (Fig. 8-9). Carefully remove the alimentary canal from the anterior esophageal region and look for the white *nerve cord* below it. This cord, with its string of *segmented ganglia,* is part of the internal segmentation of the annelid body and the chief component of the *central nervous system.* Find the *ventral nerve ganglion* in each segment, with *lateral nerves* coming from each. Dissect out a portion of the cord in the midbody, place it in a drop of water on a slide, cover, and examine under low power. How many lateral nerves come from each ganglion? Trace the rest of the nerve cord anteriorly. Near the mouth, find where this nerve separates into two *circumpharyngeal connective* nerves that encircle the anterior end of the pharynx and unite dorsally to form a "brain" (*cerebral ganglia*).

► Can you find any nerves branching from these ganglia or from the connective?

Diagram the nervous system of your specimen. Show location of ganglia, lateral nerves, and connectives; note their location and corresponding somite numbers (include only the first 15 segments in your diagram).

f. *Excretory system.* Locate the paired *nephridia* that pierce the septal walls along each side of the animal, one pair per segment. The *nephrostome,* or ciliated opening of each nephridium, drains waste fluids from the coelom. These openings can be seen anterior to the septum. Posterior to each septum is the rest of the nephridium, a winding tube with numerous associated fine blood vessels connecting to a posterior bladder-like portion, and emptying to the exterior through a *nephridiopore.* Carefully cut out a septal wall in the posterior half of your specimen. Keep the nephridium attached, mount on a slide in a drop of water, cover, and examine under low power to observe general organization. Then study the nephridium under higher magnification.

▶ What further details can you discern?

Study of a living specimen will permit you to see something of the great activity in the nephridium. Ciliary action of the nephrostome takes up coelomic wastes and moves them into the nephridial tube. Parts of the tube wall also possess cilia for maintaining rapid flow of coelomic liquid.

▶ What is the function of blood vessels encircling the nephridial tube? Specially stained permanent preparations of these organs may be available for study.

Draw a nephridium to show its principal features.

4—Histology—In a stained cross section of the earthworm, locate the structures shown in Figure 8-10 and attempt to correlate each with organs you have already seen in the longitudinal view in your gross dissection. Use high power to observe details of cellular structure. In the body wall find the *cuticle, epidermis* with glandular and epithelial cells, *circular muscle layer, longitudinal muscle layer* (appearing feathery in cross section), and *somatic peritoneum* forming the outer coating of the *coelom.* Find on the intestine the outer *chloragogue layer;* it also serves as part of the *inner* coelomic lining. Locate the *submucosa,* with its *connective tissue, muscle tissue* (how many layers?), and *blood vessels.* Finally, observe the inner layer or *mucosa,* with *connective tissue* and *ciliated columnar cells* forming the innermost lining of the intestine.

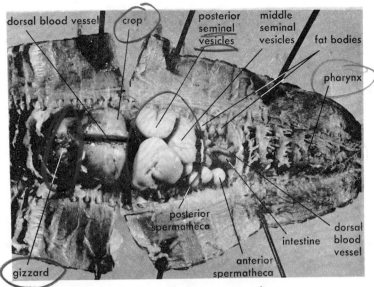

Fig. 8-7. Dissection, anterior end, showing general arrangement of reproductive organs with spermatheca and anterior vesicles removed from left side.

Locate the *dorsal, ventral, subneural,* and *lateral-neural* blood vessels now viewed in cross section. Review the part each plays in overall circulation.

Study a section through the *nerve cord,* and recognize the three clear *giant fibers,* other *nerve fibers* and occasional nerve *cell bodies,* and the outer layer with muscle cells and blood vessels. Review the function of these structures. Correlate the structures you have just seen in microscopic cross section with those you have previously seen macroscopically in longitudinal dissection.

Fig. 8-8. Further enlarged; intestine and seminal vesicle removed from left side and right posterior seminal vesicle displaced, disclosing the 4 testes sacs in which sperm funnels are found. Observe closely for *ovaries* and *egg funnels* as well.

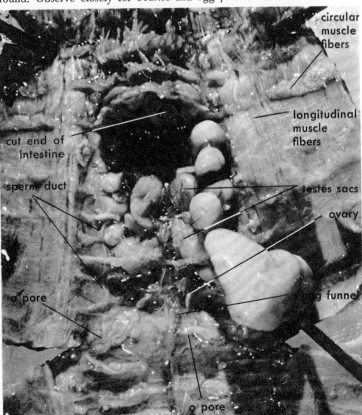

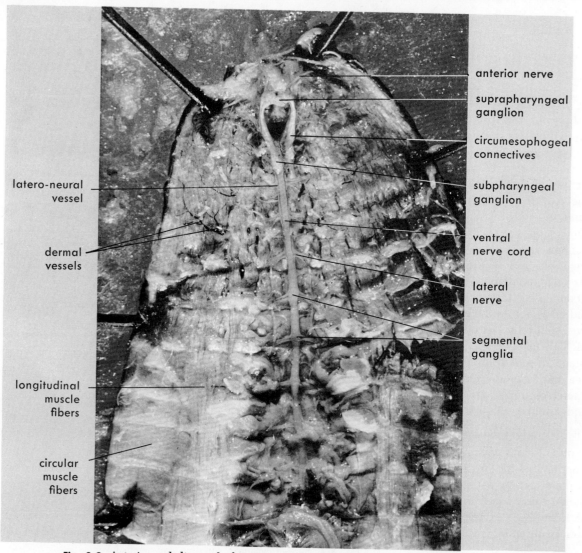

anterior nerve

suprapharyngeal ganglion

circumesophogeal connectives

subpharyngeal ganglion

ventral nerve cord

lateral nerve

segmental ganglia

latero-neural vessel

dermal vessels

longitudinal muscle fibers

circular muscle fibers

Fig. 8-9. Anterior end dissected, showing central nervous system.

This worm was once alive—it functioned. Always keep in mind this interplay between *form* and *function*. One makes it possible for the other to exist, and neither should be studied alone.

5—Special experiments—The earthworm, one of the most intensively studied invertebrates, offers excellent material for experiments on development, growth, regeneration of parts, and response to various environmental factors. Observations on habits and reactions of living worms have already been mentioned with regard to the reproductive cycle.

a. *Embryology* of earthworms can be studied by dissecting various embryonic stages from cocoons. These cocoons or capsules form, as you remember, from a ringlike girdle of tissue secreted by the clitellum, which hardens after it is slipped off the worm. As it moves anteriorly along the body, the cocoon picks up several ova and a number of spermatozoa from the pores which empty into the space between the cocoon and body wall. Fertilization occurs within the cocoon and the fertilized eggs or *zygotes* are enclosed when the cocoon shrinks and the ends pinch up.

Collect capsules from a laboratory earthworm culture in damp soil, or try to find some on ground with many earthworm castings.

Set up a regular time schedule and dissect out developing embryos at different stages. Examine them under a dissecting microscope (keeping the worms in water) or under your compound microscope if the worms are small enough. Compare these stages with newly emerged juvenile worms.

b. *Regeneration.* Growth or replacement of parts is also a fascinating study. Use your own ingenuity to set up experiments designed to answer such questions as the following:

1. Does somite replacement occur?

2. Which end can regenerate?

3. How many segments are capable of replacement?

4. What can you conclude concerning relationship between *structural specialization* and *capacity to regenerate?*

Other annelids may also be used, sometimes with considerable advantage. The freshwater oligochaete *Tubifex tubifex* can be reared in large numbers in the laboratory. It is small and easily handled. Allow about two weeks for regenerative changes to occur.

Draw the stages of change as you see them and maintain accurate records of your procedures, observations, and results.

c. *Histology.* Make your own sections by hand from a preserved earthworm, cutting transverse sections one somite thick from various points along the body length. A new razor blade is the best tool. Select a worm with a relatively undistended crop and intestine so that other organs will not be forced against the body wall. Sections can be cleared for better observation by soaking them in chloral hydrate or oil of wintergreen.

Compare your observations with those from stained tissue sections. Be sure to try several transverse sections so that you can work out the changes between anterior, genital, and posterior sections.

Be prepared to compare tissue layers and basic body type of the earthworm (for ANNELIDA) with those of hydra (for COELENTERATA) and of the frog (for CHORDATA).

d. *Symbionts* (organisms living together). Many earthworms are infected in the seminal vesicles with the sporozoan *Monocystis* (which phylum?).

The complete life cycle of this parasite can be seen on a single slide. Smear some seminal vesicle material from a living worm into saline solution (0.5 percent), cover, and examine microscopically. Encysted stages will usually be the most common. Look for large *cysts* containing *spores* at various stages of development and the *infective stage,* a spindle-shaped body with 8 *sporozoites.* Active stages include large *trophozoites* that may appear ciliated owing to the presence of degenerating worm spermatozoa around them. Review the sequence of steps in the life cycle of *Monocystis,* using the references already consulted in your study of protozoa.

Draw all stages you can find in your own material or on a stained cross section of seminal vesicle.

Rhabditis maupasi is a nematode commonly found in the excretory system or coelom of the earthworm. These are actually larval stages of a form living on decaying matter in soil. Culture of these worms with one or two decaying earthworms will yield a rich nematode harvest (see Chapter 7). These *Rhabditis* are not obligate parasites, but free-living forms capable of spending the larval part of their life cycle inside the earthworm.

e. *Other studies.* Can you devise other studies employing earthworms or other annelids to test such activities as:

1. response to an electric field
2. response to various drugs
3. method of locomotion

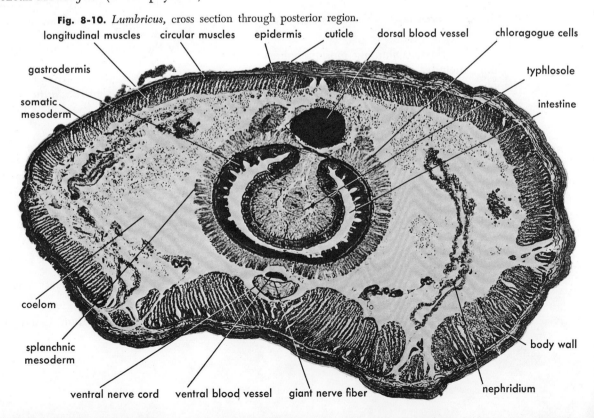

Fig. 8-10. *Lumbricus,* cross section through posterior region.

longitudinal muscles   circular muscles   epidermis   cuticle   dorsal blood vessel   chloragogue cells

gastrodermis

somatic mesoderm

typhlosole

intestine

coelom

splanchnic mesoderm

body wall

ventral nerve cord   ventral blood vessel   giant nerve fiber   nephridium

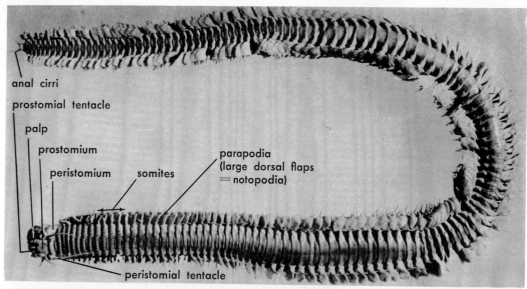

anal cirri
prostomial tentacle
palp
prostomium
peristomium
somites
parapodia (large dorsal flaps = notopodia)
peristomial tentacle

Fig. 8-11. *Neanthes,* dorsal view.

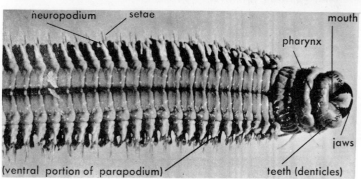

neuropodium
setae
mouth
pharynx
jaws
teeth (denticles)
(ventral portion of parapodium)

Fig. 8-12. *Neanthes,* anteroventral view.

4. manner of feeding, including peristalsis, ciliary activity, movement of setae, and circulation of coelomic fluid.

Smaller oligochaetes such as *Aeolosoma* or *Dero* may prove useful for some of these studies.

B. Class Polychaeta—*Neanthes virens* (*Nereis virens*)

This class, containing most members of the phylum, includes both relatively simple and extremely specialized and bizarre worms, especially sedentary polychaetes adapted for mud- or tube-dwelling. They all retain recognizable annelid characteristics, especially with regard to internal struc-

Fig. 8-13. *Neanthes,* anterolateral view.

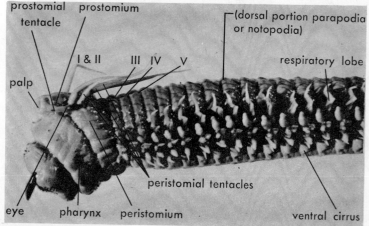

prostomial tentacle
prostomium
(dorsal portion parapodia or notopodia)
I & II
III IV V
respiratory lobe
palp
peristomial tentacles
eye
pharynx
peristomium
ventral cirrus

ture. Though their anatomy in general is much like that of the earthworm, they lack the special adaptations for terrestrial existence seen in *Lumbricus.*

Polychaetes, on the other hand, have developed many special structures absent in oligochaetes that enable them to live in the marine environment. Some, like the clamworm, *Neanthes virens* (Figs. 8-11 to 8-13), have paddlelike setae for swimming and respiration, and a formidable pair of hooklike jaws (Fig. 8-12) that evaginate and withdraw for active predation. Other polychaetes are adapted for making tubes in mud or sand. Each species constructs a highly specific type, some of which may be cemented to rocks or shells. Feeding and respiration are accomplished by a writhing mass of anterior ciliated tentacles.

1—External anatomy—If a preserved *Neanthes* is available, study its external anatomy. The *parapodia* and lateral swimming and respiratory organs will be prominent. Examine the structure of *head* and *jaws.* If your specimen was killed in an extended position, identify the *pharynx* with its *denticles* and *jaws.*

Draw the head structures you can see in dorsal view. Identify and label structures found on the *prostomium* and *peristomium.* Include one of the following views in your drawing:

a. Head (if pharynx everted): *jaws, denticles, pharynx, prostomium* with *palps* and stubby *prostomial tentacles, eyes, peristomium* (consisting of segments I and II) with 4 pairs of *peristomial tentacles* (Fig. 8-13).

b. Head (if pharynx retracted): jaws and pharynx withdrawn but *mouth* visible below peristomial tentacles; other structures as noted above.

► What are the sensory functions of tentacles and palps?

Remove a parapodium, mount it on a slide in

NOTES AND DRAWINGS

(Tear along line)

water, cover, and examine under the dissecting microscope. Note the 2 *lobes*, a dorsal *notopodium* and a ventral *neuropodium*. Each has a spine or *cirrus* (plural: *cirri*) and a cluster of bristles or *setae* around a single supporting needlelike *aciculum*. The notopodia have many fine blood capillaries coursing through them. This thin exposed surface is clearly respiratory.

▶ Why can one confidently assume this to be true?

▶ How might it be proved?

Draw and label the above structures of a parapodium.

This worm demonstrates *homonomous segmentation*—division of the body into a series of nearly equal (homonomous) segments. Later we will compare this type with a more advanced type found in higher arthropods, *heteronomous segmentation*, in which successive segments are markedly different.

▶ Why are polychaetes (especially worms like *Neanthes*) thought to be relatively primitive annelids?

▶ What is meant by the "tube within a tube" body plan?

2—Review of polychaetes—Review various polychaete examples from available specimens, your text, charts, or more complete books on invertebrate zoology. You may be surprised. They form a varied and unexpectedly interesting assemblage.

C. Class Hirudinea—*leeches*

Not a popular organism with most people, leeches are nonetheless interesting and highly adapted animals. The historical role of the medicinal leech in bloodletting is widely recognized—in fact, in some places leeches are still used for this purpose.

Although chiefly known for their bloodsucking habits, leeches are largely fresh-water predators, feeding voraciously on snails, worms, and other aquatic organisms. Some are scavengers, others parasitic. Bloodsucking species have an enormously distensible, branched gut, enabling them to feed to repletion when they do find a host and to store the bloodmeal during long periods of abstinence, often several months. Some leeches have become adapted to a terrestrial habitat, particularly in warm, moist tropical areas where they are disagreeable and in some cases dangerous pests, attacking men and animals in enormous numbers.

If specimens are available, observe them carefully and try to compare their basic segmented structure with that of other annelids. Study laboratory demonstrations or charts for internal anatomy and structures not apparent in your own specimen.

▶ Does external segmentation of leeches correspond with their internal segmentation?

▶ What structures ally leeches with other annelids?

▶ List features peculiar to leeches that enable them to become bloodsuckers or predators.

CHAPTER 9

Phylum

Arthropoda

I. INTRODUCTION

Approximately three-fourths of all animals are in the Phylum ARTHROPODA. Arthopod body organization must therefore be an extraordinarily efficient one. Great structural flexibility and high capacity to form new species are also implied by these numbers. Success of the phylum is obvious, whether measured by total numbers, species, structural variety, adaptability, or evolutionary plasticity.

The arthropod basic body type is characterized by: (1) bilateral symmetry; (2) segmentation; (3) hardened exoskeleton, usually chitinous; (4) jointed appendages; (5) strong tendency towards *tagmosis* (fusion of blocks of segments to form major regions—head, thorax, and abdomen) and towards *heteronomous metamerism* (formation of specialized appendages and segments); (6) growth discontinuous, usually occurring immediately after shedding the exoskeleton (molting); (7) no distinct trochophorelike larval form in early development, such as in annelids and mollusks;[1] (8) cephalization (increased size and specialization of brain and central nervous system); (9) tendency towards loss of coelom and formation of hemocoel; and (10) retention of certain annelidlike characters (dorsal heart with ostia; nerve ring around esophagus; ventral ganglia paired in each segment, modified by fusion of ganglia and segments).

The major groups of arthropods are classified according to their segmentation, tagmosis, and appendages. The first part to form embryologically, the head contains the most specialized appendages and therefore is probably the most useful key to relationships.

One of the most interesting aspects of arthropod biology is the extraordinary impact that the chitinous exoskeleton has had on the form, function, adaptability, and evolution of the group. Not only the term ARTHROPODA (jointed feet), but many other characters—manner of growth, circulatory and respiratory systems, size, even habitat—can be related to this tough, jointed, hollow skeleton. Limitations too—small size, short lifespan, restricted brain size—can also be traced to arthropod skeletal structure. Keep this relationship between exoskeleton and evolution in mind during your survey of the phylum, and test its applicability as you become better acquainted with the examples you review.

---

[1] Although a nauplius larva is found in CRUSTACEA, and a wormlike larva in higher insects, both are later stages in the embryological sequence.

II. CLASSIFICATION

A comparative study of ARTHROPODA is difficult, since its major elements became diversified before the earliest clearly recognizable fossils were deposited in the Cambrian Period, 500,000,000 years ago. Arthropod evolution is so vast that innumerable examples are required to get a real feeling for patterns of change and for groups that have evolved during this long period. The embryology of higher arthropods lacks phylogenetically illuminating early stages, which makes basic relationships even more difficult to trace.

We will have time to study very few examples, but these will provide a brief roundup of some major patterns of arthropod adaptation. Check all names used against the classification outlined in Chapter 2; *add generic names of examples discussed to the appropriate larger catagories in the outline.*

Two great groups of arthropods are generally recognized: Subphylum MANDIBULATA, jawed arthropods, and Subphylum CHELICERATA, arthropods whose first appendage bears clawlike pincers.[2]

The huge Subphylum MANDIBULATA contains the classes CRUSTACEA, INSECTA, and MYRIAPODA (centipedes and millipedes). In the Subphylum CHELICERATA are the classes ARACHNIDA (scorpions, whip scorpions, pseudoscorpions, spiders, sun spiders, phalangids or daddy longlegs, mites, and ticks) and MEROSTOMATA (horseshoe crabs and extinct eurypterids), along with the 4 highly specialized groups mentioned in the footnote below.

In the Subphylum MANDIBULATA, Class

---

[2] Sometimes the PYCNOGONIDA, here considered a class of CHELICERATA, is recognized as a third subphylum of arthropods. These are the "sea spiders"—strange, slow-moving, marine, somewhat spiderlike creatures. Still other small groups may be accorded a high taxonomic level because of their extremely unusual structure (or simply because we haven't enough evidence to place them phylogenetically precisely where they belong). These include the Class PENTASTOMIDA—wormlike parasites of vertebrates possibly derived from mites (Order ACARINA) but considered by many specialists to be different enough to be listed as a distinct class of chelicerates—and the Class TARDIGRADA, "water bears"—microscopic, soft-bodied, largely unsegmented, 8-legged creatures, also in the chelicerate subphylum. Others, such as the extinct TRILOBITES, probably belong as a class in the chelicerate line, though sometimes, they are classified as a distinct subphylum. The separate Phylum ONYCOPHORA, a phylogenetically important but rather rare and small group of caterpillarlike animals, shows important evolutionary relationships with the annelids (review your text discussion of *Peripatus*). Some authors list these organisms as a subphylum under ARTHROPODA, indicating uncertainty over the exact position of this ancient group.

CRUSTACEA, Subclass MALACOSTRACA, is an assemblage of water dwellers typified by crayfishes (*Cambarus*), lobsters (*Homarus*), and shrimps, all of which are included in the Order DECAPODA (malacostracans with 10 pairs of walking legs). Mantis shrimps, beach fleas, and sowbugs represent other orders of the Subclass MALACOSTRACA.

Examples of some other important subclasses in the Class CRUSTACEA include barnacles (CIRRIPEDIA) and copepods (COPEPODA). In the Subclass BRANCHIOPODA are found the most primitive crustacea, showing very little specialization of segments or appendages; examples are the fairy shrimps and brine shrimps (Division ANOSTRACA). Perhaps no animals can compare with such widespread copepods as *Calanus* in overall abundance or importance in the ecological food chain of the sea.

Our study of the crayfish as a single example of the entire Class CRUSTACEA must therefore cover a lot of biological territory, a great range of geological time, an enormous area of the earth's surface (about 4/7—all the water-covered surface of the globe), and a rich evolutionary divergence in numbers and kinds.

The two remaining classes of MANDIBULATA, the INSECTA (or HEXAPODA, 6-legged) and MYRIAPODA (centipedes, millipedes), contain many familiar examples. Despite the fact that INSECTA is by far the largest class of all, we will have time to study only one or two species. Perhaps 800,000 to a million species of insects have already been described. Some entomologists believe that this includes less than half of the actual number of living insect species. We will examine the common lubber grasshopper, *Romalea*, and the American cockroach, *Periplaneta*. (These examples are selected chiefly because of their ease of procurement.)

Whether there are one or two million kinds, insects represent a biological success story. Insect history differs markedly from that of the Class CRUSTACEA in one important ecological respect: insects have become terrestrial. They have bridged the great gap between water breathing and air breathing. Occupation of land opened a greatly varied new environment in which insects spread rapidly during the Cretaceous Period, some 100,000,000 years ago. In doing so, however, they burned their bridge to the sea behind them. Their adaptations for air breathing and for resistance to desiccation seem to have prevented reoccupation of the marine environment from which their ancestors presumably arose. A relatively small number of larval insects live in fresh water, but how many *adult* insects have you seen inhabiting ponds and streams? Some water beetles carry bubbles of air underwater, an indication of the difficulty adult insects have in returning to an aquatic environment. So far as we know, no insects live as true ocean dwellers—excluding a few at the water edge or rare water striders on surface film.

Apparently associated with the arthropod transfer to and spread over the terrestrial habitat was the development of flowering plants, which provided insects with a great variety of shelter, food, and protection. In turn, insects came to play a significant role in distribution and structural modifications of these plants, many of which possess highly specialized structures for pollination by a specific insect group—a type of evolutionary partnership.

Insects demonstrate to an unusual degree the evolutionary process called *adaptive radiation*, in which a basic structural or functional modification permits rapid occupation of a new environment. This exploitation of previously unavailable habitats is followed by diversification—formation of new species—and spread into more specialized niches within the new environment. If another evolutionary modification appears in one of the ecologically or geographically isolated groups, a new wave of habitat occupation may carry these animals into still different environments. A succession of such major structural and functional changes or adaptive breakthroughs, each producing a wave of spread and specialization, is what is meant by adaptive radiation.

When arthropods transferred from an aquatic to a terrestrial environment, their jointed exoskeleton—durable, impervious, and lightweight—determined a series of profound morphological and physiological changes that introduced adaptive radiations into the numerous habitats afforded by land and air.

First of the major changes related to the exoskeleton and influencing the evolution of insects was probably the *tracheal system,* an extensive network of air-conducting tubes branching from the exoskeleton to every cell of the organism. Tracheae, along with the strength, lightness, extensive area for muscle attachment, and other advantages of the exoskeleton, permitted early scorpionlike arthropods to become air-breathing land dwellers. Reduction of walking legs to 6 freed head appendages for specialization in feeding. Such an organism was then a true insect, capable of wide diversification of food habits and spread into a wide variety of terrestrial habitats. Insect *flight* was made possible by membranous wings, a highly organized muscular system, rapid metabolic rate, small size, and relative indestructibil-

ity—all features related to the exoskeleton. Vast new ecological realms were made available by this remarkable development (no other invertebrates and only birds and certain mammals, such as bats, have evolved the power of flight).

Metamorphosis, related to mode of growth and ultimately to the exoskeleton, provided still further specialization: the protected *egg* stage for critical and delicate early development; the wormlike *larva,* a feeding machine; the *pupa,* another protected stage for the scarcely believable transition from larva to adult; and the flying *adult,* adapted for reproduction and spread of its kind. Metamorphosis meant specialization of body form to functional needs, such as development, growth, reproduction, and distribution of the species.

Each major stage of insect evolution is marked by adaptive radiation, made possible by important morphological and physiological changes, and molded by the structural limitations and advantages afforded by the chitinous skeleton.

Although the ant may one day inherit the world, it will not, as pictured in science fiction yarns, become huge in size. Total size is restricted in insects for two reasons. First, tracheae work efficiently in small volumes, as the air moves in and out chiefly by diffusion. Very large insects simply could not exchange gases rapidly enough by tracheal respiration. Second, just after each molt the insect skeleton is soft and flexible—the period of *discontinuous growth.* Being unsupported by exoskeleton, the body at this period must be supported by the external medium. This is little problem to a lobster—but what would happen to a lobster in *air* during the molting period? It would be squashed by its own weight. Imagine what would happen to the monster grasshopper pictured in science fiction tales! Instead of becoming huge, however, the ant and his innumerable counterparts might simply multiply to the fantastic degree possible for these organisms and occupy every available square inch of ground. In this event, insects would prove an excessively burdensome competitor to man for food and space—far more dangerous to us than 10-foot man-eating insects would be.

Review the body type of the Phylum ARTHROPODA as exemplified first by crustaceans and then by insects.

▶ How do these differences permit occupation of distinct environments and subsequent divergence of the two groups?

In the second major division of ARTHROPODA, the Subphylum CHELICERATA, are the

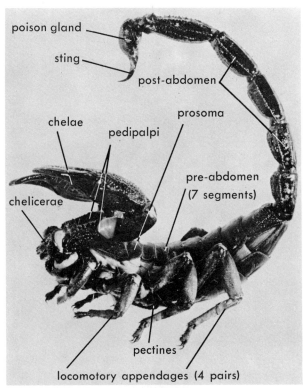

poison gland

sting

post-abdomen

chelae

pedipalpi

prosoma

chelicerae

pre-abdomen
(7 segments)

pectines

locomotory appendages (4 pairs)

Fig. 9-1. Lateral view of a scorpion.

spiders, scorpions, ticks, mites, and allied forms. Here, the general arthropod pattern is usually modified for predation as well as for existence on land. Many chelicerates are equipped with poison claws or glands and their mouthparts are usually adapted for sucking out the juices or soft tissues of their prey. Although chelicerates are among the animals most highly resistant to desiccation, few except mites have spread to the variety of habitats utilized by insects, presumably because of their more specialized food habits. The 2-sectioned body consists of *head (cephalothorax)* and *abdomen.* Six pairs of jointed, segmented appendages are hinged onto the cephalothorax. These include clawed *chelicerae* (containing the poison fangs or claws and poison ducts in forms possessing this weapon), *pedipalpi* (6-jointed, leglike structures to hold or crush prey, specialized for sperm transfer in males), and *4 pairs* of 7-jointed walking legs. Note that true antennae and mandibles, characteristic of MANDIBULATA, are entirely absent. The respiratory system also has specialized features: *lung books* in some spiders, *gill books* in king crabs, *tracheae* in the abdomen of other spiders, *direct diffusion* through the cuticle in mites. Specialization of excretory and nervous systems characterize the different chelicerate classes. The Class MEROSTOMATA includes king crabs and extinct eurypterids (huge scorpionlike predators of paleaezoic seas). ARACH-

NIDA include 9 somewhat familiar orders, among which are numerous feared and maligned examples: SCORPIONIDA—scorpions (Fig. 9-1); PEDIPALPI—whip scorpions; ARANEAE—spiders (divided into 2 suborders, trapdoor spiders and tarantulas in one, and black widows, funnel web spiders, hunting spiders, orb weavers, crab spiders, and jumping spiders in the other); SOLPUGIDA—sun spiders; PSEUDOSCORPIONIDA—false scorpions; PHALANGIDA—harvestmen or daddy longlegs; ACARINA—ticks and mites.

Chelicerate mouth structure, absence of wings, and predaceous food habits in general restrict distribution of members of this subphylum, at least in comparison with that of insects. Spiders, ticks, and mites, however, do occupy a vast area and many types of terrestrial habitat. Mites, through marked reduction of size and simplification of body structure, have, in fact, developed a different widespread adaptive radiation, enabling them to become abundant soil dwellers and to feed on a wide variety of materials from organic debris to blood. Although mites represent an extension of the arthropod type into numerous ecological niches, these tiny creatures are among the least known groups of animals.

Our detailed study of the Phylum ARTHROPODA must be confined to just 3 examples: the decapod malacostracan crustacean *Cambarus,* the crayfish; the grasshopper, *Romalea;* and the cockroach, *Periplaneta.* Familiarization with basic arthropod organization and taxonomy is needed to comprehend both the overall maze of arthropod diversity and the numbers and position of these representatives within such diversity.

III. *LABORATORY INSTRUCTIONS*

A. Cambarus

1—Classification—
Phylum ARTHROPODA
Subphylum MANDIBULATA
Class CRUSTACEA
Subclass MALACOSTRACA
Order DECAPODA
Family Astacidae
Genus *Cambarus* (in certain Western states the Pacific form, *Pacifastacus,* may be used).

2—General observations—The crayfish, a common inhabitant of fresh-water streams and ponds, often emerges at night and makes characteristic burrows and mounds in wet fields or gardens. Along with its marine relatives, lobsters and crabs, the crayfish feeds chiefly on decaying organic matter. (It is also known as crawfish.)

Observe the living crayfish in an aquarium. Watch it locate food with its antennae, tear off chunks with its large pincers (*chelipeds*), tease and macerate it with the *mandibles*, and finally pass the smaller pieces to the 5 pairs of mouthparts (*maxillae* and *maxillipeds*) that handle and ingest the morsel.

Observe walking, swimming, and respiratory movements.

▶ Which legs are involved in each process?

▶ How are the antennae used?

▶ How does the animal right itself when turned over? Pick your crayfish up by the dorsal shield (carapace). Hold it firmly!

▶ Why does the animal buck and flip its tail down so strongly?

▶ What is the function of this movement when the animal is in water?

▶ How do you suppose the crayfish digs in soft earth?

Observe the respiratory currents of a crayfish resting in a shallow pan of water and note how they are produced. Add a couple of drops of India ink near the animal and watch the particle flow into the respiratory stream.

SUGGESTION

In many areas of our southern and prairie states, it is possible to watch foraging and digging crayfish ("crawdads") at night. Seek them out with a flashlight in marshy or moist open fields and watch their pattern of movement, digging, and rapid escape. Dig a few from their tunnels and observe their action in a laboratory or home aquarium. Baked or boiled crayfish represents another biological aspect of these succulent organisms well worth investigating.

3—External anatomy (Figs. 9-2 and 9-3)— If your specimen is preserved in formalin, avoid disagreeable fumes by rinsing it overnight in tapwater before dissection.

a. *Segmentation.* Observe the *tagmata*, or grouping of segments, into 3 general regions: (1) *head*

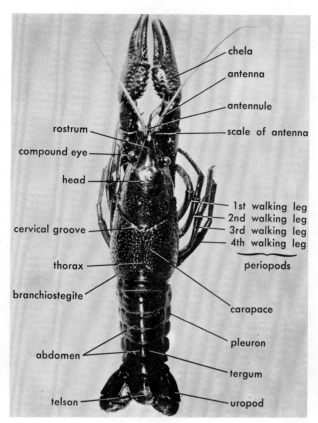

Fig. 9-2. *Cambarus,* dorsal aspect.

(somites I-V, with *antennules, antennae, mandibles,* and 2 pairs of *maxillae*); (2) *thorax* (somites VI-XIII, with 3 pairs of *maxillipeds, chelipeds,* and 4 pairs of walking legs or *pereiopods*); and (3) *abdomen* (somites XIV-XIX, with 5 pairs of swimmerets or *pleopods,* and *uropod* or tail).

▶ How many pairs of appendages are borne on each body segment?

▶ Are all appendages jointed?

▶ How do the pincers operate? (Better use a pickled specimen)

▶ What are the advantages of a hollow exoskeleton in terms of strength, variety of body movements, and protection?

▶ How does surface area for muscle attachment compare between a hollow exoskeleton and a solid endoskeleton?

▶ What are the *disadvantages* of an exoskeleton?

Observe the peg-and-socket joints between abdominal segments. The exoskeleton of each body segment is divided into a dorsal *tergum*, a lateral *pleuron*, and a ventral *sternum*. Find these parts on the abdominal and thoracic somites of your specimen.

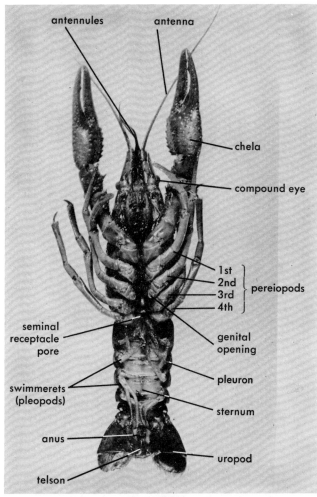

Fig. 9-3. *Cambarus,* ventral aspect.

b. *Body parts.* Before removing the appendages and studying their relationship, identify the major body parts visible *dorsally* (Fig. 9-2)—*head, antennule, antenna, cephalothorax, carapace, cervical groove, rostrum, eyes, cheliped, pereiopods, uropod, telson.* Then observe the crayfish from the *lateral* view and locate the *gill chambers* under the pleura of the carapace. Study the animal *ventrally* and observe its 19 paired appendages. First, find the anteriormost sensory *antennules,* biramous (2-branched) structures with many joints and a balancing organ or *statocyst* on the flattened dorsal surface of the basal joint. Next are the *antennae,* a pair of long, slender, many-jointed appendages with *excretory openings* at the basal segment of each. Then come the *mandibles,* or chewing jaws, followed by 2 pairs of *maxillae* for food handling. Three pairs of *maxillipeds* follow; these serve for manipulation and sensory perception of food. Then, completing the series, are the *chelipeds,* the largest claws;

4 pairs of walking legs (*pereiopods*); 5 pairs of *swimmerets;* and finally the *uropod.* Next, review the location of the following body openings: *mouth, anus* (on ventral surface of *telson,* the central portion of the tail), and *excretory pore* on each antenna. Find the *external sex organs.* Male **genitalia** open at the base of the fourth leg. A trough for transfer of spermatophores into the female seminal receptacle is formed from the fused tubular first and second swimmerets. Female oviducts open at the base of the second legs; another slit between the base of the fourth walking legs serves to receive the spermatophores. The first swimmeret in females is small or absent; the second is a typical swimmeret rather than a specialized organ as in the male. The female telson and filamentous swimmerets hold the egg cluster to form an external brood pouch for the eggs and young. Females carrying such a mass of eggs are said to be "in berry."

c. *Appendages* (Fig. 9-4). After this initial examination of your specimen you should be ready for detailed review of the appendages. Learn not only the functional and structural differences between appendages but also their relationship to a common prototype, a simple biramous appendage (rather like the swimmeret). Species thought to be more primitive show a repetition of parts with little specialization, such as the parapodia of *Neanthes.* In more highly evolved animals, specialization of appendages, especially on the head, is apparent. One sees, for example, striking differences between a brine shrimp with many similar biramous appendages and a crab, shrimp, or crayfish with much modified mouthparts that appear to be derived from more simple swimmerets. Structural change of parts repeated in linear sequence can often be traced by comparison with an unspecialized segment or appendage. This type of evolutionary modification demonstrates a relationship of parts called *serial homology.* Marked similarity of segments, a presumably primitive condition, as in the brine shrimp, is called *homonomous metamerism.* Extreme specialization of segments, as in the crayfish, is called *heteronomous metamerism.*

▶ Name several other examples of each.

Examine a sample dissection of crayfish appendages if one is available. Read the following instructions carefully before starting your dissection. Don't be alarmed by the terms. They're jawbreakers but they make sense (es-

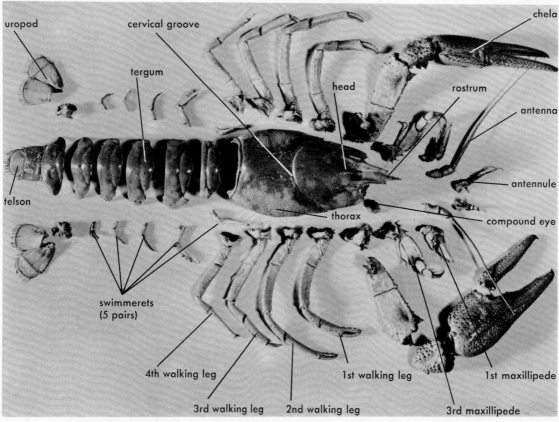

uropod
cervical groove
chela
tergum
head
rostrum
antenna
antennule
telson
compound eye
thorax
swimmerets
(5 pairs)
4th walking leg
1st walking leg
1st maxillipede
3rd walking leg   2nd walking leg
3rd maxillipede

Fig. 9-4. Disarticulated view of crayfish, male.

pecially if you have some familiarity with Latin or Greek).

Each limb consists of 3 basic portions: the stem or attachment, the *protopodite*, and 2 branches, the innermost of which is the *endopodite*, the outer the *exopodite*. The *protopodite* usually consists of 2 segments (joints), a basal *coxopodite* attached to the body, and the distal *basipodite* to which the 2 branches (endopodite and exopodite) are attached. Each appendage fundamentally follows this structural pattern, though with considerable modification towards the head, as you will soon see. In some cases, homology can be determined only by embryological study owing to loss of some portions during growth and the development of more specialized appendages. In certain cases, as in antennules, precise homology of the segments is still uncertain.

Carefully cut away the lateral extension of the carapace, the *branchiostegite*, from one side to expose the external sheet of gills (Fig. 9-5).

Your dissection will start with the uropod and work forward. The simple structure of the abdominal appendages is more like what is presumed to have been the primitive (original) crustacean biramous appendage. Each appendage should be examined critically with a hand lens or dissecting microscope. Observe the structure,

check it against its stated function, and note the *increased degree of structural specialization as you proceed toward the head*. You may find it more instructive to pin the appendages alongside the animal under water in a wax-bottom dissecting pan, than to draw them in normal extension. Afterwards the appendages can be dried and glued onto a cardboard sheet for later reference (Fig. 9-4). Be sure to remove a bit of attachment membrane with each appendage to ensure having the intact structure.

Beginning with the uropod, remove one appendage at a time from the side on which you have exposed the gills. Identify the 3 basic parts (if all are present) and pin out the appendage, carefully orienting the protopodite to the left, the endopodite anteriorly, the exopodite posteriorly. Compare the normal plane of movement of each part and of each limb with the others to get a better idea of the manner in which the entire appendage functions. From the uropod, now proceed through the simple pleopods, noting again the sexual differences and water-circulating role of these organs. The walking legs, removed next, are of interest for their endopodite specialization (the exopodite entirely disappears during development) and for their respiratory role. Special gills, *podobranchiae*, are attached to certain legs (*which ones?*). Their point of attachment is the protopodite, specifically the basal segment or

---

coxopodite, with a specialized extension to which the gill filaments attach.

► How are these gills moved?

Anterior to the pincer-bearing chelipeds are 3 pairs of maxillipeds, part of the complex food handling, grinding, and sensing mechanism. The third maxilliped, the largest of the three and most similar to the walking legs, is a good appendage to observe closely for signs of specializations that will become more marked in the anterior mouthparts. The exopodite is present in all 3 maxillipeds but the endopodite becomes progressively smaller. The first maxilliped is marked by a large, flattened extension of the coxopodite. This is the *epipodite,* a paddlelike structure that helps to maintain a water current through the gill chamber. The more anterior segments are parts of the head; their appendages form the mouthparts and related sensory organs. The second maxilla, anterior to the first maxilliped, also maintains a water flow across the gill membranes by its specialized paddle, the *scaphognathite* (which fortunately the crayfish only has to use, not to pronounce). Actually a fusion of epipodite and exopodite, this paddle may be referred to as the *bailer* for its constant sweeping action as it draws water from the gill chamber. The extremely small first maxilla or *maxillule* consists of a much reduced endopodite and larger basipodite and coxopodite. The exopodite is entirely absent, as in the walking legs.

► Can you tell where the exopodite probably was originally attached?

Next is the mandible, a heavy crushing structure (actually the coxopodite) with a cutting inner edge and a brush-like sensory projection; its much modified endopodite is called the *palp.* The basal segment of the palp is actually the basipodite. Again, an exopodite is lacking. A well-developed tendon attaches the mandible to mandibular muscles on the carapace tergum. The next appendage is the antenna. Find the opening of the kidney (*green gland*) in the coxopodite. Segmentation here is fairly typical, all parts being present. The long *flagellum,* or antenna proper, is an extension of the endopodite. Finally, examine the antennule, the anteriormost appendage, with its 2 equal divisions. These, however, are not easily homologized with the endopodite and exopodite of more typical appendages.

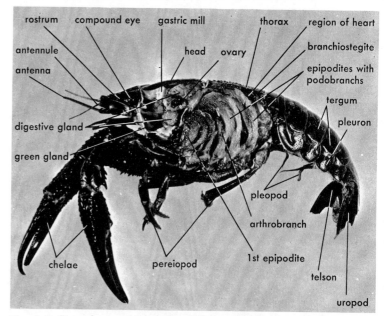

Fig. 9-5. Lateral view of female crayfish with lateral surface of cephalothorax dissected back to show disposition of parts.

Draw each appendage, *labeling* the important segments. Be able to compare each with a typical 3-part appendage and to explain its function.

► What is meant by *serial homology*?

► How would you compare serial homology with the homology represented by a comparison between the wing of a bat and a human hand?

► How does the serial homology of CRUSTACEA (heteronomous metamerism) compare with that of the ANNELIDA or primitive arthropods such as the brine shrimp (homonomous metamerism)?

► What is meant by each of these terms?

► How is anteroposterior differentiation in brine shrimp and crayfish related to habits and food-handling capacity in these animals?

► Does this differentiation imply an increased degree of nervous control?

► Is this nervous control related to fusion of nerve ganglia and increased brain size?

4—Respiratory system—Keep your specimen immersed under water in a dissecting pan. You have exposed part of the gill structure when you removed the branchiostegite from one side of the thorax (Fig. 9-5). The outermost foot gills or *podobranchiae* have already been removed, as they were attached to the walking legs and the second and third maxillipeds. The 2 gill blankets that still remain consist of 5 pairs plus a single anterior gill. These joint gills or *arthrobranchiae* (can you tell why the term is used?) are atttached to the base of the *arthropodial membrane.* The lobster possesses still another group of gills higher up on the same membrane, called side gills or *pleurobranchiae.* In *Cambarus,* side gills are lacking.

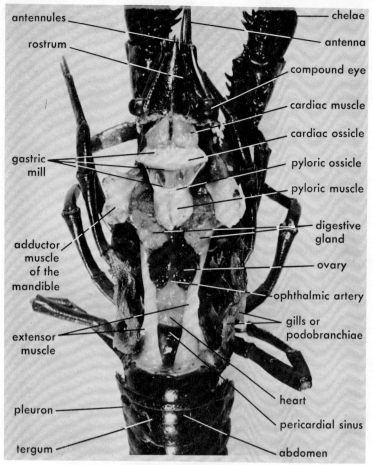

antennules
rostrum

gastric
mill

adductor
muscle
of the
mandible

extensor
muscle

pleuron

tergum

chelae
antenna
compound eye
cardiac muscle
cardiac ossicle
pyloric ossicle
pyloric muscle
digestive
gland
ovary
ophthalmic artery
gills or
podobranchiae
heart
pericardial sinus
abdomen

Fig. 9-6. Anterior end of crayfish with dorsal surface of cephalothorax dissected back to show disposition of parts.

► Are any of these gills actually inside the body?

► Is the branchiostegite the true outer wall of the thorax?

Remove an arthrobranch and examine it under a lens. Find its central axis and the many fine lateral filaments.

► What is the function of these lateral filaments?

Cut across the gill and observe the *afferent* and *efferent branchial* (gill) *vessels* visible in cross section within the central axis.

► How does walking affect the podobranchiae?

► How is a current of fresh oxygenated water kept constantly moving over the gills?

► Name the structures involved in control of this respirator stream.

► Where does actual gas exchange occur?

5—Internal anatomy (Fig. 9-6)

a. Systems to be examined in this section are *digestive, muscular, circulatory, and reproductive.*

It is difficult to separate the individual internal systems of the crayfish clearly, as they form

a tightly compacted whole, morphologically interposed one with another. We shall therefore study them as they appear—as interfunctioning parts of a single physiological complex.

A fresh specimen, newly killed or recently preserved, is best for this exercise. If available, use one that has been injected with colored latex to show the circulatory system. If it has been carefully dissected, you can still use your original specimen. Place it in water in your dissecting pan, dorsal side up; pin it out if you are using a wax-bottom pan.

With a skimming motion of your scissors, cut under the lateral margins of the cephalothorax tergum. Remove this shield after making cross-cuts behind the eyes and the posterior edge of the carapace. Over the exposed surface lies a skinlike *hypodermis* (part of which may have adhered to the carapace). This tissue, also called by a more general term, *epidermis*, secretes the exoskeleton.

Clear off the hypodermis and examine the exposed organs. You will see the gill surfaces outside the body proper in the branchial chambers. The first internal structure to locate for orientation is the *heart* in its *pericardial sinus* along the dorsal midline. The 2 dorsal pores, or *ostia*, through which blood enters the heart are visible. Later you will observe 2 other pairs of ostia in the isolated heart. The next organ to identify is the *stomach*, more descriptively called the *gastric mill* because of hardened, internal sclerites for grinding food. Look in the front portion of the thoracic body cavity for this thin sac with nearly translucent walls. Moving the sclerites are short, powerful muscle bands that pass from the posterior sclerites to the undersurface of the carapace. Find the cut edges of these muscles on the carapace shield you removed. The anterior set forms the *anterior gastric muscles;* the posterior set, the *posterior gastric muscles.*

If your specimen is a female "in berry" you will notice 2 masses of ovaries extending from anterior to the heart to merge posteriorly to it. Although male *testes* are less conspicuous, they also have the same Y-shaped gonadal pattern. The other large structure, the *digestive gland,* will be studied in more detail in a few moments.

Before continuing your dissection, trace some of the other major muscles that are visible. First are 2 pairs of *abdominal extensor* muscle bands that pass through the pericardial sinus and diverge to attach anteriorly along the floor and in

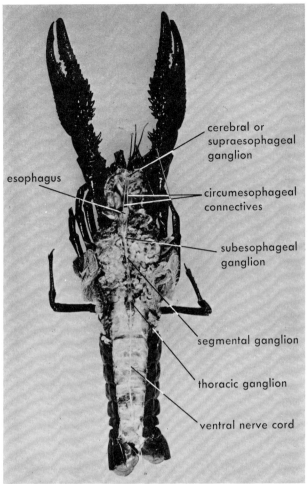

Fig. 9-7. *Cambarus,* dorsal view of nervous system.

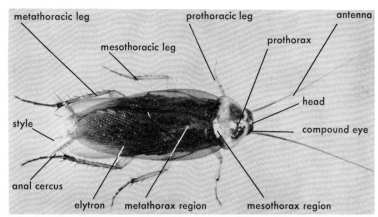

Fig. 9-8. Dorsal view of the cockroach, *Periplaneta americana,* male.

front of the exoskeletal framework. These muscles continue into the abdomen, where their dorsal-ventral position causes the abdominal sclerites to extend when the muscles contract. This extension moves the tail *dorsally,* setting the uropods in position for the stronger *abdominal flexor* muscles to deliver the powerful kick, the escape spurt you have already observed in these animals. These flexors will be seen later when you open the abdomen.

Now the specimen can be exposed for further dissection. On the side with the gills removed, cut away the inner thoracic wall and remove the shield of carapace behind the eye (do not damage the green gland under this shield). At this point you will have a lateral view of the internal organs in their normal position.

Notice the distribution of the digestive gland and ovaries (or testes), the heart with its *lateral pairs* of ostia, the coils of *vas deferens* in the male, the *green gland* or kidney. Use forceps (with caution) where necessary to move the or-

gans aside or to remove portions of digestive or gonadal tissue that obscure other organs.

Cut away the dorsal abdominal sclerites along their entire length, using two parallel incisions down the lateral margins (Figs. 9-7 and 9-8). Lift back this plate after cutting the extensor muscles of the abdomen behind the heart. Observe these thin bands under the dorsal skeleton and review their function. Then note the powerful abdominal flexor muscles forming bilateral masses on either side of the abdomen below the intestine. These are the previously mentioned muscles that give the power kick in swimming. You may also find the *posterior aorta* lying dorsal to the intestine. This important blood vessel is best seen in colored latex-injected specimens.

▶ Do any parts of the gonads or digestive gland extend into the abdomen?

At this point, pause to review what you have already examined: the gill system, major muscles, heart and posterior aorta, gastric mill, intestine, digestive gland, excretory organ, and gonads. Be able to identify each and show its structural relations to the rest of the internal anatomy.

Make an *outline drawing* of the crayfish from the *lateral aspect* and include all organs you have been able to locate. Later, add those you find in subsequent dissection.

Starting from the heart, work out as much of the circulatory system as possible, moving the organs aside to find the primary vessels. The anterior artery leaves the heart anteriorly and supplies the head. A pair of diverging *lateral cephalic arteries (antennary arteries)* emerges from the heart at the same point and supplies the gastric mill, anterior muscle groups, and kidney. Two *lateral visceral arteries (hepatic arteries)* pass ventrally from the anterior end of the heart to the digestive gland, anterior intestine, and gonads. The *posterior aorta* and *sternal artery* leave the posterior end of the heart and also pass ventrally. The sternal artery divides in the thorax and passes anteriorly to become the *ventral abdominal artery.*

You have now seen the major distributive pathways for freshly oxygenated arterial blood. Remember that this is an example of the *open type of circulation.* Blood vessels carry blood from the heart as described above, but then it passes into blood spaces (*sinuses*) and a *hemocoel* through which it flows prior to movement into branchial vessels and capillaries for oxygenation and return to the heart.

Blood sinuses of *Cambarus* carry blood to tissues and cells after which it diffuses into the *afferent branchial vessels,* is oxygenated by diffusion across fine capillary membranes in the gills, and passes out the *efferent branchial vessels.* The oxygenated blood then moves into *branchiopericardial canals* that carry it to the *pericardial chamber.* There the pool of blood enters the heart through 3 pairs of ostia and is ejected out the arteries you have just reviewed. Compare this system with that of *Lumbricus* with an intact (closed) system of capillaries and tubular veins that distributes blood to cells and respiratory centers.

Remove the heart, place it in a small dish of water, and study it under a hand lens or dissection microscope. Locate the other ostia, in addition to the dorsal pair that you have already observed.

► Can you find valves that prevent backflow through the ostia?

Now complete your examination of the genital and digestive systems. Find the *oviduct* (or *vas deferens* in the male) and note the general shape of the gonads. Trace the ducts to the genital pore on one side, and add these details to your drawing.

With care to avoid injury to the nervous system, clear away some of the gonadal and muscular tissue to locate the complete digestive system. Trace the *intestine* from the *stomach* to the *anus.* Examine the area anterior to the stomach, then find the short *esophagus,* which passes ventrally to the mouth through the nerve ring near the green gland. Don't damage either! You can locate the esophagus by cautiously inserting a rounded probe into the mouth and carefully dissecting intervening tissues from the lateral aspect. Next try to remove the entire digestive tract including the intact digestive

gland. Cut the intestine near the anus and tease it free to the stomach. Then work the digestive gland clear, cut the esophagus without damaging the nerve ring, and remove the entire alimentary canal. Let the structure float free in water and observe its pores, especially connections of the digestive gland ducts to the stomach. Add this system to your drawing, or place it in a separate drawing if that is more convenient. *Label* completely.

Cut the gastric mill from the rest of the gut, slit it ventrally, and examine its parts carefully. Find the heavy, toothlike projections and move the sides of the organ to see how they operate.

► What had your crayfish been eating?

Pin out the gastric mill, let it dry to show more clearly the teeth or *ossicles.* Study it under the dissecting microscope. Determine the pattern of food flow into the cardiac section, the pressure chamber and valves leading to the intestinal connection, and the opening from the digestive gland.

b. Nervous system

1. The *sense organs* to be studied include the many *sensory hairs, compound eyes,* and *statocysts.* Sensory hairs over the entire body provide the animal with touch receptors on the otherwise relatively insensitive exoskeleton. Hairs on the mouthparts and antennae probably have chemotactic as well as tactile receptors. Nerve cells lying near tactile hair bases are stimulated by movement of the hair.

The characteristic arthropod eye is a compound structure formed by a bank of many *ommatidia* (like cells of a photographic light meter) covered by a thin, transparent, cuticular *cornea.* A cross section of the eye made with a razor will disclose black radiating lines marking separate ommatidia or visual units, which emanate from a central white *optic ganglion. Pigment cells* around each *rhabdome* and the *crystalline cone* may be seen by microscopic examination of a portion of the eye that has been placed in a drop of water on a microscope slide.

The statocyst, or gravity receptor, is located in the basal segment of each antennule. Remove the remaining antennule and examine the basal segment under a dissecting microscope or hand lens. Search for a thin sac attached to the dorsal wall of this segment. As the crayfish moves, sand grains placed in this sac by the animal stimulate sensitive tactile hairs.

▶ What function does the organ serve and how does it work?

▶ What equivalent organs have you already studied in other groups?

Some rather weird experiments can be performed by placing a newly molted crayfish in a tank of clean filtered water to which iron filings have been added. The animal will place these filings in its statocysts, since no sand grains are available.

▶ How will the crayfish orient itself if you hold a magnet over its head? At the side of its head?

It would be interesting to see if these reactions eventually disappear and if the animal learns to associate normal positioning of its body with a different stimulus, such as produced by a magnet held in a dorsal position for a long period. Why not try it?

2. *Central nervous system* (Fig. 9-7). The *ventral nerve cord,* in the midventral portion of the animal above the ventral abdominal artery, lies below the abdominal flexor muscle and under a shelf of connective tissue and *apodemes* (ingrowths from the ventral exoskeleton serving for muscle attachment).

Expose the nerve cord from the dorsal surface by stripping away the *dorsal flexor muscles* of the abdomen and cutting carefully through the thoracic apodemes on either side of the midline. It is sometimes simpler to make a single cut, spread the opening apart with the fingers to locate the cord, and then cut away projecting tissues. Expose the nerve as completely as possible.

Count the abdominal ganglia and note the somites in which they lie.

▶ Can you find *lateral nerves* arising from the abdominal portion of the nerve?

▶ Are they connected to ganglia?

▶ How many *thoracic ganglia* are there per segment?

▶ What appears to have happened to the anterior ganglia?

▶ What is the evolutionary significance of this development?

▶ Can you trace any thoracic nerves from the cord?

A worthwhile special anatomical study would be to work out the peripheral nerve connections. Notice the space for the sternal artery between the sixth and seventh thoracic ganglia. Trace the cord anteriorly and dissect clear the *subesophageal ganglion,* which is a fusion of the esophageal nerve ring (*circumesophageal connectives*) and the brain (*cerebral ganglion*). The dorsal part of the nerve ring is sometimes called the *supraesophageal ganglion.* Locate the central pair of *optic nerves,* the *antennulary nerves* bordering them, and the lateral pair of *antennary nerves.* Trace these nerves to their respective organs.

Draw the complete ventral nerve cord and brain, showing location of ganglia and lateral nerves.

B. Romalea and Periplaneta

1—Classification—
Phylum ARTHROPODA
Subphylum MANDIBULATA
Class INSECTA
Subclass PTERYGOTA
Division HEMIMETABOLA
Order ORTHOPTERA
Species *Romalea microptera* (lubber grasshopper)
Order BLATTARIA
Species *Periplaneta americana* (American cockroach).

2—Introduction—Our representative insects are members of the Order ORTHOPTERA—grasshoppers, crickets, and related forms—and of the closely related Order BLATTARIA—cockroaches, wood roaches, and their allies. These are in the Division HEMIMETABOLA, a group of insect orders characterized by *gradual metamorphosis* in which immature forms are merely smaller editions of their parents, with wings gradually developing externally, eyes like those of the parents, and sexual organs undeveloped until the last *instar* (stage) is reached. Growth is discontinuous, as is typical of arthropods. Because of the hard exoskeleton, growth is possible only during a brief period after each molt, when the cuticle is soft and can be stretched. Internal pressures, such as blood (hemolymph) and air, exerted against the soft cuticle at this stage expand the larval skin, creating space for internal growth until once again the larva is literally bulging at the seams.

Other hemimetabolous orders include DERMAPTERA (earwings), PLECOPTERA (stoneflies), ISOPTERA (termites), EMBIOPTERA (embiids), ODONATA (dragonflies and damselflies), EPHEMEROPTERA (mayflies), MALLOPHAGA (biting lice), HOMOPTERA (cicadas, scale insects, aphids), and THYSANOPTERA (thrips).

Varied and numerous as these insects are, they are far less so than the Holometabola, the so-called higher insects, characterized by *complete metamorphosis*. In holometabolus orders, the life cycle can be divided into 4 clearly distinct stages: *egg, larva, pupa,* and *adult*. Each stage of holometabolous insects is an extreme form of morphological specialization. The larva, usually a worm or grub, is a voracious eater, and represents the growth stage. The sexually mature adult, the flying stage, is specialized both for reproduction and distribution. The egg and pupa represent periods of protected, active bodily reorganization, each ending in dramatic structural and functional change. Growth is confined to successive larval instars, as adult insects do not molt. Such limited adult "growth" as occurs is only a distension with eggs as in queen bees or ants. There is no such thing as a "baby fly" (except the wormlike grub, of course). Small adult flies are simply small species, or dwarfed flies hatched from poorly fed larvae. Specialization of body structure and stage of development to the metabolic and ecological needs of the higher insects represents a unique type of adaptation of the entire life cycle to distinct functions and diverse habitats.

Compare larval and adult stages of the *beetle, mosquito, honey bee,* and *butterfly*.

The largest of insect orders is the Coleoptera (beetles). Lepidoptera (moths and butterflies) and ever-present Diptera (true flies) are also giant groups. Siphonaptera (fleas) are among the most specialized. Hymenoptera (bees, wasps, and ants), with their complex social organization, are perhaps the most highly developed of all arthropods. Lesser known orders of Holometabola include the Neuroptera (lacewings), Mecoptera (scorpionflies), and Trichoptera (caddisflies).[3]

This makes quite a collection, some 27 orders, give or take a few, and about a million species, give or take a couple of hundred thousand. Name a terrestrial or fresh-water environment and it will have insects. Atomblast an island and insects will be among the first to repopulate it. Prolific, adaptable, varied, rapidly evolving, insects are here to stay. It's still questionable whether man can

[3] A few other insect groups are placed in a separate subclass, the Apterygota, owing to certain primitive or highly distinctive characteristics. Included are wingless forms like the Diplura (japygids) and book-loving silverfish or Thysanura (bristletails). Still more primitive, scarcely even conforming to the strict definition of insects, are the tiny Protura and equally small but very abundant Collembola (springtails).

devise insecticides as rapidly as his insect targets can become resistant to them by mutation and natural selection. It's a race in which we are far from ahead. Our knowledge of insects and reasons for the ubiquity of this highest group of arthropods is of more than academic interest.

SUGGESTIONS

Make an insect collection representing at least 10 orders and 50 families. Key out your specimens; label, pin, and mount them on composition board in cigar boxes. Available textbooks and guides, such as F. L. Jacques' How to Know the Insects, and federal or state publications on entomology are excellent sources for methods of killing, preserving, pinning, and labeling. Make careful notes of date, locality, habitat, and other collecting data. Use as many techniques as possible for collecting and searching different habitats. Develop your acuity and sense of observation for the characteristic habits and habitats of different orders. If you do this conscientiously and for fun as well as knowledge, you will be rewarded by a far more satisfying and instructive lesson in entomology and biology than any laboratory can provide.

3—External anatomy—Both the large lubber grasshopper (*Romalea microptera*) and the unpopular American cockroach (*Periplaneta americana*) (Figs. 9-8, 9-9, and 9-10) are useful in these dissections. The cockroach is easier to dissect and may be considered a somewhat more representative insect than the grasshopper, owing to its lack of specialized jumping adaptations.

a. Identify the major body segments—*head, thorax,* and *abdomen*.

► How do these segments compare with those of the crayfish?

The insect exoskeleton, a complex, many-layered structure of chitin and other materials, is covered by a thin but critically important outer waxy layer that prevents desiccation. Some "desiccant" insecticides now being developed abrade or dissolve out minute pores in this wax and allow rapid evaporative water loss, which quickly kills the insect.

Head somites are 6 fused segments. The thorax consists of 3 segments (*pro-, meso-,* and *metathorax*), and the abdomen of 11, including the terminal reproductive organs. A tendency towards fusion is as marked in insects as in other arthropods.

Movement is restricted to soft sutures between sclerites and segments. Growth, or body expansion, is limited to stretching during the brief period after molting of the old exoskeleton and before hardening of the new one.

Review how the exoskeleton *limits* as well as *permits* evolutionary change in insects.

Notice that each thoracic somite consists of several sclerites. On a thoracic or abdominal somite locate the *tergum, pleuron,* and *sternum.*

▶ What, then, would be the *metapleuron,* the *mesosternum,* and so on?

▶ How many sclerites are there per tergum? Per pleuron? Per sternum?

b. Closely examine the *head.* Locate the compound eyes (with many small facets or *ommatidia*) and simple eyes *(ocelli)* between them *(how many?).* Head sclerites, from dorsal surface of head down the face, include the *epicranium, frons* (below the attachment of the antennae), *clypeus,* and *labrum* (upper lip). The "cheek" areas are termed the *gena.* The other mouthparts will be examined later.

c. The thorax is divided into 3 body segments, as already noted.

▶ To which segments are the legs attached?

Identify the following leg segments starting from point of attachment and extending to the terminal claws: *coxa, trochanter, femur* (bearing a few spines), *tibia* (very spiny), *tarsus* with 5 joints, a number of *pads,* and a terminal pad *(pulvillus)* bearing a pair of hooks or *claws.* Find the corresponding parts in each leg along one side of the body.

▶ How do they differ?

Spread the forewing *(elytron)* and the flying wing or *hind wing.* Note the segments to which they attach.

▶ How do the 2 wing pairs differ in structure?

▶ How do they differ in beetles? In bees? In flies?

▶ What functional advantages do these differences afford?

The abdomen has 11 segments, though the terminal genital plates 9 to 11 are difficult to discern. Segment 1 is interrupted in *Romalea* by the *tympanum* (function?) and the metathorax.

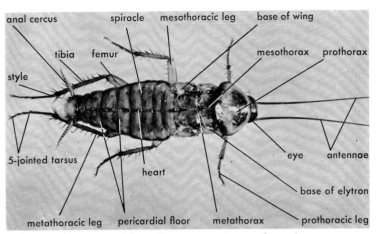

Fig. 9-9. Dorsal view of *Periplaneta americana,* male, with wings removed.

Segments 2 to 8 are complete rings bearing *spiracles* on each side. These are the breathing apertures for gas exchange into and from the tracheal network. (Did you also notice the two pairs of spiracles on the thorax?)

The tip of the abdomen shows sexual dimorphism. *Romalea* females possess 2 pairs of pointed ovipositors, digging structures for egglaying in soil. Near the upper pair of ovipositors, a pair of small sensory projections—the *cerci* (singular: *cercus*)—mark the border between the 10th and 11th segments. The male grasshopper has a prolonged genital plate extending backwards and upward from the 9th sternite.

Cockroaches lack specialized digging structures. The female has large cerci with a pair of triangular ventral *podical plates* between them. The anus opens between these plates at the posterior tip of the insect. The male has cerci plus a pair of fine terminal spines, each called a *style.*

Draw a lateral view of your insect showing relationships of body sections and somites and parts you have identified.

d. *Mouthparts* (Fig. 9-11). Much of the multiformity among insects is reflected in the diversity of their mouthparts, manner of feeding, and types of food. Compare mouthparts of a *mosquito,*

Fig. 9-10. Ventral aspect of *Periplaneta americana,* female.

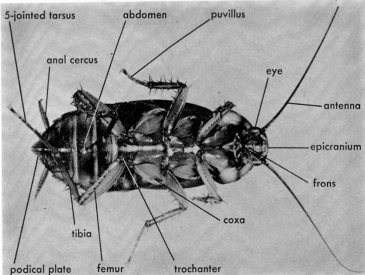

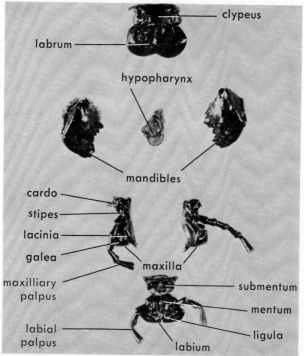

Fig. 9-11. Isolated mouthparts of the grasshopper, *Romalea*.

butterfly, tiger beetle, and *mayfly.* All of this extraordinary functional difference can be homologized to the same structural elements. Mouthparts of roaches and grasshoppers are thought to be fairly conservative or nonspecialized; hence, they are useful for demonstration of basic anatomy.

As you identify and remove each part, place it on a clean sheet of paper in the same orientation as in the natural or intact insect head (Fig. 9-11). Remove the *clypeus* and *labrum,* already identified. This will expose the powerful *mandibles* or jaws (usually black or brown). Notice the serrated inner surface.

▶ Can you determine probable food habits on the basis of the mandibles?

Observe that the mouthparts are paired, rather like legs. They appear, in fact, to be serially homologous with legs (compare with crayfish and annelids) and to be derived from leglike appendages.

Separate the mandibles with a needle and remove them with forceps. Next are the *maxillae,* rather complex sensory food handlers (and chemoreceptors) to which *maxillary palps* are attached. In addition to the palps, find 2 other projections—the rounded *galea* and sharp, pointed, hairy *lacinia.* Remove the maxillae and add them to the array of mouthparts.

The *labium,* or lower lip, underlies the maxillae and bears a second pair of sensory palps or "feelers." Though the labium appears to be single, it actually is a pair of maxillalike structures fused along the midline to form a plate, or *mentum.* Removal of the labium reveals a narrow, tonguelike *hypopharynx.* Arrange all the mouthparts in their correct relative position and review their names and functions in the food-handling process. Glue the mouthparts in this position; label them and their principal parts.

4—Internal anatomy

a. *Introduction.* Few animals are so well packed as insects. Miniaturization is carried to a degree that would astonish even our satellite designers. There is a high survival premium for efficient packaging of internal organs into the limited available space. Consequently, dissection of insects requires dexterity and patience to avoid destruction of one organ system while another is being disentangled from its neighbors.

Several dissection techniques can be followed. If the specimen is small and difficult to handle, it is advantageous to embed it in wax before dissecting. Melt some clear paraffin and pour it into a glycerine-coated watch glass. (Glycerine allows easy removal of wax.) Trim off the legs as close to the body as possible. Holding the specimen by the wings, carefully immerse it in the wax halfway up the pleurites, deeply enough to allow the wax a firm grip on the body. Keep the insect in place until the paraffin hardens on the surface, then speed the hardening process by placing the watch glass in cold water. After it has hardened, remove the entire wax piece by slipping it from the glass. If the wax is still malleable, it can be pinned to the wax bottom of your dissecting tray without cracking. You now have a firmly held insect ready for dissection under a binocular microscope or under water.

A somewhat simpler method is to pin the insect directly to the dissection tray through the base of the metathoracic legs and forewings after trimming off the other legs and hind wings close to the body. The wax embedding method permits a somewhat more controlled dissection and allows microscopic examination of the specimen during work. Either technique can be satisfactory or discouraging, depending upon one's interest and patience. The result, however, is your introduction to a remarkable, complex animal as successful in its realm as man is in his, yet constructed on a markedly different body plan.

b. *Dissection.* Open the dorsal surface of the abdomen to disclose the *heart, aorta,* and general disposition of internal organs. Loosen one of the terga near the end of the abdomen; then make a lateral cut from this edge of the loosened dorsal plate to the first abdominal segment. Raise this loosened flap and work it free, being careful not to damage the heart and aorta directly under the plate. Continue to cut forward toward the head, then across the top of the prothorax behind the head, and slowly work free the entire exoskeletal shield. Check the midline of the inner surface of this shield to see whether the heart was stripped off the abdomen. You will find it to be a delicate tube, either dorsal to the thin mass of *alary muscles* adhering to the removed portion of the exoskeleton, or still intact on your specimen. Examine the heart closely and try to locate the *ostia.*

▶ How do the ostia function in circulation?

▶ What sort of circulation is typical of insects?

▶ How does insect circulation compare with that of annelids?

The *digestive, excretory, reproductive, tracheal (respiratory),* and *nervous* systems will next be studied in this gross dissection. The *skeletal* system consists essentially of the exoskeleton, with its internal projections (*apodemes*) that serve as additional surfaces for muscle attachment. The extremely complex *muscular system* is too difficult to work out in a brief laboratory period. In fact, the cockroach is said to have about 10 times as many separate muscles as man! And you will observe that these separate muscles are not grouped and tied to tendons as in vertebrates. Grouping ends of muscles to a tendon attaches them to a single point on a bone, a necessary development in vertebrate structure. The insect has more muscles, yet each has a separate point of attachment and insertion, allowing for considerable diversity and flexibility of movement. All of this of course is due to the fact that the insect exoskeletal tube offers about 10 times more surface area for attachment relative to the animal's bulk than does the human solid endoskeleton.

Closely connected to the nervous system are various recently discovered hormonal centers that trigger the various steps of maturation and metamorphosis. These structures should be re-

viewed in your textbook rather than on the specimen. Details of the sensory apparatus are other important structural and functional aspects for interesting study in more advanced courses.

Remove the heart, with its adjacent *pericardial floor* and alary muscles, by carefully stripping it from the exposed surface of the insect without damaging the underlying organs. Pick off the covering layer, largely *fat body.* Examine the glistening white tubes spreading through the fat body and covering the crop and other organs visible below it. These tubes form the tracheal or respiratory system.

c. *Tracheal system.* Another anatomical feature related to the exoskeleton is the air-tube or tracheal system, which supplies oxygen from the outside air directly into tissues and cells without a blood carrier, as in most other animals. In this highly efficient system for gas exchange by diffusion, air flows rapidly through major tubes and numerous smaller branches that penetrate tissues and reach each cell. If the rest of the insect were to disappear you would see remaining a tight network of fine interlacing branches reaching around the cells, just as capillaries do in our own bodies. Air passes from the *spiracles* and thence to the major tracheal *ducts,* then to *air sacs* and a multiplicity of smaller tubes lined with spiral *taenidia* that keep the channels open. Remove a bit of muscle tissue, place it in a drop of water on a slide, tease it apart with needles, and then press a coverslip down carefully. Examine the preparation under a compound microscope; observe numerous tracheal branches among the muscle fibers. *Draw* a group of fibers and accompanying tracheae.

If your specimen is freshly killed, air sacs and large tracheae will be glistening white and filled with air. If it is preserved, the ducts will be harder to see but their location should nonetheless be sought. Trace one duct from a spiracle to its primary divisions, the air sacs, and into smaller divisions. Use a blunt probe to push the intervening organs aside without damaging them.

▶ How does the development of a tracheal system obviate the need for capillaries to each cell?

d. *Digestive system.* Remove the overlying mantle of tracheae and remaining fat body tissue to expose the *crop,* largest portion of the alimentary canal. Carefully work the crop loose without breaking attachments at either end and lift it out, holding it to one side with a pin placed against the inner margin of the crop. Avoid damaging the reproductive organs in the posterior portion of the body. As you lift the crop free, the *stomach* and coiled *intestines* will appear. These are marked anteriorly by fingerlike *gastric caeca*, and at the start of the hind-gut by numerous hair-like *Malpighian tubules,* which form the excretory organ. Work the coils loose and try to expose the complete digestive system. In the thoracic region it will be necessary to cut away most of the heavy limb and wing musculature. As the anterior end of the crop is lifted from the thorax, look for the paired *salivary glands* that lie ventral to the *esophagus* but extend halfway into the thoracic cavity.

▶ Where do these glands empty?

The anterior part of the alimentary canal consists of an anterior *foregut (stomadeum)* including the *mouth, esophagus, crop,* and *proventriculus* (gizzard). This latter structure grinds like the gastric mill of the crayfish. In some insects, a muscular sucking organ—the *pharynx*—is found at the anterior end of the esophagus.

▶ Name several examples of insects with a pharynx.

The middle section of the alimentary canal, the mid-gut (*mesenteron*), consists of *gastric caeca* and *stomach (ventriculus)*. Most digestion takes place in this region.

The beginning of the third region, the hind-gut (*proctodeum*), is marked by Malpighian tubules, as already noted. The hind-gut consists of an enlarged anterior and a slender posterior portion of intestine and the heavy-walled *rectum* ending at the *anus*. The fore-gut and hind-gut are both derived from ectodermal infoldings, whereas the mid-gut is formed from endodermal tissue. (Fore-gut and hind-gut linings are therefore shed, along with the exoskeleton, during molting.)

Disentangle these structures and lay out the intact digestive system, leaving it attached at mouth and anus. Remove interfering bits of fat body and tracheae, but do not damage the reproductive system.

e. *Excretory system.* The thin, brownish Malpighian tubules between the stomach and intestine have previously been identified as excretory in function. These blind ducts in the hemocoel around the gut are washed by bloodflow emptying from the arteries. Their function is apparently to ab-

sorb differentially metabolic waste products from blood and to pass them into the intestine. Products not later reabsorbed in the hind-gut are passed out the anus with undigested food wastes.

f. *Reproductive system.* Expose the reproductive organs in the posterior end of the abdomen. This highly complex system is markedly similar in general organization and symmetry in the two sexes. The male grasshopper or roach, however, has a single mushroom-shaped, combined *testis*. Reproductive products from the testes are passed through a medial *vas deferens,* the sperm duct (the "stem" of the mushroom), and out the *ejaculatory duct*. More typically in other insects, the testes are paired with separate *vasa deferentia* and *seminal vesicles,* the sperm storage organs. The seminal vesicles then join to form a single ejaculatory duct, receiving seminiferous material from a pair of *accessory glands* near this juncture. Sperm pass out the ejaculatory duct through a specialized copulatory organ, the *penis,* which is usually associated with a complex external *intromittent organ*.

The female system is also paired and, as in the male, the gonads (*ovaries*) are really two clusters of smaller units. Each ovary consists of a group of tapering *ovarioles*. Eggs are produced in the narrow tips and passed posteriorly into enlarged *follicles* (egg chambers), which feed into an oviduct, one per ovary. The two oviducts then unite into a common oviduct, which passes into an enlarged, egg-holding *vagina*. The vagina in turn leads into the external *ovipositor,* or egg-laying mechanism. The dorsal wall of the vagina is connected to two other important structures. One is the *spermatheca* (seminal receptacle), a small bulb for storing sperm received at copulation. It also allows sperm to pass a few at a time through a small duct into the vagina for insemination of newly produced eggs. A pair of *accessory glands,* also attached to the vagina, secrete the special gluelike material that surrounds the eggs at laying.

Few of these smaller structures can be discerned in your specimens. However, in female specimens you should find the 2 ovaries with their ovarioles, the paired oviducts leading to the common oviduct, and the many-branched accessory glands that, with the spermatheca, empty into the vagina. Find the central, composite testis in the male, with the medial ejaculatory duct into which the accessory glands empty. Between the testis

NOTES AND DRAWINGS

(Tear along line)

and ejaculatory duct is the coiled *vas deferens* and the enlarged seminal vesicle. Lay these organs out, free from fat body and tracheae, so that they can be seen clearly.

1. *Draw a full-page outline* of the dorsal view of your dissection. Sketch in the alimentary canal along one side, and label all parts. Add the excretory system and the reproductive system, spread out as in your own dissection, and label as far as visible. Leave space in the midline for adding the ventral nerve cord.

g. *Nervous system* (Fig. 9-12). Expose the ventral nerve cord by carefully picking away overlying muscle, tracheae, and fat body tissues. Work from the posterior end, exposing each ganglion in turn. Remove the rectum and reproductive organs to expose the terminal ganglia. To show the anterior ganglia, cut the esophagus, place it to one side, and remove the salivary glands. Cut the exposed dorsal sclerites of the head away from the neck area to a point between the eyes. Use fine pointed scissors or forceps so as not to damage the brain. This should expose the entire nerve cord, showing the *abdominal, thoracic,* and *cranial* ganglia.

▶ How many of each ganglion type are there?
▶ In what segments are they located?

Find the *subesophageal ganglion* with its *circumesophageal connectives* joining the *cerebral ganglion* or *brain* (also called *supraesophageal ganglion*).

▶ Can you find nerves stemming from each ganglion?

Note that all ganglia are paired, joined transversely by commissures, and to the posterior and anterior ganglia by connectives. Even apparently single ganglia consist of fused pairs of ganglia. Considerable modification of the nervous system with a marked tendency towards fusion of anterior ganglia is found among insects. This is particularly evident in the so-called higher orders, especially in some DIPTERA and HYMENOPTERA. Remember, however, that throughout the Phylum ARTHROPODA the pattern of the nervous system shows a marked uniformity,

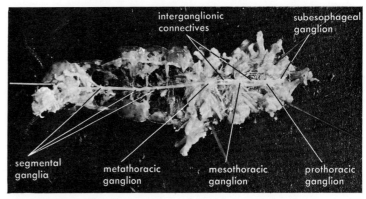

Fig. 9-12. Ventral nerve cord of *Periplaneta americana*, dorsal ganglion removed.

a similarity that can be extended back to include even the ANNELIDA.

▶ What phylogenetic relations does this similarity suggest?

In a further dissection, clear away the tissue around the brain to show the precise location of the subesophageal ganglion and its connection to the brain and to the next posterior, or *first thoracic,* ganglion. A group of apodemes (*tentorium*) in the head serves as an area for attachment of numerous muscles controlling movements of the mouthparts and antennae. This structure must be cut on each side and removed to expose the subesophageal ganglion.

Add the nervous system to the drawing of your dissected insect, and have your instructor check your work. Be prepared for an oral review of all these systems, including names and functions of important parts.

▶ How do these organ systems compare in general with those of CRUSTACEA?
▶ How would you compare their general degree of specialization?
▶ How has the exoskeleton affected *size, growth pattern, type of flight, feeding habits,* and *general habitats* of insects and provided them with both biological advantages and limitations?

Redescribe the arthropod basic body type, then modifications as seen in the Classes CRUSTACEA and INSECTA. Finally, tell how these major structural adaptations are related to the way of life and distribution of these two large, important classes of animals.

In sum, don't despise the lowly insects. They appear able to take over any time we radiate or explode ourselves out of existence.

I. INTRODUCTION

How can such a huge and varied assemblage as chitons (Figs. 10-1 to 10-3), clams (Figs. 10-4 to 10-7), snails (Figs. 10-8 to 10-11), and octopuses (Figs. 10-12 to 10-14) be placed in the same phylum? As with frogs and man, which share a single phylum, these animals all have the same essential body organization. The *molluscan basic body type* is typically *unsegmented and soft* with an *epithelial mantle* that secretes a *calcareous shell,* an *anterior head, ventral foot, dorsal visceral body mass,* and *ctenidia* (gills). Special aspects of the nervous system, mouth, body cavity, and gut further characterize the Phylum MOLLUSCA.

Of particular biological interest is the manner in which molluscan body organization has undergone such marked variation in the 6 classes within this phylum. Adaptive patterns in these classes apply principally to means of nutrition and degrees of motility associated with protection or food getting. For example, in the octopus specialized structures and functions are chiefly for speed and predation, in the clam for filtering fine food material, in the snail for gliding and protection, and in the chiton for algal grazing and adherence to wave-beaten rocks. Each evolutionary pattern is sufficiently distinct and important to characterize an entire class of mollusks.

II. CLASSIFICATION

A. Class AMPHINEURA—chitons (Figs. 10-1 to 10-3)

Chitons are mollusks with 8 calcareous linked plates surrounded by a variable fleshy girdle (mantle). Their elongate, flattened body bears a well-developed foot for clinging to rock surfaces. Chitons have a small head without tentacles, numerous gills on either side of the foot between foot and mantle, a single gonad, and separate sexes. They are algal feeders and occur chiefly in marine intertidal areas.

B. Class PELECYPODA (or LAMELLIBRANCHIATA)

PELECYPODA are bivalves—clams, scallops, oysters, mussels, and so on (Figs. 10-4 to 10-7)—which, as the name implies, have 2 symmetrical valves forming a shell. The dorsally hinged valves are tightly closed by well-developed adductor muscles. The key to understanding this specialized but large mollusk group is its manner of feeding. Bivalves are essentially water pumping and filtering organisms enclosed in a protective shell. Aided by enlarged,

CHAPTER 10

Phylum

Mollusca

curtainlike gills covered with cilia and mucus-secreting cells, oral palps, and excurrent and incurrent siphons, bivalves feed by filtering food from an internally controlled water flow. Other characteristics of the group are secondarily related to the mode of feeding: loss of both head and rasping radula, loss of motility (except in scallops, which swim by clapping their shells together), and protection by a heavy shell with powerful adductor muscles. Four orders of pelecypods are separated by structural details of the gill system.

C. Class GASTROPODA

This class includes snails, whelks, limpets, slugs, and nudibranchs (Figs. 10-8 to 10-11), all characterized by a single, well-developed spiral shell (in typical snails) and an embryological phenomenon called *torsion*. During development, the body of the embryo twists 180° with reference to the head and foot. Differential rates of growth cause the visceral mass to turn counterclockwise so that the anus is moved to an anterior position and the gills posterior. This growth pattern in effect allows withdrawal of the head into the shell mantle cavity prior to withdrawal of the foot. The latter structure is often equipped with a tough doorlike operculum that blocks the shell opening. Thus the delicate head with its exposed sense organs is well protected by the shell and the covering foot.

▶ Had torsion not occurred, where would **foot, gills, and head** be located with respect to the shell opening, upon withdrawal of the snail into its shell?

The large head has tentacles and a well-developed rasping radula. Marine, fresh-water, and terrestrial gastropods[1] are mostly slow-moving plant feeders and scavengers, though some are active swimmers and others are predators or even internal parasites.

D. Class CEPHALOPODA—squids and octopuses (Figs. 10-12 to 10-14)

These animals are highly modified for motility and active predation. They possess a large head and eyes, a highly developed brain and central nervous system, 8 or 10 arms with rows of sucking discs encircling the head, a mouth with a horny beak and radula, and a large siphon for controlled, rapid movement. The group includes the nautili (Order TETRABRANCHIA), and cuttlefishes, squids, paper nautilus, and octopus (Order DIBRANCHIA).

E. Class SCAPHOPODA—tooth shells or elephant-tusk shells (example: *Dentalium*)

These animals live in a slender, tusk-shaped tubular shell. Adapted to life in mud or sand, often at great depth, they are seldom seen alive. The mantle is fused along its midventral line and the shell is open at both ends. Small ciliated tentacles and a knob-shaped foot that protrude from the larger opening carry food particles into the mouth. The radula and other alimentary organs are present, but gills have been secondarily lost.

F. Class MONOPLACOPHORA—primitive, segmented mollusks (example: *Neopilina galathae* [Fig. 10-15])

These animals were discovered off the coast of Denmark by Professor H. Lemche in 1957. The group is living proof (a so-called "missing link") of relationship between annelids and mollusks. Collection of living specimens was one of the most significant—and unexpected—biological finds of the century. Internal structure of these animals had previously been surmised only from impressions of muscle scars and other hard parts on the 300,000,000-year-old fossils. We therefore find a mollusk with annelidlike segmentation (5 pairs of nephridia, gills, hearts, and retractor muscles of the foot, plus 3 such pairs of muscles in the head), along with typically molluscan characteristics such as mantle and shell and anterior mouth and radula. This remarkable animal, though it defies the definition of MOLLUSCA, establishes the relationship of mollusks with annelids and is sufficiently distinctive to justify erection of this new class within the phylum.

---

[1] Gastropods are divided into 3 subclasses, each defined by adaptive changes in general structure. In the Subclass PROSOBRANCHIA—primitive snails with characteristic torsion, well-developed shell, and unspecialized gills—are limpets, slipper shells, abalones, periwinkles, cowries, rock shells, and oyster drills. Gastropods of the Subclass OPISTHOBRANCHIA have secondarily lost the pattern of torsion: they have a reduced shell (or none at all) and a modified single gill and nephridium. Bizarre and often brilliantly colored nudibranchs are in this group along with sea hares and other tectibranchs. Often called sea slugs, opisthobranchs play an ecological role in the ocean similar to that of familiar slugs on land (the latter are in the Subclass PULMONATA, considered next). Members of this third Subclass, PULMONATA—characteristic land and fresh-water snails and slugs—have a lunglike vascularized chamber in the mantle cavity instead of gills; hence, the name PULMONATA. This important evolutionary modification enables pulmonates to become air breathers and occupy terrestrial habitats. *Helix*, the European garden snail, is a typical pulmonate gastropod (as well as the epicure's delight).

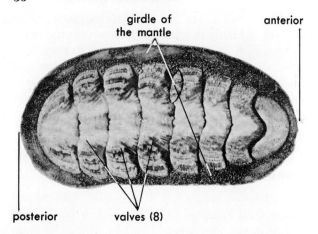

Fig. 10-1. *Stenoplax,* external anatomy, dorsal view.

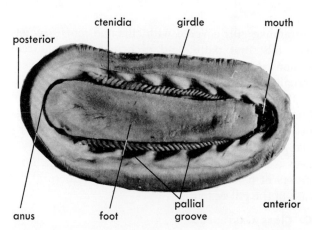

Fig. 10-2. *Stenoplax,* external anatomy, ventral view.

We shall review several evolutionary patterns by studying representatives of 4 major molluscan adaptive types—a chiton, clam, snail, and squid. As is often necessary, these organisms are samples selected from their respective classes for availability and convenience. They should be considered as one of many and not as definitive prototypes.

III. LABORATORY INSTRUCTIONS

A. Class AMPHINEURA—chitons (Ischnochiton, Chiton, Stenoplax, Cryptochiton, Chaetopleura, Tonicella)

Almost any available form of these intertidal rocky-coastline animals shows essentially the same anatomical structure. Different genera vary chiefly in size, shape, and form of the girdle, and other external characteristics. Chitons are among the simplest mollusks, rather like a presumed ancestral type, although clearly not so primitive as *Neopilina*.

1—External anatomy. Carefully observe your specimen. Notice the 8 overlapping dorsal plates or valves surrounded by a fleshy *girdle* of the *mantle* (Fig. 10-1). These plates do not indicate segmentation, but are secondary adaptations permitting the animal to bend and cling to rocky surfaces by its large ventral foot. The chiton can also coil up in a defensive posture like the familiar sowbug. Note linkage and markings of the plates, and extent, thickness, and type of girdle. *Draw* a dorsal view, showing relationship of the parts you see.

Study the animal ventrally and observe the large, flat muscular foot, usually flanked by protruding portions of many *gills* that lie in a *pallial groove* between foot and mantle (Fig. 10-2). Pry into this groove and find the gills if they are withdrawn. The mouth, surrounded by a circular mass of tissue, is just a small opening in the head. An *anus* is visible at the posterior end. Try to locate the paired *genital openings,* each with a *nephridiopore* behind it, in the pallial groove on each side about a fifth of the body length from the anus.

2—Internal anatomy

a. Remove the foot by inserting the sharp point of scissors or the blade of a scalpel into the foot alongside the pallial groove, near the mouth. Extend this cut posteriorly, but not deeply, around the entire foot; however, be sure to leave both the mouth and anus attached to the remaining portion of the animal. Carefully remove the large plate cut from the foot and expose the internal organs (Fig. 10-3). Observe gills in the pallial groove (several to many depending upon the genus). Much of the exposed tissue between loops of coiled, elongated *intestine* is the glandular filamentous *digestive gland* or *liver.*

▶ What does the length of the intestinal tract indicate about food habits of this animal?

Expose the *stomach* and trace the intestine to the *anus.* Note the *pharynx,* a portion of the gut connected to the *mouth,* with an enlarged *buccal capsule,* containing the many-toothed, rasping *radula.* Cautiously cut the tissue around the mouth to expose this capsule and observe the red muscular attachments that control radula movement. A *subradular* organ anterior to the buccal capsule secretes digestive enzymes.

b. Probe carefully around the pharynx and locate the encircling *nerve ring* just anterior to the buccal swelling. This ring consists of *cerebral* and *pleural ganglia* and their connectives. Two pairs of central nerve cords arise from this ring, one passing to the foot, the other out to the girdle. Fine cross connectives join the ventral nerves.

c. Dorsal to the intestine lies the large single gonad, either a *testis* or *ovary*. Sever the connection between pharynx and buccal capsule; remove the intestine to expose the gonad. Try to locate 2 ducts that carry gametes laterally and ventrally out the 2 gonopores in the pallial grooves near the anus (already observed in the intact animal). If possible, trace these gonadal ducts.

d. The aorta, dorsal to the gonad and just beneath the mantle, carries blood pumped from the 3-chambered heart (2 *auricles* and a posterior *ventricle*). Locate the heart in a special *pericardium* between the gonad and anus. Paired vascularized *nephridia* that drain this cavity carry waste liquids from the pericardium to the *nephridiopores*.

▶ Where are the nephridiopores with respect to gonopores?

▶ What is the function of blood vessels associated with the nephridial ducts?

e. Cut out the pharynx, split the tube, and remove the radula. Lay the organ out flat on a slide in a drop or two of water, cover with coverslip, press flat, and examine the structure microscopically. Observe the neatly arranged rows of fine teeth that characterize the radula.

▶ List important chiton characteristics that help adapt them to their environment.

B. Class PELECYPODA—clams and relatives

The fresh-water forms of this class are: *Anodonta, Margaritana, Lampsilis, Unio*; the marine forms are: *Venus, Pecten, Ostrea, Crassostrea, Mytilus, Mya.*

1—General aspects—In a casual appraisal of MOLLUSCA we might think of bivalves as typical of the phylum. Actually, from tiny fingernail clams to the 500-pound *Tridacna* of the Pacific reefs, they are among the most specialized of animals, and far from typical mollusks. The name **PELECYPODA,** meaning hatchet-foot, reflects the laterally compressed body. As already mentioned, this class is modified for a passive filter-feeding existence, having lost the head and developed a complex

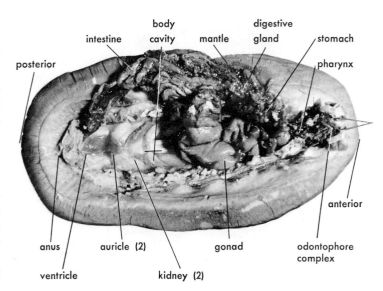

Fig. 10-3. *Stenoplax*, internal anatomy.

sheet of gill-derived tissues for screening microorganisms out of an induced water current. Food particles, rolled into a mucus-laden ball, are passed by ciliary action to the oral palps and mouth. Fresh-water pelecypods possess a distinct specialization: a parasitic larva, called a *glochidium*, which hooks or clamps onto the flesh or gill filaments of fish. The host provides a safe, nourishing location for larval development and serves as an agency for their dispersal in an otherwise harsh fresh-water environment with extreme temperature and water-level fluctuations. The young clams later escape from the cysts in which they are embedded, and, if they fall into appropriate mud or sand bottoms, develop to familiar adult clams.[2]

2—External anatomy—Examine the empty shell of a clam. The paired valves are joined by a tough *hinge ligament*, which holds the toothlike projection of the shell together at a swollen *umbo* junction. Orient a pair of valves *umbo* up and open edge below. The shorter, rounded end is anterior; the opposite end, through which siphons protrude, is posterior; the umbo end is dorsal; the open or gaping edge is ventral. Usually the clam digs into mud by shoveling with its foot. The anterior end remains in the substrate with the posterior, siphon-bearing end pointed upward. Note the rough shell with concentric *lines of growth* and characteristic grooves and markings. Break off a piece of shell and observe the

---

[2] Generally, the fresh-water clams *Anodonta* or *Unio* are used in laboratories near major rivers, but marine clams such as the quahog, *Venus*, the soft-shelled clam, *Mya*, the mussel, *Mytilus*, or the edible oysters, *Ostrea* or *Crassostrea*, are equally useful. Each has similar structures but is modified in body shape, shell form, and organ arrangement. Illustrations and descriptions in the ensuing discussion are based on *Anodonta* and *Venus.*

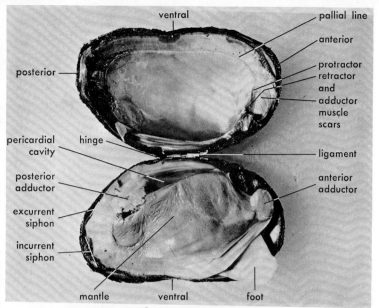

ventral / pallial line / anterior / protractor retractor and adductor muscle scars / ligament / anterior adductor / posterior / pericardial cavity / hinge / posterior adductor / excurrent siphon / incurrent siphon / mantle / ventral / foot

Fig. 10-4. *Anodonta,* internal anatomy.

layers under a hand lens: first is the thin, horny outer layer (*periostracum*), which protects the rest of the shell from dissolved carbon dioxide in water.

▶ What reaction occurs between carbonic acid and the shell?

▶ How would strong alkali affect the shell?

▶ *Test your answers experimentally* and record the results.

The next layer is the *prismatic* layer, the crystalline calcium carbonate portion of the shell. Below it is the irridescent mother-of-pearl inner *nacre*, or nacreous layer.

▶ Which is the oldest part of the intact shell?

▶ How old was the specimen you are examining?

▶ Why are shells from limestone-rich waters thicker than those in other areas?

▶ Study the microscopic structure of these layers in a prepared slide and *draw* a small portion of such a cross section.

Observe the inner surface of a valve. Notice the smooth rounded areas at the anterior and posterior ends. These are *muscle scars*, points of attachment of valve-closing and foot-moving muscles. They include the large scar where the *anterior valve adductor* was attached and the small scar marks where the anterior foot protractor (behind the anterior adductor) originated. Muscles attached to these scars withdraw and extend the foot. The posterior end is marked by a large *posterior adductor muscle* scar (another strong muscle that helps close the valves) and by the scar of the small *posterior retractor* of the foot.

▶ Why are the adductors so much larger than other muscles?

88

▶ How is the shell opened in the absence of specific muscles for this purpose?

Next, locate the *pallial line* that marks the outer margin of mantle attachment. It is a long ridge following the curve of the shell, extending between the 2 adductor scars. It also marks the margin of the retractor muscle of the mantle.

Draw the outside of one valve and the inner surface of another showing the above morphological features.

3—Internal anatomy

a. *General aspects.* Formalin-preserved specimens will be available for dissection. Orient the animal, identifying *right, left, dorsal, ventral, anterior,* and *posterior* surfaces. Separate the valves slightly, insert a scalpel, and cut across the adductor muscle as close as possible to the muscle scars on the right valve to prevent injury to other organs. Then twist off the right valve and cut the dorsal hinge ligament attaching it to the other member.

▶ What other structure helps attach valves at this point?

▶ Identify each visible muscle on the left valve.

You can study exposed organs of the *right* side of the animal as it lies in the *left* valve. Find the cut muscles and see how they operate to close the valves and control movement of the foot. The organs form a central *visceral mass* and are covered with a sheet of bounding mantle epithelium (Fig. 10-4). The mantle both encloses the body cavity and secretes the entire shell. Organs visible through the mantle include a fleshy *foot* protruding through the anteroventral margin; the greenish brown *digestive gland* in the dorsoanterior region; the *pericardial cavity* (reduced coelom) posterior to the digestive gland; and the *nephridium*, a dark triangular organ ventrolateral to the digestive gland. The *pericardial gland*, sometimes called *Keber's organ,* is anterolateral to the digestive gland. This brief examination provides you with a general orientation to pelecypod anatomy.

Float the specimen in water to facilitate seeing detailed structures in a more natural position, each in proper relation to surrounding organs. Locate the siphons. The larger *incurrent siphon* has *sensory papillae* inside the margin; the *excurrent siphon* lies just above it.

► What is the function of these sensory papillae?

Both siphons are actually tubes formed by fusion of posterior ends of the mantle. Probe carefully into the incurrent siphon.

► How does this siphon connect to the mantle cavity?

Remove the exposed half of the mantle, carefully cutting it out with scissors. Below it lies the *visceral mass, foot,* and sheetlike *gills,* 2 on each side of the visceral mass. The *alimentary canal* coils back on itself in the visceral mass and then passes posteriorly through the *pericardial cavity* to its terminus at the *anus,* above and slightly behind the posterior adductor muscle. The inconspicuous mouth between the anterior adductor muscle and foot is bordered by a pair of small triangular *oral palps,* which aid in passing food-laden mucus balls into the slitlike mouth.

b. *Water conduction and respiratory system* (Figs. 10-5 and 10-6). The water current entering the clam via the incurrent siphon carries (1) food particles into the mantle cavity, (2) dissolved oxygen to the mantle and into gill water tubes where respiratory exchange occurs. Dissolved carbon dioxide and wastes are carried out via the excurrent siphon. Microorganisms or bits of organic matter are trapped from the passing water by cilia and mucus on the gill surfaces and on the foot and mantle. Food particles are then enclosed in small mucus balls and passed "hand-over-hand" by ciliary action to the oral palps where edible portions are selected. Acceptable food is transferred into the mouth and rejected items are

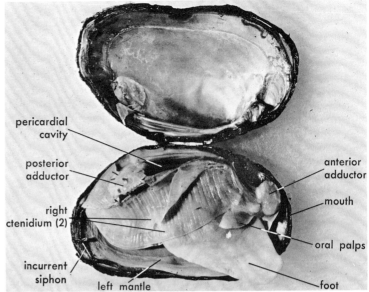

Fig. 10-5. *Anodonta,* internal anatomy. Mantle tissue removed to show oral palps and ctenidia.

passed by other cilia down the foot and through the gap between valves to the outside. Water from which food has been selected flows into the mantle cavity, through numerous pores (*ostia*) into the gills, and into many vertical cilia-lined *water tubes* bordered by vertical *gill bars.* Fine capillaries that parallel the water tubes permit rapid respiratory exchange by diffusion through the thin intervening membranes. The water stream, with dissolved carbon dioxide, passes dorsally up the water vessels and posteriorly through water-collecting *suprabranchial chambers* (1 above each pair of gill tissue sheets, 4 in all). Each collecting chamber then drains the thoroughly used water out through the excurrent siphon. Fluid wastes from the kidneys also flow into the suprabranchial chambers via *nephridial ducts.* These nitrogenous and other wastes enter the ducts after exchange from nephridial capillaries. The freshly cleansed blood flows from kidney capillaries directly into the gill circulation where

Fig. 10-6. *Venus,* internal anatomy; digestive, circulatory, and reproductive systems.

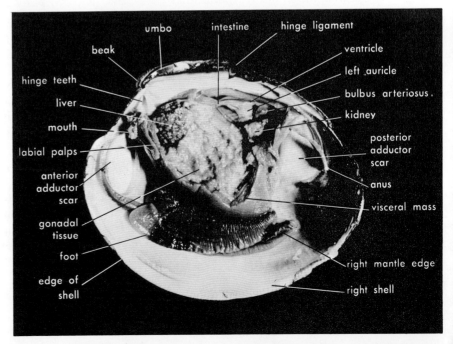

respiration occurs, then passes into veins that conduct it back to the heart.

Cut a piece of gill tissue, float it in water, and examine it under a hand lens or dissecting microscope. Find the ostia and vertical gill bars on each side of the rows of ostia. Each gill, suspended in the mantle cavity on either side of the visceral mass, is composed of 2 sheets. Each sheet in turn is formed by 2 *lamellae*. Water tubes are formed when the 2 lamellae of each sheet partially fuse. A single, W-shaped gill therefore consists of 2 gill sheets (4 lamellae) on each side of the visceral mass. Pelecypod gills have evidently undergone considerable modification and enlargement in conjunction with the filter-feeding mode of nutrition.

Review this remarkable use of water flow for ingestion, respiration, and excretion, and name the associated organs responsible.

► What is meant by "ciliary-mucus-filter-feeding"?

► How can *structure, distribution,* and *biological success* of these headless mollusks be attributed to their specialized mode of feeding?

c. *Excretory and reproduction systems.* Carefully remove the exposed mantle and gill tissue, leaving the inner right suprabranchial chamber intact.

Trace the excretory system from the *pericardial pores* in the pericardial wall to *nephridial ducts* and *nephridia* (dark organs ventral and lateral to the pericardial cavity), and then to the *excretory ducts* leading from the nephridia to the inner (medial) suprabranchial chambers. You will have to cut the intestine and move it away from the pericardial cavity in order to search the walls for pericardial pores and nephridial ducts leading to the kidneys. Cut open a nephridium and try to trace out the loop of the excretory duct. Find *excretory pores* draining the nephridia into the anterior end of the inner suprabranchial chambers. A fine wire probe is useful for exploring these ducts.

Nephridial ducts form a flattened U-loop within the kidney, the upper arm quite thin-walled, the lower arm spongy and vascular, surrounded by numerous fine blood vessels. Diffusion of metabolic wastes and resorption of usable salts and other materials occur across the thin capillary and excretory walls. *Notice that the kidneys drain the coelom,* or what is left of it in these animals—the *pericardial cavity.*

► How does this compare with the activity of nephridia in annelids?

► Could this functional similarity constitute evidence that the pericardial cavity is a reduced coelom?

► How is the *circulatory* system employed in disposal of excretory fluids in the kidney?

Two openings are found in each inner suprabranchial chamber. The upper one is the excretory pore, the lower one the *genital pore.* *Genital ducts* lead from the highly branched *gonad,* enmeshed in the intestinal loop in the basal portion of the foot, to the suprabranchial chambers via the genital pores.

The inner suprabranchial chambers also form *brood pouches* for glochidial larvae of fresh-water clams. Study microscopically several preserved glochidia or some taken from the brood pouch of a ripe living female.

► Why are the adductor muscles of these larval clams so well developed?

► Review the life cycle of a fresh-water clam.

► What is the probable adaptive advantage of parasitism at the larval stage in the life cycle of fresh-water clams?

d. *Digestive tract* (Figs. 10-6 and 10-7). Trace the alimentary canal from mouth and oral palps, along intestinal windings through the base of the foot, through the pericardial cavity, and out to the anus at the margin of the posterior adductor muscle.

Remove the body from its remaining valve. Cut the mantle and gill tissue from both sides; note the previously identified foot retractor muscles and their function. Carefully dissect away muscle and tissue of the visceral mass on the right side of the medial intestine. The pasty material surrounding the intestine is largely gonadal (Fig. 10-6). The *digestive gland* lies anterior to the intestinal loops, surrounding the stomach or swollen portion of the gut (Fig. 10-7).

Pin out the specimen in your dissecting pan. Keep it clean with water squirted from a medicine dropper. Relate the following parts both structurally and functionally, including ducts or tubes by which they are connected: *mouth, oral palps, esophagus* (short tube posterior to the mouth), *pericardial cavity* (with *rectum* passing through it), *anus, excurrent siphon,* and *posterior adductor muscle.* Inside the coiled intestine you may find a gelatinous, rodlike, *crystalline style* in a special intestinal outpocket. This rod apparently releases a digestive enzyme supplied by gradual

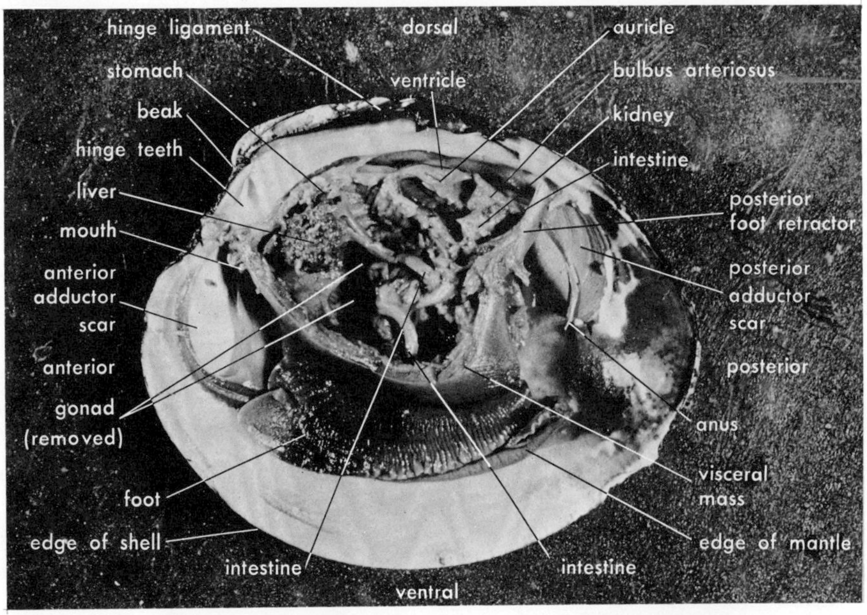

Fig. 10-7. *Venus*, internal anatomy; digestive, circulatory, and reproductive systems.

Labels on figure: hinge ligament, dorsal, auricle, stomach, ventricle, bulbus arteriosus, beak, kidney, hinge teeth, intestine, liver, mouth, posterior foot retractor, anterior adductor scar, posterior adductor scar, anterior, gonad (removed), posterior, anus, foot, visceral mass, edge of shell, edge of mantle, intestine, intestine, ventral

wearing of the style at the end entering the gut near the stomach.

Draw, in diagrammatic outline, the relationship of these parts. Review their function.

▶ How can you account for the lack of a radula and well-developed head in this class of mollusks, compared with gastropods and cephalopods?

e. *Circulatory system.* Examine your specimen from the dorsal aspect. Find the pericardial cavity. Open it anterior to the posterior adductor muscle. Identify parts of the heart (previously seen in your search for excretory pores). Locate the muscular *ventricle* enclosing the intestine (rectum), 2 delicate anterior *auricles* that connect the ventricle to the lateral margins of the pericardial cavity, and the *bulbus arteriosus* anterior to the ventricle. These organs deliver blood from the mantle and gills to the ventricle. The blood is then pumped anteriorly via the bulbus arteriosus and *anterior aorta* to the alimentary canal, foot, and mantle. It passes posteriorly via the posterior aorta to the alimentary canal and mantle. Blood sent out to various organs returns via a vein and capillaries to the nephridia and then by capillaries into the gills before it returns to the heart.

▶ What is meant by "open system" of circulation?

▶ How does this system work?

▶ What are some of its advantages? Disadvantages?

SUGGESTION FOR A SPECIAL EXPERIMENT

Set up a kymograph to show the pumping action of a living clam heart and effects of acetyl choline, adrenalin, and other chemical agents known to affect heart rate.

f. *Nervous system.* In the clam, the principal nerves are connected to 3 ganglia of the central nervous system. These small yellowish ganglia with their white connectives are all located near major muscle areas. Included are (1) paired *cerebropleural ganglia* at the posterior margin of the anterior adductor muscle, below the base of the palps; (2) *pedal ganglia* between the foot and visceral mass; and (3) a single *visceral ganglion*, on the ventral surface of the posterior adductor muscle.[3]

▶ Is the nervous system as highly developed in PELECYPODS as in the other classes of mollusks?

▶ Does your answer fit the way of life characteristic of these groups?

g. *Recapitulation.* Review (for an oral quiz by your instructor) the primary organs and their function in the digestive, excretory, circulatory, nervous, muscular, respiratory, water-conducting, and reproductive systems. Try to trace water current, blood flow, food passage, nerve control of major muscle groups, digging activity, shell closure, and sperm or egg passage in the clam. Return first to your specimen for review rather than your text.

C. Class GASTROPODA—*Helix*

1—External anatomy

a. *Observations. Helix,* the common European garden snail and escargot of gourmets, is one of

---

[3] By careful dissection, the following nerves around these ganglia can also be exposed: *cerebropedal connectives* between ganglia (1) and (2), and *cerebrovisceral connectives* between (1) and (3).

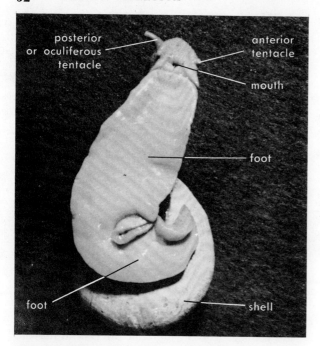

Fig. 10-8. *Helix,* ventral view.

a vast array of mollusks included in the class GASTROPODA. Many common fresh-water snails, such as *Physa, Planorbis, Helisoma,* or *Lymnaea,* make excellent study specimens.

Observe these or young *Helix* in a watch glass Fig. 10-8). Study movement and action of head and tentacles; reactions to a bit of meat, to strong light, to moderate probing with a needle, to a few crystals of menthol, and to 1 percent sodium chloride, mild acid, or alkali. Observe the shell shape (whorls, spire, aperture, color, texture). Watch for the occasional movement of the pneumatopore or respiratory opening.

▶ How many eyes does the snail have?
▶ Where are the eyes located?
▶ How does the mouth function?

To study the normal feeding pattern, observe aquatic snails feeding on algae-coated glass surfaces of an aquarium. Watch for a wedge-shaped object protruding briefly from the mouth

opening. This is the top of the buccal mass in which the radula is embedded. The rasping, tooth-covered surface of this organ scrapes off bits of algae or other plant materials, which are then engulfed. Garden snails and slugs feed on vegetation; many others feed on decayed matter. Most marine gastropods are scavengers. Others, such as the oyster drill, adapted for predation, use the radula to bore through shells of other mollusks. Still others are highly modified, worm-like, internal parasites.

It is interesting and useful to observe aquatic snails in an aquarium. You can see feeding and locomotory habits, chemical stimulation from various foods, mucus threads the snail uses for movement in water or to help it support itself at the water surface, responses to light, breathing rates at various temperatures, and effect of desiccation. Life cycle and patterns of reproduction and development can also be studied in aquarium specimens. Your observations should suggest better controlled experiments by which the snail's responses to various stimuli can be more critically tested.

A convenient way to observe muscular action of the foot and appearance of the snail's ventral surface is to place the animal in a drop or two of water on a slide, invert the slide over a small dish, and watch the foot under a dissecting microscope (Fig. 10-8).

b. *Shell.* Examine an empty shell for whorls, growth lines (*why are they irregular?*), spire, aperture, and thickened edge or collar. In marine snails, the collar is often drawn out into a lip to enclose the respiratory siphonal canal.

▶ Which is the oldest portion of the shell?
▶ How does the shell grow?

Study a bisected or broken shell and note the axis (*columella*) about which the shell twists.

▶ How can you tell a right from a left twist in the shell (right or left with respect to the opening)?

Study the variety of shell types in your local collection or museum display. Compare *Helix* with *Lymnaea, Physa,* a limpet, abalone, and moon shell. An interesting and biologically enlightening hobby is to collect these abundant, varied, and often beautifully colored marine gastropods and pelecypods. Shell collecting has started many lifetime hobbies and successful careers in biology as well.

Fig. 10-9. *Helix,* lateral view with shell removed.

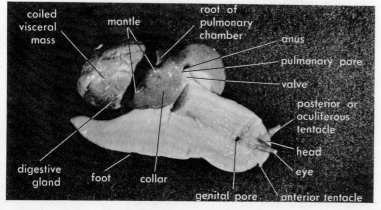

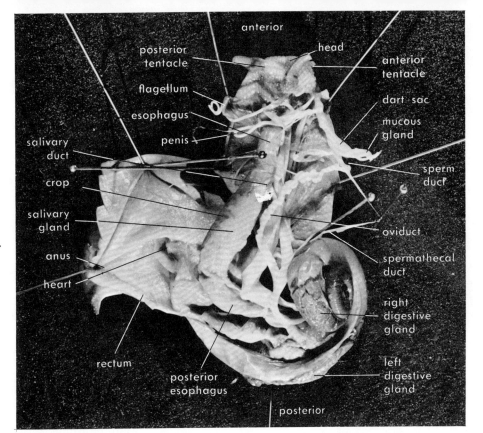

Labels on figure:
anterior
posterior tentacle
flagellum
esophagus
penis
salivary duct
crop
salivary gland
anus
heart
rectum
posterior esophagus
head
anterior tentacle
dart sac
mucous gland
sperm duct
oviduct
spermathecal duct
right digestive gland
left digestive gland
posterior

Fig. 10-10. *Helix*, internal anatomy.

▶ Do snails have the same 3-layered shell seen in the clam?

▶ Why are nudibranchs and tectibranchs still considered gastropods, though shell and body torsion may be lost?

▶ Cite a few examples to show how various shell types adapt the snail to its particular habitat.

2—Internal anatomy

a. *Initial dissection.* Study an extended, preserved *Helix* and identify external characters already discussed: *shell, whorls, spire, collar, aperture, anterior tentacles, posterior tentacles* with terminal *eye,* mouth with 1 ventral and 2 lateral lips, *genital pore* (right side of head), *pedal gland opening, foot, mantle, pulmonary pore,* and *anus* (located on right side of mantle under shell collar).

Remove the shell (Fig. 10-9) by cutting around the spiral to the terminal coil or by carefully cracking the shell and removing the chips. Be careful not to damage the tissues, which may have been made hard and brittle by the fixative. The central columella may have to be freed from the body by cutting the columella muscle.

Observe the *visceral hump.*

▶ How many coils does it make?

Notice the thickened collar (for shell secretion) at the base of the mantle and the thin,

vascular *respiratory mantle cover* elsewhere. Locate the *nephridium* or *kidney* (second half-turn of the visceral mass) anterior of which is the *heart.* The dark, lobed *digestive gland* dominates the rest of the visceral hump. Final whorls show the whitish *albumen gland* and *hermaphroditic gonad,* the *ovo-testis.*

Next, lay back the intact mantle (both roof and floor) by the following procedure: cut from the genital pore back to the base of the collar; then make a parallel cut on the other side of the head; connect these 2 cuts behind the tentacles and lay back this tissue flap. Then continue the initial cut (on the right side of the snail) around the collar, and follow the whorls of the body. This will expose the internal organs and permit you to fold back the entire roof and floor of mantle tissue. The rectum, vascularized lung system, and heart are contained in this tissue flap, which should be laid back and pinned out (Fig. 10-10).

This exposure of internal organs essentially completes your dissection—all that remains is to spread the organs so that the digestive, reproductive, and nervous complex can be identified. Be sure that the specimen is covered with water so that the organs float freely. Place the reproductive organs (*dart sac, penis, flagellum, oviduct, sperm duct, spermathecal duct, mucous gland*) to one side, preferably the right. Separate

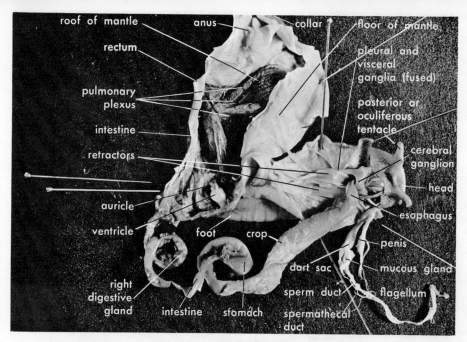

Labels on figure:
roof of mantle — anus — collar — floor of mantle
rectum — pleural and visceral ganglia (fused)
pulmonary plexus — posterior or oculiferous tentacle
intestine — cerebral ganglion
retractors — head
auricle — esophagus
ventricle — foot — crop — penis
dart sac — mucous gland
right digestive gland — sperm duct — flagellum
intestine — stomach — spermathecal duct

Fig. 10-11. *Helix,* internal anatomy.

them carefully and place pins against (not through) them at appropriate points (Fig. 10-11). Cut through connective tissue that may prevent laying out the parts, such as tissue connecting the spermatheca and the albumen gland to the digestive organ. Then move the crop somewhat to the left to allow the sexual organs the fullest degree of display possible. Have your teaching assistant check your dissection before you proceed to dismember your beast further.

b. *Excretory system.* Each organ system should be traced out as completely as possible. Locate the following in the excretory system:

1. Kidney—large structure in roof of mantle cavity, in second half of first coil of visceral mass.

2. Renal duct—passing parallel to the rectum, out to the anterior end of the mantle cavity, and to an *excretory pore* at the edge of the respiratory pore. These relationships have been disturbed, however, by the dissection.

c. *Digestive system.* Locate the following:

1. Perivisceral cavity—the blood space or *hemocoel* of large blood sinuses in which internal organs are bathed.

2. Buccal mass (with nerve ring)—*esophagus* (passing through the nerve ring), *radular retractor muscle, crop* (thin-walled tube from esophagus to base of visceral hump), *salivary glands* (alongside crop) with ducts passing through the nerve to the top of the buccal mass.

3. Stomach—wider than crop, forming second coil of visceral hump. Near the stomach-intestine junction are 2 small ducts leading to the large *diges-*

tive glands. The right digestive gland is the terminal coil of the spire; the left forms the bulk of tissue embedding the intestine.

4. Intestine—a thick, S-shaped tube, eventually returning to the main body whorl as the *rectum,* which passes through the mantle cavity and exits via the *anus* next to the excretory and respiratory pores at the right collar margin. These pores, you will note, were moved with the mantle during your dissection.

Trace the *rectum,* following the cut posterior margin of the mantle roof, and find its terminus at the *anus.* Review the digestive system to understand better the connections to the rectum in the mantle cavity.

d. *Reproductive system* (Fig. 10-10). Starting with the tip of the coiled visceral hump, find the following:

1. Ovo-testis—protandrous (the male developing first), found on the inner surface of the coiled digestive gland.

▶ What is the biological importance of protandry?

2. Hermaphroditic duct—tight coils running from gonad to base of the large whitish *albumen gland,* where the fertilization chamber is located. Here eggs are fertilized and then coated with albumen.

3. Common duct—the prominent duct with separate male and female portions leading from the hermaphroditic duct.

The common duct consists of a thin male half for sperm passage and a larger convoluted female half where calcareous shells are secreted around eggs moving down the duct. Note the incomplete septum dividing the ducts.

4. *Oviduct and sperm duct*—produced by separation of the common duct into distinct units. Joining the sperm duct halfway between the origin of this duct and the *penis* is the *flagellum*, a long narrow tube for compressing sperm bundles into *spermatophore* groups.

5. *Penis*—protrusible terminus of the sperm duct, which can be extruded through the common genital pore and withdrawn by the retractor muscle (previously cut when the mantle floor was removed).

6. *Oviduct*—a thick-walled, separate tube continuing from the female portion of the common duct to the vagina and joined by the *spermathecal duct*, the blind end of which is a swollen *spermatheca*. In this sac is stored sperm from the male organ of another snail received during hermaphroditic copulation. The spermatheca is found in the upper coils near the junction of hermaphroditic and common ducts. The long spermathecal duct runs parallel to the common duct, and joins the oviduct near the vagina. Another small diverticulum joins the spermathecal duct near the anterior end of the common duct. Sound complicated? It is! Work it out on your specimen and check with the photographs. Appreciate that structural complexity is not an exclusively human or even vertebrate characteristic.

The final portion of the reproductive system includes the *vagina*, joined by 2 branched *mucous glands*, and a *dart sac* (a muscular organ producing a calcareous spine for stabbing into the side of the other snail as a precopulatory stimulus). The entire complex, joined at the vagina, opens externally via the common genital pore near the base of the right posterior tentacle.

e. *Nervous system* (Fig. 10-11). Careful dissection is also necessary to expose this system. Cut the esophagus anterior to the nerve ring, then cut the adjoining salivary gland ducts and radular retractor. Move the crop aside, pull the anterior stump of the esophagus out from the nerve ring, and pin it aside. Then dissect the ganglia and nerves of the ring free of enclosing connective tissue. Observe the concentration of ganglia in this area.

▶ What is the significance of this concentration?

Find the *cerebral ganglia* with a small pair of nerves leading to the *buccal ganglia* near the bases of the salivary gland ducts on the buc-

cal capsule. Other nerves from the cerebral ganglia lead to the body wall, mouth, and eyes. The fused posterior ganglia, *cerebropedal, cerebropleural*, and *visceral ganglia*, form a ring around the cephalic aorta.

Return now to the pinned-out mantle tissue. The exposed thin inner lining is the floor of the mantle overlying the foot and viscera. Dorsal to it (actually pinned down below it in your preparation) is the vascularized roof of the mantle cavity embedding the lunglike *pulmonary plexus, pericardium, heart* and connecting major blood vessels, *rectum*, and *anus*.

f. *Circulatory system.* Locate the large branchial "lung" vein or pulmonary plexus just identified. It returns aerated blood to the heart. Follow the plexus to the pericardial cavity into the thin-walled large *auricle* and small muscular *ventricle*. The latter pumps blood out the *aorta*. This major vessel almost immediately divides into a *visceral branch* (along the ventral surface of the liver, from which it branches to the entire visceral mass) and a *cephalic branch* to the head and foot, encircled by the fused posterior ganglia already observed. In the snail's "open" circulation, blood bathes the organs directly, flowing through large sinuses or blood spaces. Blood returns to the heart through sinuses (forming a hemocoel) rather than by closed veins (*as in what previously studied animal?*). En route back to the heart, blood is collected in a large *afferent branchial vessel* located near the collar, and then passes through the lung capillary bed (plexus) *or* to the kidney capillaries. After aeration or excretory exchange, blood returns to the heart from the hemocoel and is again pumped into the general circulation.

A final examination of whatever is left of your snail can include dissection of the buccal mass to expose the anterior "jaw" (a rubbing surface for the radula); the ventral radula in its *radular sac;* and the *odontophore* or ventral muscle mass, which moves the radula in its belt-like grinding action. Dissect out the radula and examine it microscopically.

▶ How does the *Helix* radula compare with that of the chiton?

SUGGESTION

Compare radulae of several snail species to see their marked differences, mount each in balsam

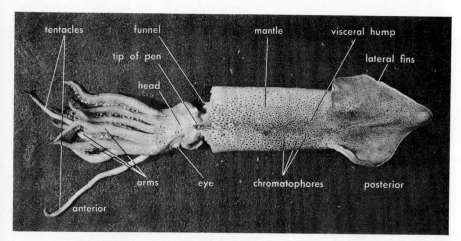

tentacles　funnel　mantle　visceral hump

tip of pen　lateral fins

head

arms　eye　chromatophores　posterior

anterior

Fig. 10-12. *Loligo opalescens,* dorsal view, male.

on a slide, and identify them by their radular pattern with the aid of any standard taxonomic reference on these snails.

▶ Could a taxonomic key based on these differences be made?

▶ What general features adapt *Helix* to terrestrial life?

Review essential organs of each system and be able to tell how they are adapted to this animal's mode of life. All of this in an ordinary garden snail!

D. Class CEPHALOPODA—*Loligo,* the common squid

1—General aspects—Rapid movement, rapid response—this is the evolutionary pattern demonstrated by the squid, octopus, and other cephalopods. The structure of squids and octopuses indicates active predation, rapid swimming, complex behavior, and a degree of intelligence probably unique among invertebrates. Observe how CEPHALOPODA represent a highly specialized but still recognizable example of the molluscan basic body type.

▶ Where is the shell or the remnant of it? The mantle?

▶ What are the other typically molluscan features?

▶ What structures are unique to the CEPHALOPODA? Does this imply great age of this group?

▶ Name several fossil representatives of the class. How do these fossil forms differ from modern counterparts?

▶ What, then, has been the general evolutionary trend within the cephalopods?

2—External anatomy (Fig. 10-12)

a. *Symmetry and orientation.* Formalin-preserved, frozen, or freshly captured specimens may be used. Examine the general body form and gross features, color pattern, mouth, head and eyes, mantle, movable funnel, and mantle cavity (Fig. 10-12).

▶ What is the general pattern of symmetry?

Morphological orientation and directional orientation of the squid are distinctly different. Your first requirement, therefore, is to decide which end is up. The tip of the cone-shaped body is morphologically dorsal; the arms and tentacles are morphologically ventral, and the funnel is the posterior surface. But in swimming, the animal moves with arms leading and the funnel held below. Therefore, from the standpoint of *directional* as opposed to *morphological* orientation, the morphologically ventral arms become functionally anterior, and the morphologically posterior funnel becomes functionally ventral.

▶ What then, would be the *functional* orientation of the morphological dorsal surface? Review these changes of orientation. *Dissection directions will utilize functional orientation.*

b. *Arms, tentacles, mouth, and surrounding membranes.* In the squid, the molluscan *foot* is modified into 5 pairs of *arms* surrounding the mouth. Four pairs, equally long, are nonretractile, and have 2 rows of suckers. One pair (the *tentacles*) is longer, retractile, and has specialized suckers only at the tips. To capture swimming prey, the tentacles dart out rapidly, grab a fish or crustacean, and draw it back to the other 8 arms. Suckers of these arms anchor and move the victim to the horny jaws that bite and poison it.

▶ Observe how the suckers vary in size. Note the *cup* and attachment *pedicle* or stalk of each.

Remove a sucker and examine it microscopically. Note the chitinous toothed ring supporting the edge of the cup with the basal portion forming a small piston.

▶ How does the sucker function?

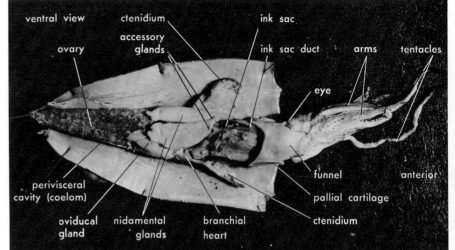

Fig. 10-13. *Loligo opalescens*, internal anatomy, female.

Labels on figure:
ventral view — ctenidium — ink sac — ovary — accessory glands — ink sac duct — arms — tentacles — eye — periviscreal cavity (coelom) — oviducal gland — nidamental glands — branchial heart — ctenidium — funnel — pallial cartilage — anterior

Locate the lower left arm—the *fourth left*—and see if it shows a modification in which size of suckers decreases and size of pedicles increases. This asymmetry marks the male, and is called *heterocotyly* (different arm). The male fourth left arm is modified for transfer of the sperm-bearing *spermatophore* to the *horseshoe organ* on the female's buccal membrane. Expose the mouth of your specimen to observe this membrane connecting to the bases of the arms. The outer portion is the *buccal membrane;* the inner, the *peristomial membrane.* The buccal membrane has 7 projections, each with suckers, whereas the peristomial membrane lacks suckers.

▶ Are the dark, chitinous, beaklike *jaws* visible through the mouth opening?

The ventral jaw usually overlaps the dorsal. If your specimen is a female, look for the horseshoe organ (sperm receptacle) on the buccal membrane below the mouth.

Around the dorsal surface of the head, note the crescentic opening which receives respiratory water currents passing into the mantle cavity.

On the dorsal surface of the skin, observe the numerous tiny dark spots, the pigment cells (*chromatophores*). Contraction or expansion of each cell by special enclosing muscle fibers restricts or spreads pigment to account for the extremely rapid blanching or darkening that sweeps over the living animal, often seen as rhythmic pulsations.

c. *Eyes.* Remove and examine an eye under the dissecting microscope. Identify *cornea, iris, pupil, lens,* and *aquiferous pore* (small opening in front of each eye) that leads into the eye chamber and presumably functions for pressure equalization. The *olfactory crest,* a fold of tissue behind each eye, partly covered by the mantle, is thought to have an olfactory function (for example, it may serve as a water-tasting organ).

d. *Supporting and locomotory structures.* The rest of the squid's body is covered by the mantle, the free anterior edge of which is called the *collar. Pallial cartilages* on either side of the funnel can be seen as lateral projections. A dorsal projection is produced by the anterior end of the *internal shell* (the *pen*). The mantle forms a graceful posterior *cone,* with 2 lateral *fins* for locomotion and guidance. Three sets of muscles (*longitudinal, transverse,* and *vertical*) activate the fins to make slow rhythmic movements or powerful strokes for rapid forward locomotion.

The funnel, projecting from beneath the mantle, is not homologous with the siphons of clams. The later are derived from fusion of posterior portions of the mantle. The funnel and arms of cephalopods are thought to be derived from the *foot* of an ancestral mollusk.

▶ How does the function of the cephalopod funnel compare with that of the clam's siphon?

▶ How does the funnel action control direction and speed of the animal's movement?

▶ Locate the transverse muscle fibers clearly grouped on the ventral surface of the fins.

3—Internal anatomy (Figs. 10-13 and 10-14)

a. *Dissection.* Expose the internal organs of your specimen by making a longitudinal incision on the ventral surface of the visceral hump along one side of the midventral line. Then make a longitudinal cut along the funnel and pin out this thick wall of mantle tissue. Keep the specimen under water to facilitate observation and separation of the organs. Observe the set of *valves* and *interlocking cartilages* by which the incurrent

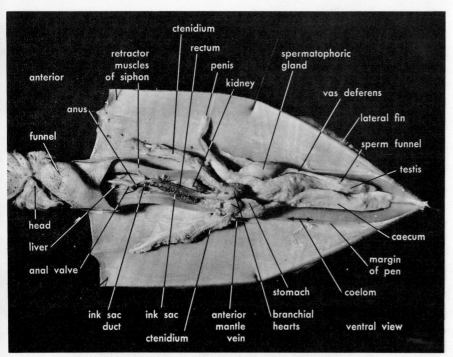

Labels on figure:
ctenidium
rectum
retractor muscles of siphon
penis
spermatophoric gland
anterior
kidney
vas deferens
anus
lateral fin
funnel
sperm funnel
testis
head
liver
anal valve
caecum
margin of pen
stomach
coelom
ink sac duct
ink sac
anterior mantle vein
branchial hearts
ventral view
ctenidium

Fig. 10-14. *Loligo opalescens,* ventral view, male.

water flow is restricted to the dorsal openings and the excurrent flow is confined to the funnel. Review the function of this water-flow pattern. Cartilaginous grooves fit into cartilaginous ridges dorsally and ventrolaterally where the inner surface of the mantle anteriorly joins the body. Entry of water is restricted to the dorsal openings by 2 large saclike valves at the base of the siphon (preventing inflow). Incoming currents therefore must first pass over the 2 large gills (*ctenidia*). Two anal valves at the base of the siphon mark the terminus of the *rectum*. Note the functional relationship of these valve openings. Water movement out of the mantle cavity is controlled by *circular* muscles, which squeeze the mantle cavity, draw the collar down tight on the head, and expel water out of the funnel. Contraction of *radial* muscles actively expands the cavity, drawing water into the cavity through the openings between collar and head.

Identify the major organs of your specimen (Fig. 10-13). The black or silvery *ink sac duct* lies dorsal to the rectum. The basal swelling of this duct forms the sac. As is commonly known, ejected ink provides an escape screen for the octopus or squid.

Gills along the lateral border of the viscera have already been identified. Notice the enlarged round *branchial heart* at the base of each gill.

▶ Can you guess the function of the branchial heart?

In the male (Fig. 10-14), the *testis* occupies the posterior end of the mantle cavity dorsal

to the *caecum* in the cone-shaped body tip. The *penis* is a muscular duct on the left side of the *rectum* (as always, the *animal's* left). The paired *kidneys,* elongate or triangular structures between the gill bases, are clearly visible in the male. In the female (Fig. 10-13), kidneys are covered ventrally by a pair of large, white, elongate *nidamental glands.* Each has a small *accessory nidamental gland* at its anterior tip. These glands may be red or orange-speckled before egg laying. The entire conical tip of the mantle cavity may be filled with eggs, as the large ovary in this region sheds eggs directly into the *perivisceral* (coelomic) *cavity.*

b. *Reproductive system.* Having already identified the major reproductive organs, review this system and try to clarify functional relationships of the parts. The sexual apparatus is not only complex, but intricate behavior patterns have also evolved that ensure proper fertilization and placement of eggs. The male's large, single testis opens into the coelom through a slit in the wall. Sperm are picked up by a ciliated funnel (*sperm bulb*) and passed into the *posterior vas deferens* or *sperm duct.* The duct, at first a slender coiled tube white with sperm, may become considerably enlarged by its contents. Two glands straddle the vas deferens. Anteriormost is the *spermatophoric gland,* which receives the sperm and packs them into complex *spermatophores.* The second, the *spermatophoric organ,* receives finished spermatophores and stores them before ejection through the enlarged *anterior vas deferens* that passes near the dorsal surface of the left kidney. The vas deferens ends at the muscular ejaculatory penis. The sperm are therefore bundled, packaged, and stored before being used in the complex copulatory act. Examine spermatophores from the spermatophoric sac. Each spermatophore consists of an elongate outer *tunic* enclosing the *sperm mass*. A *cement body* and coiled *ejaculatory organ* at the anterior end of the spermatophore (near the end bearing an elongate cap thread) complete the structure. When the cap is broken, the coiled ejaculatory organ below it springs out, dragging the cement gland and sperm mass with it. The cement gland sticks to whatever it is thrown against and holds the sperm masses on or near the point—usually near unfertilized eggs. Spermatophores are generally transferred by the male's specialized arm (*which one?*) to the female horseshoe organ, or they may be thrust by the male directly into the female mantle cavity.

The female genital system (Fig. 10-13) consists of the *ovary*, which empties numerous eggs into the coelom, and an *oviduct*, which picks up the eggs with a ciliated funnel. The funnel and adjacent portion of oviduct are embedded in the egg mass, and are thus difficult to locate and more easily traced from the anterior portion. Observe the flared opening of the oviduct through which eggs pass from the coelom into the mantle cavity (look in the area halfway down the left gill). The thick-walled, glandular, anterior portion of the oviduct forms the *oviducal gland*. Trace the oviduct back to the ovary through its several loops, removing the left gill and its branchial heart if necessary. Identify again the nidamental glands and the accessory nidamental glands. These glands secrete the outer capsules of the egg masses. The oviducal gland (in the oviduct) forms spherical capsules around individual eggs, which are therefore encased in their individual packets, surrounded by a fluid, jelly-like matrix, and then extruded through the funnel, fertilized, and placed by the female on an appropriate rock or substrate below the low-tide zone. The female octopus guards and constantly aerates her eggs by controlled water movements. The jelly covering the eggs hardens to enclose a cluster of several dozen eggs in a finger-shaped protective envelope that adheres by its basal cementing material in the case of the squid eggs. In an aquarium with running sea water, development of young squids can be observed through these protective membranes.

c. *Respiratory and circulatory systems.* The cephalopod circulatory system is closed. (*How does this compare with that of the clam and of the earthworm?*) The major flow pattern of the blood is best seen in injected specimens but can also be worked out in ordinary specimens. *Branchial hearts* receive venous blood returning from passage throughout the body. Principal veins are the large pair of *postcavae* (singular: *postcava*) or *posterior mantle veins*. Blood from the head returns through the *anterior vena cava* (or *cephalic vein*), which receives blood from 2 large vessels the right and left *precavae*. Find where the precavae pass through the kidney tissues and join the postcavae as they enter the branchial hearts. From the branchial hearts, blood passes out the *branchial arteries* into a fine capillary bed in the gills where O_2-CO_2 exchange occurs, then flows back through the *branchial veins* into a large *systemic heart* between and somewhat anterior to the branchial hearts. Remove the *pericardium* to examine the median systemic heart. Oxygenated blood is pumped out of the heart and passes forward to the head through the *anterior aorta* (to the right), or through the *posterior aorta* that divides into a *median* and 2 *lateral mantle arteries*. Near its point of origin, the posterior aorta also gives off branches to the ink sac, rectum, branchial hearts, and gonoduct. Both the veins entering the heart and the arteries leaving it are protected from backflow by semilunar valves.

d. *Excretory system.* Expose the paired kidneys. Observe again the anterior vena cavae passing through the kidney tissue. A pair of *papillae*, each enclosing a *nephridiopore*, is seen as a small projection on the anteroventral surface of each kidney. The large, bilobed urinary gland is enclosed by kidney tissue.

▶ Are relationships of kidney, gills, and heart (direction of blood flow) the same in the Classes CEPHALOPODA, PELECYPODA, and GASTROPODA?

e. *Digestive system.* Expose the muscular, bulbous *buccal mass* in the head by cutting through the base of the funnel and tissues overlying the mouth. Lay these parts to either side, and dissect through the muscles, cutting open the head along the median line. The *radula* and *radular muscle* are enclosed in tissues between *mandibles* of the beak. Try to dissect out the radula and examine it microscopically as you did with the snail and chiton. Be careful, however, not to damage ganglia of the head region. A pair of buccal *salivary glands* lie in muscular tissue posterior to the buccal mass, and their ducts enter the posterior portion of the buccal cavity. Trace the thin *esophagus* from buccal mass to *stomach* along its loop through the *digestive organ* (liver). Posterior to the muscular stomach is the *caecum*, a long sac (considerably shorter in starved specimens; compare Figs. 10-13 and 10-14) extending out to the end of the cone. Try to locate the U-shaped *pancreas* anterior to the stomach. A single *hepatopancreatic duct* carries fluids from both these organs into the caecum. Near the junction of the esophagus and stomach, find the *intestine,* which passes forward between lobes of the pancreas, narrows into the rectum (previously identified), and ends at the *anus* near the funnel base. Again trace the digestive system from mouth to anus, naming and stating the primary function of each portion.

f. *Nervous system.* Cephalopods are said to be the most intelligent of invertebrates. You have already noted how this can be correlated with the predatory habits and activity of these animals. In addition to massing of nerve ganglia in the head region, a definite skull-like structure—the *cephalic cartilages*—has developed.

▶ What is the advantage of this structure?

Extremely rapid nerve conduction is possible through *giant nerve fibers,* which originate in the cephalic ganglia, pass through the *stellate*

Fig. 10-15. *Neopilina Galatheae,* ventral view. (Photograph courtesy of Dr. Henning Lemche.)

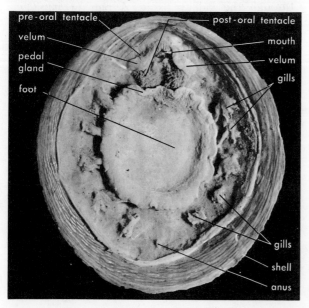

ganglia, and end in the circular muscles of the mantle. Find the stellate ganglia embedded in the dorsal surface of mantle tissue, near the tip of the gills. Trace the giant nerve fibers—some of the largest (and fastest conducting) nerves of this type known, and a favorite research tool of nerve physiologists the world over. The largest fibers innervate the most distant muscles.

▶ How does this difference in fiber size make possible the nearly simultaneous contraction of the mantle?

▶ What does this function imply about integration of movement and degree of swimming control?

Dissection of the central nervous system, a rewarding challenge, requires care and skill, but promises the interested observer a view into a brain that shows striking developmental parallels between cephalopod and vertebrate nervous systems. Expose as much of the squid brain as possible without destroying primary nerves; then identify the various ganglia and their connectives.

Perhaps the simplest method is to cut a sagittal section through the head with a razor. This will expose the *dorsal ganglia* and the *cerebral* and small *suprabuccal ganglion* behind the buccal mass. Below the esophagus the main brain elements can be identified: the *visceral ganglion,* the anterior *pedal ganglion,* and the *propedal ganglion* closer to the mouth. Note also the cephalic cartilages that form a protective skull-like shield of overlapping plates about the brain.

A demanding but more illuminating dissection is from the dorsal surface so that the entire brain and its contributory nerves can be isolated. Remove the skin, dorsal muscles, and upper portion of the cartilaginous skull, being careful not to destroy the postorbital nerves passing through the dorsal cartilaginous shield. Dissect laterally to clear tissues from around the optic ganglia and major connectives. The "white bodies," or white blood cell centers, should be removed to expose the ganglia more fully. Work out the relationships of the different ganglia and their connectives. Contrast this view with that obtained in the sagittal section. Then dissect anteriorly to expose the buccal ganglia and nerves, and the fused nerve ring of ganglia about the esophagus. Continue posteriorly to show the medial visceral nerve and giant nerves to the stellate ganglia.

▶ Which ganglia are paired?

NOTES AND DRAWINGS

(Tear along line)

► Does the cerebral ganglion appear to be derived from a pair?

► What other evidence of fusion can you find?

► How does the squid brain compare with that of the clam? The snail?

► What correlation can be made between muscular activity, brain size, and ganglion concentration?

Cut off one eye and optic ganglion to view the brain both dorsally and laterally; place the eye in a separate dish of water for later examination. Review the parts of the newly exposed brain.

► Does the cerebral ganglion give off nerves? What might this imply?

Observe the relatively large proportion of the brain that seems to be associated with the eyes (*optic nerves, optic ganglia, oculomotor nerve* to the *eye muscles*).

Now check the structure of the dissected eye. Remove it from enclosing tissues. Observe the short optic nerve that connects it to the optic ganglion. Locate the *anterior* and *posterior chambers*, with the *lens* between.

► How does the eye focus?

► How does this compare with methods of focusing among vertebrates?

Find the *cornea, iris,* and *pupil*.

Draw the squid eye; name primary parts. Compare the function and position of these parts with those of the vertebrate eye. This similarity of eye structure in two such divergent groups represents one of the most remarkable examples of evolutionary convergence in nature.

g. *Skeletal system.* The *pen,* a chitinous, translucent, middorsal internal shell, has already been identified. Remove it and note its relationship with the *nuchal cartilage* at its anterior end in muscle tissue near the collar. *Infundibular cartilages* lie laterally along the base of the funnel and these in turn articulate with *posterior mantle cartilages* (*pallial cartilages*) in mantle tissues. *Cephalic cartilages,* which serve as a skull, have already been observed. Notice the somewhat irregular arrangement of these plates, and the number of foramina for blood vessels and nerves.

► Is the skeletal system of the squid a basic molluscan feature?

► What is the chief function of the cartilages?

Some authorities say that the pen is a nonfunctional remnant of the heavier and more typical external shell seen in the related Pearly Nautilus or extinct Ammonites. Others feel it might be a new and useful structure, rather than a vestigial relict.

► What information would be required to choose properly between these alternative views?

Review the names and chief characteristics of the 6 mollusk classes and their representatives studied.

► What is the *basic body type of mollusks*?

► Which would you consider a "typical mollusk"?

Correlate feeding habits and degree of motility in each class with the pattern of evolution and structural adaptation exemplified by that class.

CHAPTER 11

Phylum

Echinodermata

I. INTRODUCTION

Sea stars, sea urchins, brittle stars, sea cucumbers, and feather stars are all echinoderms (a word meaning "spiny skin"). They form a large phylum of specialized marine organisms that are interesting both for their striking body form and their evolutionary role as possible precursors of the vertebrate line. Though adults of most echinoderms show *radial symmetry,* zoologists have learned that this does not ally sea star with jellyfish. Even a hundred years after the time of Linnaeus, the superficial similarity of echinoderm and coelenterate symmetry caused confusion as to the basic differences between these two phyla. Further research made it clear, however, that the radially symmetrical pattern of coelenterates is present in *each stage* of their life cycle. This was therefore recognized as a basic phylogenetic characteristic called *primary* radial symmetry. In echinoderms, on the other hand, larval stages are actively swimming *bilaterally symmetrical* animals. Radial symmetry in this phylum is an evolutionary modification found only in *adults* and is associated with a sessile, creeping existence. This is considered *secondary* radial symmetry, an indicator of subsequent modification or specialization added later in the evolutionary history of the group. Though this interpretation probably won't interest the sea star, it tells us that adult symmetry is not a reliable index of the phylogenetic history of ECHINODERMATA. It also helps clarify our thinking about the importance of larval stages in working out evolutionary antecedents, applied, as we shall soon see, in the question of vertebrate origins. Finally, it permits classification of echinoderms with other eucoelomate animals with which they have close structural and embryological ties, and releases them from an artificial alliance with coelenterates with which they have no basic similarity.

Our review of ECHINODERMATA starts with a description of its basic body type, then a study of examples of its 5 classes and their structural and functional characteristics. The embryological and phylogenetic importance of the phylum is discussed in a subsequent section.

Approach your specimens with questions and the same curiosity applied to the strange and wonderful beasts you picked off the beach as a child. Opportunities to acquire knowledge of living animals in their natural environment are offered by several university marine biological stations where summer courses in marine biology stress living activities and ecological interrelationships. A lifetime of interest in marine life usually results from such a study.

II. CLASSIFICATION

The fundamental adult morphological pattern of this ancient phylum is *pentamerous* (5-armed), forming a secondary radial symmetry around an oral-aboral axis (aboral indicates the side away from or opposite the mouth). The adult develops embryologically from a bilaterally symmetrical larva that undergoes a striking metamorphosis, changing to a body form adapted to slow-moving life on the ocean floor.

Perhaps the most unique characteristic of echinoderms is the *water-vascular* system, which consists of numerous water-filled tubes ending in a large number of *tube feet* that control motility and, to a varying degree, respiration. Other echinoderm characteristics include a spacious coelomic (perivisceral) cavity lined with ciliated peritoneum developed in the embryo by the *enterocoelous* (outpocketing) method. An endoskeleton of calcareous plates, ossicles, or spines, appears to be external but is actually covered by a thin epidermis. Additional features are ciliated organs; lack of head, brain, or segmentation; minute gills or dermal papillae protruding through fine pores in the skeleton and epidermis; and a simple nervous system of circumoral ring and radial nerves to the arms. Many extinct groups and an extensive fossil record are known. Living representatives are divided into the following 5 classes.

A. Class ASTEROIDEA—sea stars (Figs. 11-1 and 11-2)

This class includes such typical echinoderms as the predaceous star-shaped or pentagonal sea stars. In some species, the number of arms may be multiplied to 50. Ossicles are separate, permitting movement; short spines and pedicellariae are present; 2 or 4 rows of tube feet line the open ambulacral grooves in each arm. Oral surface is ventral; madreporite is aboral. *Asterias, Pisaster, Patiria, Henricia, Solaster,* and *Pycnopodia* are common genera. Sea stars are often called, inaccurately, starfish.

B. Class OPHIUROIDEA—brittle stars (Figs. 11-3 and 11-4)

Similar to sea stars, brittle stars have a central disc to which highly flexible, jointed limbs attach. Tube feet, confined to 2 rows and lacking suckers, have a sensory function. Pedicellariae and anus are lacking; madreporite is aboral. Typical genera are *Gorgonocephalus* and *Ophiothrix*.

C. Class ECHINOIDEA—sea urchins (Figs. 11-5 to 11-9)

These spiny, herbivorous echinoderms are constructed as though their tentacles were folded back into a ball and fixed into a calcareous skeleton (test), then covered with long, sharp, movable spines and 3-jawed pedicellariae. The test is globular in sea urchins and disc or heart-shaped in sand dollars. Tube feet are long, slender, and equipped with suckers. Mouth and anus are central or lateral. The large gut fills much of the test cavity (except during spawning periods). Typical genera are *Arbacia, Strongylocentrotus,* and *Echinorachnius.*

D. Class HOLOTHUROIDEA—sea cucumbers (Figs. 11-10 and 11-11)

Sausage-shaped garbage collectors, sea cucumbers are among the chief clean-up organisms of the ocean bottom. They represent a different evolutionary direction among echinoderms—the adult phase retains the larval bilateral symmetry. With their sausage shape and warty papillated skin, sea cucumbers are well named. They vary in length from an inch or so to several feet, with body wall consistency from leathery to papery. Arms, spines, pedicellariae, and skeleton (except for scattered tiny plates in body wall) are all absent. Tube feet are present. The mouth with tentacles is at one end of the body and the anus is at the other, the latter often bearing a respiratory complex called the respiratory tree (which may be ejected with other organs in a sticky mass when the sea cucumber is attacked or disturbed). Examples: *Thyone, Leptosynapta, Stichopus.*

E. Class CRINOIDEA—sea lilies and feather stars (Fig. 11-12)

These stalked, flowerlike echinoderms have 5 arms that branch to 10 or more, each bearing 5 branchlets or pinnules to form a cuplike central disc (calyx). No spines, pedicellariae, or suckers arise from the tube feet lining the open ambulacral grooves. In sea lilies, a long jointed stalk with rootlike projections may attach the animal to the substrate. In feather stars, the calyx may lack a stalk and be free-swimming with motile, gripping cirri and a mouth and anus on the upper (oral) surface. Examples: *Metacrinus, Antedon,* and *Heliometra.*

► Review the general definition of the phylum. Describe a generalized echinoderm body type.

► Define the classes and state in what way the general adaptive pattern—feeding habits and locomotion—of each is related to its structure.

► Explain how sea stars, sea urchins, sea cucumbers, brittle stars, and crinoids still can be combined in the same phylum in spite of their remarkable variation.

III. *LABORATORY INSTRUCTIONS*

A. CLASS ASTEROIDEA—Pisaster[1]

1—Observations

a. Seeing living sea stars or other echinoderms, especially in their natural habitat, makes all the difference in an appreciation of their movements, feeding methods, and natural appearance. A field trip to an intertidal zone is particularly helpful in this regard, but a surprising amount of information can be obtained by observing echinoderms in a marine aquarium. With low temperatures and proper aeration, these animals remain alive and active for several weeks. They can then be studied at leisure for righting reactions, response to various stimuli (such as a molluscan prey), and feeding methods.

Watch their locomotion. Observe coordination of tube feet, sucking action on glass wall of aquarium, and righting reaction.

► Which arm leads in general movement?

► Does the sea star have an anterior end?

If possible, observe normal feeding reactions, including seeking, finding, opening, and digestion of prey. The last step involves eversion of the stomach and *external* digestion. To see the reaction to food, place a bit of meat near the mouth of an inverted sea star. The feeding posture may be preserved for more detailed observation by collecting and quick-freezing sea stars in the act of opening clams. The tube feet will remain in position and the stomach everted for digestion of the molluscan victim.

► How are the tube feet of a sea star able to pull open even the largest mussel?

[1] Our principal organism for study is the sea star *Asterias* (from the Atlantic Coast) or *Pisaster* (from the Pacific Coast). Though numerous distinct species are found, each in a specific habitat and locality, their structure is markedly similar. Photographs used here are of the giant Pacific sea star *Pisaster gigantea*.

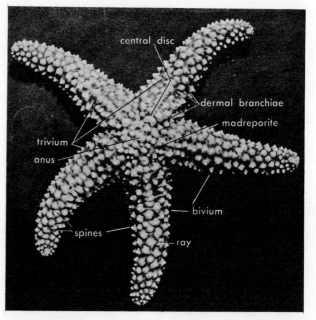

Fig. 11-1. *Pisaster gigantea,* aboral view.

► How does the sea star sense the presence of its prey?

External structures best seen in the living specimen include the soft respiratory papillae or *dermal branchiae,* which may be withdrawn or everted, and tiny pincers or *pedicellariae.* The latter go quickly into action when the surface of a living specimen is slowly stroked with a camel's hair brush. Under a dissecting microscope, pinching tips of the pedicellariae can be seen adhering to the brush hairs.

► Could these pedicellariae explain the freedom of sea star from surface-encrusting hydroids and other organisms?

► Almost any surface in the intertidal zone is soon encrusted with organisms, yet sea stars are nearly always clean. How is this phenomenon advantageous to the sea star?

b. The following are suggestions for additional experiments on asteroids.

1. Test the effect of water drippings from a living sea star on oysters or other clams when the latter are open and "pumping."

2. Test the effect of various types of meat or clam tissue on the feeding reaction of a sea star.

3. Quick-freeze a sea star in the act of opening a mussel; study the position of the tube feet pulling open the mollusk valves and note the everted, baglike stomach.

4. Test the ability of sea stars to adhere to

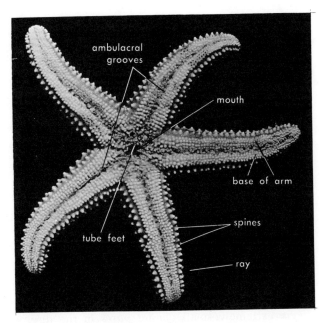

Fig. 11-2. *Pisaster gigantea,* oral view.

a silica or grease-coated aquarium glass surface.

5. Observe the action of *cilia*, both inside the body cavity and on the outer surface. To do this, inject powdered carmine or India ink into the body cavity and watch the dermal branchiae under a binocular dissecting microscope.

▶ What causes the particles to move?

▶ How is this movement related to respiration and to internal circulation of fluids?

2—External anatomy (Figs. 11-1 and 11-2)

a. Using a preserved or freshly killed specimen, find the disc and aboral *madreporite* (small, colored plate markedly off center on the disc). A pair of arms, the *bivium*, borders the madreporite. The other arms form the *trivium*. The *anus*, a fine pore in the center of the aboral surface, can be located with a pin. Turn your specimen over and observe the *mouth* on the ventral or oral surface. Around the mouth is a soft membranous zone, the *peristome*, and a protective circle of movable *oral spines*. Examine the other spines.

▶ Can you find an epithelial lining over these spines?

▶ Are the spines therefore a portion of an *ectoskeleton* or of an *endoskeleton*?

▶ What forms the remainder of the skeleton?

Study the ventral *ambulacral grooves* in the arms. Two or 4 rows of tube feet are found, depending on the species. Observe their arrangement and position.

▶ What is the function of tube feet?

▶ How are they interconnected?

b. Examine the animal's aboral surface more closely, using a hand lens or dissecting microscope. Keep the specimen submerged so as to float up the smaller structures. These include the previously mentioned papillae or *dermal branchiae*, small fingerlike projections with a respiratory and perhaps excretory function. These thin-walled structures, representing the major surface in contact with the aquatic environment, have internal cilia that maintain a moving current of blood cells and body fluids. They therefore offer an excellent means for respiratory and excretory exchange. Search for the still smaller *pedicellariae*, some of which are stalked, others attached basally. They can be seen as tiny white specks among papillae and spines. Examine microscopically an aboral surface scraping in a drop of water covered by a coverslip. Try to locate some pedicellariae jaws. Rock or press gently on the coverslip while you watch the specimen. This motion will sometimes cause the pedicellariae to roll over or even to open. Attempt to work out the scissorlike action of the tiny snap jaws.

c. *Drawings.*

1. Make a large *outline drawing* of a sea star, placing the external dorsal structure on one arm and external ventral structure on another arm. Later, add internal structures in the disc outline. These can be drawn in the remaining arms to give you a composite drawing of major internal systems and of external anatomy on a single page.

2. Sketch a group of spines, papillae, and pedicellariae to show their normal arrangement. Select a pedicellaria from your microscopic preparation, and draw it in lateral view to show the 4 articulations and attached muscles.

3—Internal anatomy (preserved specimen)—As an example of echinoderm organization, you will be provided a sea star, *Pisaster*, for study of skeletal, digestive, reproductive, water-vascular, and nervous systems.

a. *Skeletal system.* This can be examined on a dried or pickled specimen. Dry sea stars should be soaked in potassium hydroxide to dissolve fleshy portions and to demonstrate the pattern of plates or ossicles forming the internal framework, with openings for feet and mouth. However, many plates are embedded individually and will fall free in the KOH. Therefore, compare dried and macerated specimens. Portions of the body wall can be removed and studied to show structure and pattern of the inner skeletal framework.

Cut one arm off your preserved specimen and study the cross section of the stump. Make several more cuts if needed to locate the arrangement of *ossicles* with their fixed *dorsal spines* and movable *ventral spines* along the ambulacral groove.

b. *Digestive system.* Digestive organs are best seen by removing the dorsal (aboral) body wall (Fig. 11-13). *Hepatic caeca,* large paired organs, are suspended by mesenteries from the roof of each arm.

Make all dissections under water to expose other organs with greatest facility and clarity. Cut the tip from one arm, then make 2 lateral cuts extending towards the disc. Raise the roof (careful!) by trimming the mesenteries attached to it so as not to disturb the digestive glands. Then cut across this roof or shield where it joins the disc.

Next, remove the aboral disc by making a circular cut, then loosening adherent mesenteries as before. Avoid cutting out the madreporite; allow it to remain attached to the specimen. For additional views, cut from the exposed aboral area out to the tip of one or more remaining arms, then remove the excised body wall from disc outward (Fig. 11-14).

You have exposed the large *coelom* and mesenteries supporting the organs.

► How are these mesenteries related to the coelom?

Carefully probe around the digestive glands.

► How are the small groups of digestive glands attached?

► How many combined glands are in each arm?

Trace the connection between the digestive glands and disc. Note where the 2 *hepatic ducts* of each arm join and enter the *stomach.* Observe that the stomach has 2 portions, a small aboral *pyloric stomach* connecting with the hepatic ducts, and the large, whitish, bag-like *cardiac stomach* that lies ventrally and is the portion everted through the mouth while feeding. Five pairs of *retractor muscles* (one from each arm) attach to the stomach walls. Notice the great distension of this bag owing to its many pleats and folds.

► What is the functional importance of such a large sac?

► Why is external digestion advantageous to the sea star?

Dorsal to the pyloric stomach, near the center of the stomach, is the single pair of small, lobed *rectal caeca.* These are attached to a fine *intestine* passing dorsally to the aboral disc and opening externally by a small *anal pore.*

c. *Reproductive system.* A pair of buff-colored glandular *gonads* lies under the hepatic caeca in each arm, usually ventrolaterally, alongside the ambulacral groove (Fig. 11-15). Gonads vary in size from insignificantly small to those filling most of the coelomic space, depending upon the breeding cycle phase at time of capture. *Gonoducts* between the arms send sexual products out via extremely small *genital pores* in the disc, 1 per gonad (2 per arm), around the periphery of the aboral disc.

Make a microscopic examination of the gonadal tissues and products to determine the sex of your sea star.

d. *Water-vascular system.* The water-vascular system, a unique internal water-pressure system, consists of a *madreporite* leading ventrally through a *stone canal* (Fig. 11-16) to a *ring canal* circling the mouth, and branching out into each arm via *radial canals.* Nine small swellings, *Tiedemann bodies,* on the inner margin of the ring canal probably are related to formation of certain cells in water-vascular fluid. Between each pair of radial canals is the *Polian vesicle,* also of uncertain function. Tube feet, basic units of the water-vascular system, lie alongside the radial canals, each tube foot connected to the canal by a short *lateral canal.*

A tube foot consists of a tubular portion protruding into the ambulacral groove, and an internal swollen *ampulla.* This system, which serves as a fluid-pressure mechanism operating the tube feet, provides echinoderms with slow motility, adherance to the substrate, and prolonged sucking action for opening the strongest bivalve (by alternately holding with one group of tube feet, then another).

First locate the ampullae lined up along both sides of each ambulacral groove. Apply pressure to one ampulla and note the effect on its tube foot.

► How do these ampullae control liquid pressure in the external tube feet?

Next, find the radial canal in the center of the ambulacral groove of the cut arm. Dissect further in this cut portion until you can discern the lateral canal between the radial canal and a tube foot. Trace the radial canal towards the disc and find its connection to the ring canal. Expose the ring canal in turn and find its inner swellings, the Tiedemann bodies. (Note that 2 are found between each pair of arms except on the bivium, where the tenth space is occupied by the stone canal.) The ossicle-reinforced stone canal rises from the ring canal and emerges to the outside via the madreporite. This structural complex, operated by valves and reservoir chambers to control and maintain internal water pressure in the tube feet and in their suction discs, permits the system's remarkable operation.

Retrace the entire system, its components and functioning. Consult your text and laboratory charts for clarification of structures not visible in your specimen.

Drawing: Complete your outline with details visible in *dorsal view* of the disc. Include both portions of the *stomach, rectal caeca, hepatic ducts,* portions of *digestive* and *reproductive glands,* and visible parts of the *water-vascular system.*

▶ How is respiration accomplished in the Asteroidea?

▶ How are wastes excreted?

e. *Nervous system.* Nervous coordination in sea stars is difficult to study morphologically, hence the nervous system will be described only briefly. *Radial nerves* pass from the ambulacral groove of each arm (near the radial canal) to an *oral ring* or *nerve ring* (also near the ring canal, at the outer margin of the peristomial membrane). Coordination of arm movement is centered in *ganglion cells* at the junction of each radial nerve and the nerve ring, and the nerve ring serves to coordinate arm movements for directed activity. Local nerve centers are found in the stomach wall, near various muscles and movable spines, and near the tube feet and ampullae. These complete the readily visible branches of the nervous system. In addition, a *subepidermal nerve net* serves as a more independent network for control of local reactions.

f. *Circulatory system.* Circulation in sea star is accomplished by coelomic fluids that move by action of the ciliated peritoneum lining the coelom. This fluid carries a large number of specialized coelomocytes, many of which are amoeboid wandering cells. The cilia-directed currents of coelomic fluid appear to have replaced the blood system of other organisms, as evidenced by the presence of a nonfunctional vascular system in sea stars. This *haemal system* consists of an *axial sinus* (outer surface of the stone canal), a *haemal ring,* remnants of branches into the arms (*radial haemal canals*), and branches along the hepatic duct.

g. *Suggested experiments.*

1. *Circulation*

i. Open an aboral flap in a living sea star placed in a pan of sea water and trace coelomic currents with a few drops of India ink or carmine. Observe particularly ciliated cells of the peritoneum.

ii. Inject these dyes into the pyloric caeca and trace the particles under a dissecting microscope.

iii. Observe passage of particles in distended dermal branchiae.

2. *Reproduction*

i. Fertilization of sea star ova in sea water (in *clean* glassware previously washed and preferably soaked overnight in sea water) can easily be observed and the developmental stages followed. This is now a standard procedure for embryological study. Consult Chapter 17 and appropriate texts or manuals for details.

ii. Stained preparations of *zygotes, segmentation stages, blastula, gastrula,* and early *bipinnaria* larvae can be studied, identified, and drawn. Be sure

Fig. 11-3. *Ophioderma panamensis,* aboral view.

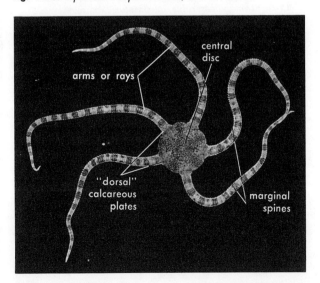

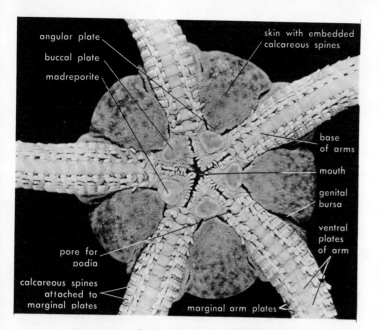

labels, clockwise from top left:
angular plate
buccal plate
madreporite
skin with embedded calcareous spines
base of arms
mouth
genital bursa
ventral plates of arm
marginal arm plates
calcareous spines attached to marginal plates
pore for podia

Fig. 11-4. *Ophioderma panamensis,* oral view.

to observe the sequence through the blastula and gastrula stages.

> **3.** *Field observation.* Visit a marine intertidal zone and study the habits and distribution of as many echinoderms as you can discover. List the species encountered and their habitats. Record observations on food, numbers, and any particular activities observed or tested.

B. Class OPHIUROIDEA—brittle stars, serpent stars, basket stars

1—Observations and external anatomy—Study dried or bottled museum specimens of brittle stars or other ophiuroids (Figs. 11-3 and 1-4).

▶ How do they compare with asteroid sea stars?

Fig. 11-5. *Strongylocentrotus purpuratus,* aboral view.

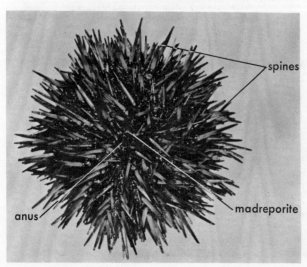

labels:
spines
madreporite
anus

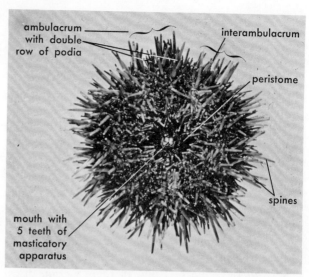

labels:
ambulacrum with double row of podia
interambulacrum
peristome
spines
mouth with 5 teeth of masticatory apparatus

Fig. 11-6. *Strongylocentrotus purpuratus,* oral view.

▶ What is the chief characteristic of the Class OPHIUROIDEA?

Notice the absence of pedicellariae and position of the *madreporite.* Observe *ambulacral grooves* and *tube feet* emerging from lateral margins of these grooves.

▶ Can you locate an *anus*?

▶ What permits the unusual motility of brittle stars' arms?

C. Class ECHINOIDEA—sea urchins, *Strongylocentrotus* (Figs. 11-5 to 11-9)

1—Introduction and observations—Sea urchins (*Arbacia* on the East Coast, *Strongylocentrotus* on the West Coast) are striking and intriguing echinoderms. As noted previously, they structurally resemble a sea star with its

Fig. 11-7. *Strongylocentrotus franciscanus,* aboral view of test.

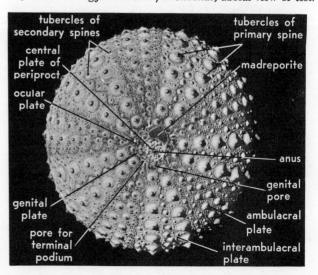

labels:
tubercles of secondary spines
tubercles of primary spine
central plate of periproct
madreporite
ocular plate
anus
genital plate
genital pore
pore for terminal podium
ambulacral plate
interambulacral plate

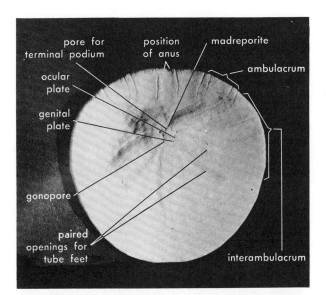

Fig. 11-8. Sand dollar, *Dendraster excentricus,* aboral view.

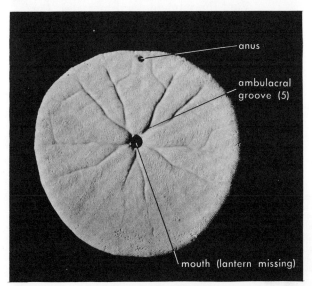

Fig. 11-9. *Dendraster excentricus,* oral view.

arms folded back and with a dense covering mat of spines. Their way of life, however, is totally different, as sea urchins are algae-grazers rather than predators. Sea urchin structure, characterized by a spined protective test, a large coelom, and a greatly enlarged digestive system seems to have evolved along defensive and herbivorous lines.

▶ How are these structures related to the habitat and distribution of sea urchins?

Examine living sea urchins. Compare their appearance and habits with those of sea stars. Locate the elongated *tube feet* and *pedicellariae* among the numerous spines. If possible, observe these structures on a specimen crawling on the glass of a marine aquarium.

2—Internal anatomy—Study either living or preserved specimens for internal structure. Cut the test along its equatorial axis using heavy scissors or bone-cutters. Notice the extremely large *intestine* and digestive apparatus, adapted for herbivorous life. Observe the pentamerous pattern of the *gonads, ampullae,* and test. Cut around the *peristomial membrane,* remove the mouth and entire feeding apparatus, and study the unusual complex jaw apparatus, *"Aristotle's lantern,"* a chuck-and-bit type of rock scraping mechanism. Observe its complex array of muscles for movement of the 5 parts—some 92 separate muscles have been identified.

▶ What characteristics mark echinoids as a distinct class?

▶ What characteristics mark echinoids as echinoderms?

▶ What does the name ECHINOIDEA mean?

▶ How do other animals in this class vary from sea urchins?

D. Class HOLOTHUROIDEA—sea cucumbers, Stichopus, Thyone

1—Observations—Among the most specialized echinoderms, sea cucumbers have slender elongate bodies that are bilaterally symmetrical along the oral-aboral axis. Presumably this is an adaptation for directed, crawling movement, derived from an ancestral pentameral pattern that initially was adapted to sessile or slow-moving life. (As noted earlier, the pentameral pattern is in turn probably derived from an even earlier bilaterally symmetrical free-swimming form.)

Sea cucumbers feed by scavenging the ocean bottom. Their flowerlike anterior tentacles (Fig. 11-17) entrap material in mucus or scrape together debris or other available food particles.

The holothuroids are of added interest because of their capacity to cast out their internal organs, to fragment, and to eject en-

Fig. 11-10. *Cucumaria,* external view.

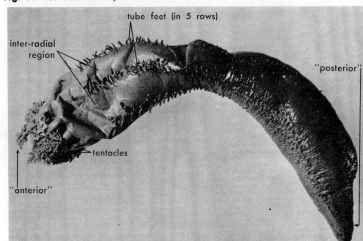

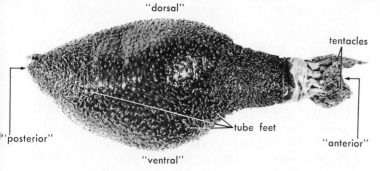

Fig. 11-11. *Thyone*, external view.

"dorsal"

tentacles

"posterior"

tube feet

"anterior"

"ventral"

tangling viscous tubes of the respiratory mechanism. By these defensive mechanisms sea cucumbers trap a potential predator or satisfy it with a partial meal. Perhaps best known is the capacity of certain species to eject the respiratory apparatus through the cloaca when severely disturbed. The loss of organs is not fatal to the former owner and they are rapidly regenerated.

2—External anatomy—Examine the external surface of a sea cucumber. Note its leathery, sometimes warty appearance with many tube feet and numerous embedded ossicles that can be felt under the skin (Figs. 11–10 and 11–11). Specialized sensory and respiratory tube feet on the dorsal surface are usually in 2 zones or tracts, and locomotory tube feet in 3 ventral zones. Notice how this repeats the basic pentamerous pattern.

Find the retractile oral tentacles (Fig. 11–17).

▶ How many are there? Describe their function.

3—Internal anatomy

a. Dissection of a large sea cucumber like *Stichopus* or *Thyone* demonstrates very well the fundamental echinoderm pattern (Figs. 11-18 and 11-19).

arm

oral end

mouth

pinnules

calyx

jointed cirri

Fig. 11-12. The crinoid *Heliometra glacialis*.

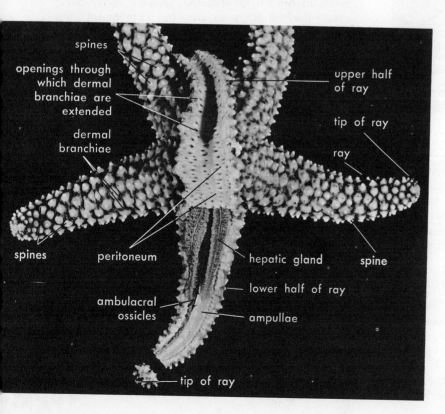

spines

openings through which dermal branchiae are extended

dermal branchiae

upper half of ray

tip of ray

ray

spines

peritoneum

hepatic gland

spine

ambulacral ossicles

lower half of ray

ampullae

tip of ray

Fig. 11-13. *Pisaster gigantea*, internal anatomy, aboral view.

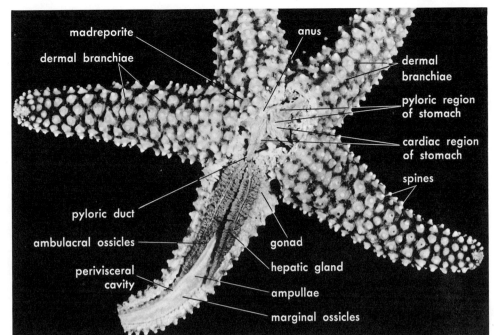

Fig. 11-14. *Pisaster gigantea,* internal anatomy with aboral region of disc removed to show disposition of parts.

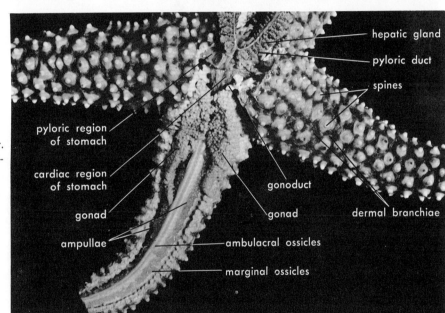

Fig. 11-15. *Pisaster gigantea,* internal anatomy. Hepatic gland displaced aborally to show disposition of underlying organs.

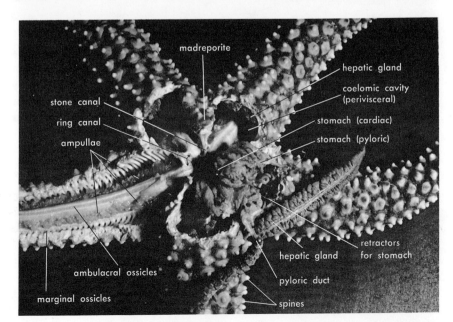

Fig. 11-16. *Pisaster gigantea,* internal anatomy. Gonads removed.

Fig. 11-17. *Cucumaria,* external anatomy.

► Which internal systems show evidence of pentamerism?

Work out the long digestive tract, including *tentacles; mouth;* short *esophagus;* enlarged *stomach;* long, looped *intestine;* muscular *cloaca* (attached by numerous mesenteries to the body wall); and *anus.* Extending forward into the *coelom* from the cloaca are 2 *respiratory trees* with many small branches. The cloaca

Fig. 11-19. *Parastichopus californicus,* internal anatomy.

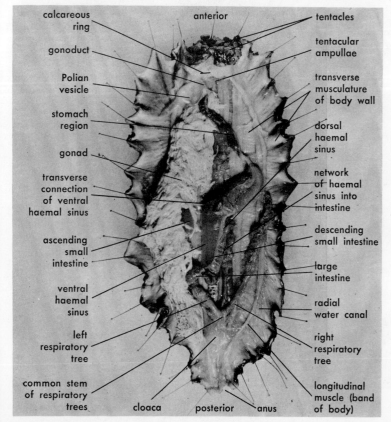

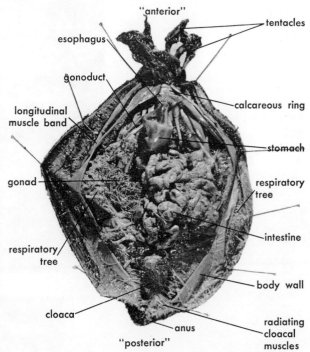

Fig. 11-18. *Thyone,* internal anatomy.

pumps water through these trees; hence it serves for egestion, excretion, and respiration.

b. The water-vascular system consists of a *madreporite* that usually opens directly from the coelom, a *ring canal* around the esophagus, and 5 longitudinal *radial canals* that connect along the body wall to the feet. The tube feet follow 5 longitudinal internal *muscle bands.* Blood vessels line the intestine. The brushlike *gonad* has fine tubules joining a *gonoduct* opening near the tentacles on the dorsal surface.

Make a pinned-out dissection of your specimen to show these organs.

Draw the internal anatomy of your specimen.

► What features adapt this class to its mud or sandy-bottom marine environment?

► What features make sea cucumbers a distinct class?

► What features ensure its inclusion within the Phylum ECHINODERMATA?

E. Class CRINOIDEA—sea lilies

1—Observations and external anatomy—

If specimens are available, study these strange sessile or crawling echinoderms (Fig. 11–12). Observe the ringed stalk and the 5 petallike arms, each divided and subdivided.

NOTES AND DRAWINGS

(Tear along line)

► To what type of habitat are these organisms best adapted?

The ringed stalk is attached to the substrate by rootlike *cirri,* and topped by a *calyx* from which the 5 *arms* emerge. Each arm divides into 2 branches and again into small branchlets or *pinnules.* A large *anal tube* also protrudes up from the calyx. Some crinoids lack the stalk and swim by arm movement.

Relatives of this class include numerous fossils in the Classes CARPOIDEA, CYSTOIDEA, BLASTOIDEA, and EDRIOASTEROIDEA, all of which are placed with CRINOIDEA in the Subphylum PELMATAZOA. These groups are combined on the basis of the skeleton, especially the calyx, as this is the fossilized portion that is most distinctive.

Echinoderms in which the mouth is *ventral* and which lack a stalk are in the Subphylum ELEUTHEROZOA, which includes all classes *except* crinoids and their related extinct classes.

I. INTRODUCTION

A prime lesson in introductory biology courses is that man learns about man by first studying other animals in order to adopt a truly comparative perspective. When we can view comparatively both our similarities and differences from other organisms, we will have come a long way along the path symbolized by Socrates' maxim, "Know thyself."

Many courses in zoology begin with the CHORDATA, the phylum that includes humans, so as to approach the unfamiliar from the familiar. But, unexpectedly, we often find that we are less familiar with ourselves and with our phylum than we had supposed. Hence, we follow here an evolutionary sequence from structurally simple to more complex animals. By the time the Phylum CHORDATA is reached, we know that we are getting close to home and wonder how we fit in the overall picture.

Many of us will be surprised to find, however, that the large, varied group of chordates includes certain wormlike or sac-shaped animals that aren't even vertebrates. It may even be disconcerting to learn that among true vertebrates, most are fishes—some 75 percent, in fact. All of this should serve to orient our thinking along strictly biological lines, free from preconceived human-oriented views.

CHAPTER 12

Phylum
Chordata

II. CLASSIFICATION

A. General

The Phylum CHORDATA should first be examined as one of several phyla in the Superphylum ENTEROCOELA[1] (outpocketing coelom) linked by basic embryological criteria. Just as annelids, mollusks, and arthropods are placed in the Superphylum SCHIZOCOELA, so echinoderms, chordates, and a few smaller phyla are combined in the ENTEROCOELA.

▶ What embryological traits distinguish ENTEROCOELA from SCHIZOCOELA?

▶ Define the Phylum CHORDATA. What unites it with ENTEROCOELA?

▶ Why is it considered a distinct phylum?

---

[1] This assemblage is also called the DEUTEROSTOMA (new mouth), a name derived from another embryological trait of this collection of phyla. Other terms, such as "Echinoderm-Chordate line," also symbolize the same general group.

B. *Related Phyla*

One of the least known of the several phyla linked with chordates in the **ENTEROCOELA** is the POGONOPHORA, a recently discovered phylum of wormlike creatures with an appearance strikingly similar to the younger stages of some chordates. The other small but distinct phyla united in this assemblage have also been placed there on embryological grounds. A good example is the Phylum CHAETOGNATHA, the arrow worms (*Sagitta*)—active, common, torpedo-shaped predators of marine plankton. The wormlike Phylum PHORONIDA is also thought to be in the enterocoel complex, although this position is still conjectural. Major phyla in this group are: ECHINODERMATA, HEMICHORDATA (included as a CHORDATA subphylum by some authors), and CHORDATA. HEMICHORDATA, as the name "half chordates" implies, do not possess all of the accepted chordate characteristics. They appear to lie somewhere between echinoderms and chordates. Such chordate features as paired pharyngeal gill slits and a notochord are found in the hemichordates, although even the latter structure in these insignificant but phylogenetically important worms is in dispute. At the same time, their larval form (*tornaria*) is so close to some echinoderm larvae that the two have often been confused, even by experts. This tie-up of larval characters with what are considered to be basic chordate features has brought about the strange alliance of starfish and frogs, separated by acorn worms, such as *Balanoglossus* of the Phylum HEMICHORDATA.

C. Phylum CHORDATA

The true chordates consist of the following several subphyla.

1—Subphylum TUNICATA (or UROCHORDATA), **the tunicates or sea squirts.**—These are highly modified, sessile, filter-feeding animals with motile larvae. The larval chordate characteristics (notochord, dorsal hollow nerve cord, pharyngeal gill slits) are lost during metamorphosis into adults.

▶ Can you account for a possibly adaptive loss of chordate features in sessile adults of this group?

2—Subphylum CEPHALOCHORDATA, **lancelets or Amphioxus**—These small, fishlike, mud- or sand-dwelling filter feeders are important animals from a theoretical standpoint. They represent an evolutionary stage in which chordate characteristics (notochord, dorsal hollow nerve cord, gill slits) are well developed, but typical vertebrate characteristics are absent. No course in zoology is complete without a look at diagrams or slides of this shy little creature. Its two-inch long, fishlike shape, chordate characteristics, and simplified enterocoelous (deuterostome) embryological pattern mark Amphioxus as a primitive chordate of great interest, a prototype of what might have been an ancestral vertebrate. Except for annelidlike ciliated nephridia, the lancelet's organ systems are strikingly similar to those of true vertebrates or other simple chordates.

The above groups are combined in a general grouping, the PROTOCHORDATES or ACRANIATA (without heads), in contrast to higher chordates in the Subphylum CRANIATA or VERTEBRATA.

3—Subphylum VERTEBRATA, **higher chordates**—We are now dealing with vertebrates or higher chordates—including ourselves. Here is where we can say animals are truly animals in the layman's sense.

The Subphylum VERTEBRATA is defined as craniate chordates with visceral arches, vertebrae, and a brain. It, in turn, is divided into several classes of fishes, and the classes of amphibians, reptiles, birds, and mammals. The old term for fishes, PISCES, is now used as a superclass designation to include 4 distinct classes. The other superclass, TETRAPODA, includes all 4-legged (or originally 4-legged) vertebrates.

a. Superclass PISCES.

1. Class AGNATHA—jawless fishes, the most primitive true vertebrates, lack limbs and jaws. The first records of true vertebrates from early fossil deposits show they were abundant members of the sea-bottom fauna some 400 or more million years ago. Fossil AGNATHA are characterized by heavy bony armor and probably a mud-sucking, filtering mode of feeding. Their highly specialized descendants, the lampreys and hagfishes, are still alive—in fact, they are far too abundant in the Great Lakes where lampreys have nearly destroyed the entire fishing industry. Survival of modern remnants of this ancient class is probably related to their specially adapted rasping and bloodsucking mouthparts, which enable them to feed on other fish. This parasitic way of life frees the lamprey from competition with later evolved forms. Larval lampreys, *Ammocoetes*, very well illustrate their primitive vertebrate form.

2. Class **PLACODERMI**—ancient armored fishes, now entirely extinct. The class is marked by development of a primitive type of jaw suspension that enabled **PLACODERMI** to replace the more primitive jawless fishes, although they themselves died out in competition with still more efficient forms.

3. Class **CHONDRICHTHYES**—cartilaginous fishes: sharks, rays, skates, and chimaeras. It is doubtful whether these fishes preceded true bony fishes in evolution, as often is assumed. In fact, fossil evidence opposes this view, since earliest remains of modern fishes are actually bony fishes (Class **OSTEICHTHYES**). Sharks and other cartilaginous fishes probably evolved from bony fishes rather than the reverse, or perhaps the two groups evolved in parallel fashion from placoderm ancestors.

The all-cartilaginous skeleton therefore appears to be a comparatively recent adaptation (though still several hundred million years old). Another important adaptation in the group is a capacity to retain *urea* in blood and tissues, thus raising internal osmotic pressure to a point nearly equal to that of the salt water environment.

▶ Why is this such a valuable adaptation?

Sharks, as typical fish, as fearsome predators, or as modern derivatives of an ancient lineage, are always interesting. We will study a common offshore form, the dog shark or spiny dogfish, *Squalus acanthias.*

4. Class **OSTEICHTHYES**—bony or higher fishes. Enormously varied and numerous, **OSTEICHTHYES** represent, as noted earlier, some 75 percent of described vertebrate species including nearly all fresh-water fishes and the preponderance of marine species. Most members of the class, in turn, belong to the Teleost group, an assemblage of some 29 orders of so-called higher bony fishes.

The example we shall study is the familiar yellow perch, *Perca flavescens.*

One subclass of **OSTEICHTHYES** of special importance to students of evolution is **CHOANICHTHYES**, fish with nostrils connected to the mouth cavity and with paired fleshy or limblike fins. These are presumed precursors of the **TETRAPODA**, 4-legged, land-dwelling animals. Familiar **CHOANICHTHYES** include the lungfish and the remarkable "living fossil" *Latimeria,* discovered a few years ago off the coasts of South Africa and Madagascar. Until recently, this fish was presumed to have been totally extinct for over 75 million years. It's never too late to find something new.

▶ What even more ancient invertebrate "living fossil" can you name?

b. Superclass **TETRAPODA.**

1. Class **AMPHIBIA**—salamanders, frogs, toads, and caecilians (or **APODA**—tropical, limbless amphibians)—are the first tetrapoda or land-dwelling, limbed vertebrates. Amphi, meaning "both," implies life both in water and on land.

Amphibians require abundant moisture, as their soft skin is not protected against water loss. Nearly all amphibians depend on water for egg laying and early development, though some frogs breed in damp moss instead of water. Certain toads are remarkably resistant to drying, whereas others, such as the Mexican axolotyl and a few frog species, never leave the water. In general, we think of amphibians as transitional creatures, not perfectly adapted to water or to land but somewhat adapted to both, the ancestors of purely terrestrial animals.

In a later section we will study the anatomy of the familiar leopard or grass frog, *Rana pipiens,* as a typical member of this class. Although salamanders are more truly "typical" amphibians, they are less easily obtained than are frogs.

2. Class **REPTILIA**—snakes, lizards, turtles crocodiles, and alligators, along with numerous extinct forms (many different groups are linked by the common name "dinosaur")—are reptiles. They represent the completed transition from water to land, owing principally to adaptations that reduce water loss, including dry scaly skin; efficient encased (internal) lungs for aerial respiration (as opposed to the external gills or skin of amphibia); internal fertilization; and eggs protected from desiccation by a relatively impervious, often limy shell and by embryonic membranes enclosing the developing embryo in an aquatic environment. A free larval stage is lacking; the egg, usually placed in a warm, sheltered spot, provides protection and nourishment (yolk) for prolonged embryonic development. The young thus pass through the fragile early stages of life without excessive hazard from violent temperature and humidity changes characteristic of the land environment. They can then emerge essentially as young adults. Internal improvements probably accompanying these changes were the bellows method of breathing and improved systems of blood circulation and heart structure. More efficient limbs and superior muscular coordination are also related to survival in an air medium where rapid, controlled movements are highly advantageous. The variety of reptilian adaptations is clearly evident when we compare turtles, snakes, lizards, and crocodiles and perhaps throw in a 25-ton *Brontosaurus,* a giant marine "sea serpent" like a mosasaur, or the 25-foot flying *Pteranodon* for ample good measure.

3. Class AVES—birds. Structurally, birds are feathered, beaked, flying, reptilelike animals with physiological adaptations for temperature control. The evolutionary transition from reptiles to birds was gradual, marked by a number of intermediate stages. Evidence for these changes comes from fossil, embryological, and anatomical studies. Structural and physiological adaptations of modern birds, highly specialized for aerial life, make them among the most successful, efficient, and complex living things.

4. Class MAMMALIA—warm-blooded, fur-bearing tetrapods with mammary glands—in other words, us. Mammals, a very early offshoot from reptilian ancestors, stemmed not from specialized but from very primitive reptile stock at about the time the earliest reptiles were themselves evolving. Temperature-regulating mechanisms gradually evolved, with hair as the chief insulator. Probably warm-bloodedness (homeothermy) developed in mammals about the same time it independently appeared in birds. The story of mammal evolution is really one of progressively greater degrees of protection from, or control over, the environment. Homeothermy provides freedom from rapid fluctuations in internal temperature. A greater constancy of the internal environment results. Viviparity (young born alive) and lactation allow longer incubation and greater protection of embryos and young over longer periods. Unusually complex adaptive *behavior* patterns and *parental training* are associated with these longer periods of contact between parent and offspring and the high degree of integration in the central nervous system (CNS) that developed. Beyond this, one can envisage gradual evolution of social and learned patterns of behavior. Among primates at least, this resulted in an extraordinary flowering of mental development and an extreme level of environmental control, as demonstrated by man.

Structurally, mammals represent a peak of efficiency in nerve-muscle coordination and respon-

siveness, ultimately resulting in the high order of intelligence and adaptability that characterize the class. Structural specialization correlated with different habitats and food habits is particularly marked in various patterns of tooth specialization. In fact, differences between types of teeth and changes in jaw and middle-ear formation are primary structural criteria for separating mammals from reptiles. Major organ systems also reflect this increased degree of control and coordination with outward structural improvements.

We will study one of the most abundant and successful members of the class, the Norway rat, *Rattus norvegicus* (Chapter 14). Wily, prolific, and omnivorous, this rat and its close relative *Rattus rattus* are found almost wherever man is, and sometimes in far greater numbers. The mantle of successor to man as a dominant mammal may yet fall on these adaptable and widespread members of the largest order of mammals—the RODENTIA.

III. LABORATORY INSTRUCTIONS

A. Subphylum CEPHALOCHORDATA—**Amphioxus** (scientifically named *Branchiostoma*)

1—Observations—This animal lives in sandy offshore and intertidal areas where it feeds on small organisms filtered through its pharyngeal gill basket. Such a function implies that the most primitive chordate gills were used for feeding rather than for respiration, a supposition apparently confirmed by fossil evidence of earliest vertebrates.

Amphioxus, which lacks vertebrae or bony rings around the notochord, is not a vertebrate. However, it does possess the chief chordate characteristics in almost diagrammatic clarity.

2—Anatomy—Stained whole mount specimens or plastic embedded specimens are excellent for studying both external and internal structures (Fig. 12–1).

Orient your specimen—the blunt end is anterior, the dorsal surface is more pointed than the flattened ventral surface. Find the

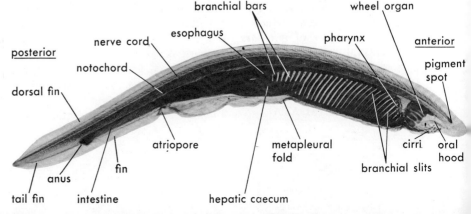

Fig. 12-1. Amphioxus, whole mount, lateral view. (Copyright by General Biological Supply House, Inc., Chicago.)

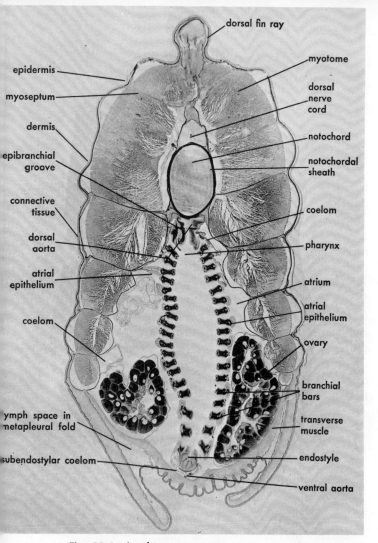

Fig. 12-2. Amphioxus, transverse section through pharyngeal region, female.

oral hood enclosing the mouth and an upper *vestibule* equipped with stiff *cirri,* which the animal uses as strainers for food selection. A single posterior *fin* passes from a median opening, the *atriopore,* and extends to the tail and around to the dorsal surface, where it forms the *caudal fin* and then the *dorsal fin.* The *anus* is on the midventral line anterior to the tail.

Observe the V-shaped muscle segments, *myotomes,* with *myosepta* (connective tissue partitions) between them.

▶ **Can Amphioxus properly be called a seg-mented animal?**

Trace out the digestive tract. Locate the oral hood and cirri, and the wheel organ (fingerlike projections at the posterior inner surface of the hood). The mouth leads directly into the *pharynx,* which is a complex food-sifting chamber of *gill bars* (or *branchial bars*) and, alternately, *gill slits.* The bars, skeletally supported to form a feeding gill basket, are markedly similar to those in *Balanoglossus,* the most primitive protochordate (Phylum HEMICHORDATA).

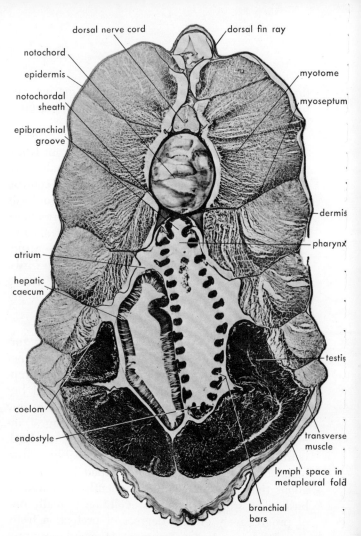

Fig. 12-3. Amphioxus, transverse section through pharyngeal region, male.

The *atrium* surrounding the gill basket receives water passing from the pharynx through the gill slits, and then out the atrio-pore.

The digestive tract posterior to the pharynx continues as a short *esophagus* and wider *stomach* (midgut). The *liver* (or *hepatic caecum*) is an outgrowth from the midgut, which then narrows into the *intestine* (hind-gut) and terminates in the anus.

Find the notochord dorsal to the di-gestive tract.

▶ **How far anteriorly does the notochord run?**

Locate the *neural tube* above the notochord; it is marked by a row of black spots, which are very simple eyes consisting of 1 ganglion and 1 pigment cell. Notice the extremely small anterior vesicle forming the brain.

Draw your specimen and identify as many structures as you can.

3—Histology (cross section)—Study a stained Amphioxus cross section taken through the pharynx (Figs. 12–2 and 12–3) or the intes-tine (Fig. 12–4). Under low power, you should be able to identify: *epidermis, dorsal fin* with its supporting *fin ray, metapleural* folds (or *ventrolateral* folds), *myotomes* (filling much of the dorsal and lateral spaces), *neural tube, atrium, pharynx, gill bars, gill slits, liver, gonads* (if present, ovary cells have large nuclei, testes appear striated or streaked), and *nephridia* (portions are attached to outer surface of dorsal gill bars).

  Draw what you can identify in this section.

  ▶ Review evidence for relationships between hemichordates, tunicates, and primitive vertebrates. Consider embryological and structural similarities, and general organization of digestive, nervous, circulatory, and excretory systems.

  ▶ Does any evidence oppose this conclusion of a phyletic relationship?

  ▶ Which view seems stronger? Why?

B. Subphylum VERTEBRATA, **Class** AGNATHA, **Order** CYCLOSTOMATA—lampreys and hagfishes

1—Adult lamprey

a. *External anatomy.*

  1. We begin our survey of true vertebrates by examining the adult and the Ammocoetes larva of these most simple and presumably most primitive living vertebrates, which are contemporary representatives of the AGNATHA—the most ancient class of fishes.

  ▶ Define the term AGNATHA.

  ▶ Why are these fishes considered primitive?

  ▶ What structures or characteristics enabled the cyclostomes to survive for so long?

  Observe a demonstration specimen of an adult lamprey. Find the *dorsal* fins and *caudal fin* with *fin rays.* Note the absence of paired ventral fins.

  2. Study the head. Note absence of a lower jaw and presence of a toothed funnel and toothed tongue (an effective sucking and rasping device). The lamprey attaches by the suction funnel, then rasps away the host's flesh with the toothed tongue.

  Note, too, the single dorsal opening to the olfactory sac instead of paired nasal openings. This is another primitive characteristic typical of living and fossil agnathids.

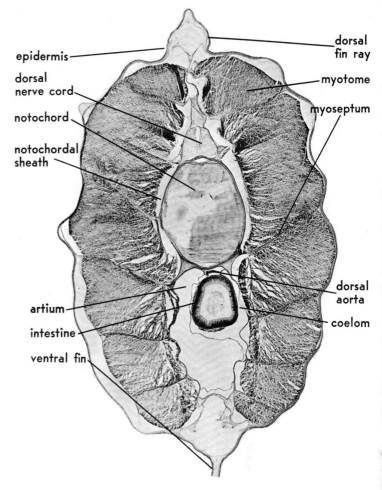

Fig. 12-4. Amphioxus, tranverse section through intestinal region.

  ▶ How many gill slits are there behind each eye?

  3. The musculature, like that of Amphioxus, is divided into myotomes (segments) with myosepta between them. A cloacal pit lies on the midventral line in front of the trunk-tail juncture. Inside it are an *anus* and posteriorly a *urogenital papilla.*

b. *Sagittal section (anterior end).* If a plastic-embedded or demonstration section of the preserved animal is available, study it for structural details of feeding and respiratory apparatus.

  Find the *buccal funnel, teeth,* and *tongue.* Observe the large muscles that control the rasping tongue. Follow the buccal cavity to the *esophagus* (upper, smaller tube) and *pharynx* (lower, larger tube), which opens externally through 7 gill clefts or slits. These slits open into larger gill pouches that in turn connect to external slits.

Fig. 12-5. Ammocoetes, whole mount, lateral view.

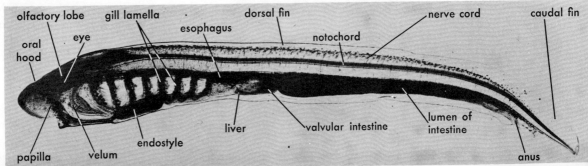

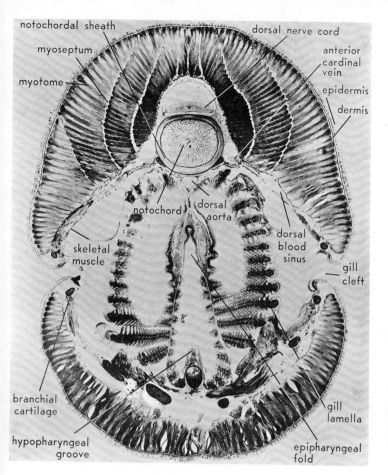

Fig. 12-6. Ammocoetes, transverse section through pharyngeal region.

▶ How does the lamprey respire? Trace the path of the water current produced.

▶ Trace the passage of food.

Next, find the *notochord,* for which the phylum is named. In lampreys, this structure is still an essential supporting element, as the vertebrae are only small arches straddling the neural tube. A cartilaginous skull and complex gill basket form the rest of the skeletal system.

The *nervous system* consists of a dorsal hollow nerve cord over the notochord and an anterior enlargement, the brain (just above the anterior edge of the notochord).

2—Ammocoetes larva (Figs. 12–5 to 12–8)

a. *Introduction.* This peculiar larval form is sufficiently distinct to have once been named *Ammocoetes,* as it was originally thought to be a separate genus of adult fish. Actually it is a long-lived cyclostome *larva* that burrows in stream beds and filters up small food particles or organisms much as Amphioxus does. Of considerably more evolutionary interest than the adult, this larva illustrates many primitive vertebrate characteristics that are later masked by specialized adult cyclostome characteristics.

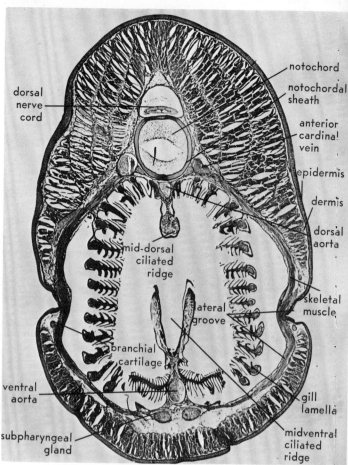

Fig. 12-7. Ammocoetes, transverse section through pharyngeal region but posterior to area shown in Fig. 12-6.

▶ Why are larval forms more often of phylogenetic significance than are adult structures?

▶ Name at least 3 other examples in which larvae and not their adult forms are of primary importance for determining phylogeny.

b. *Anatomy.* Study a *whole mount* preparation (Fig. 12-5) and observe how similar Ammocoetes is to Amphioxus.

▶ What does this similarity imply?

Notice the oral hood with papillae that serve as food strainers; then observe the gill region with the brain above it. The brain is divided (front to rear) into *olfactory bulb* and *olfactory lobe* (parts of the *telencephalon*). The *eyes,* the *infundibulum* below the olfactory lobe (which equals the posterior lobe of the *pituitary*), and the *pineal body* above the olfactory lobe are parts of the *diencephalon.* The midbrain (*mesencephalon*) consists largely of the *optic lobes.* The hindbrain, *rhombencephalon,* the largest division, consists mostly of the *medulla oblongata,* contact center for automatic reactions of the body. From the medulla, the *spinal cord* extends posteriorly above the supporting notochord.

These parts of the CNS are characteristic of all vertebrates, but you will find a remarkable change anteriorly in other vertebrate classes. *Keep the basic divisions in mind, however,* and try to develop a critical comparative viewpoint to help you relate successive evolutionary stages.

Compare the remaining organs with the adult structure and identify as many as you can. Notice the pharynx with its gill pouches, and gill lamellae in the pouch walls.

c. *Histology*—cross section of Ammocoetes (Figs. 12-6 to 12-8).

1. *Pharynx* (Figs. 12-6 and 12-7). This is a favorite cross section for viewing parts of a primitive vertebrate. Locate the heavy *epidermis* or outer surface, then the connective tissue and muscle blocks (*myotomes*), which are especially thick on the dorsal surface.

Then find the *neural canal,* containing the rather flattened *spinal cord* and below it the *notochord* flanked by *cardinal veins.* Below this is the *dorsal aorta.* Most of the section consists of the pharyngeal region with gill lamellae on the pharynx walls.

2. *Trunk* (Fig. 12-8). This section should show the *dorsal* and *ventral fin fold, neural canal* and *spinal cord, notochord, dorsal aorta, cardinal vein,* and *myotomes* enclosing the body cavity (*coelom*). Depending on the section cut, you will also be able to locate the *esophagus* and *pronephric* (excretory) *tubules* and the *heart,* or in a more posterior section the *liver* and *intestine,* and possibly the *mesonephric tubules.*

▶ What basic vertebrate characters can be seen in Ammocoetes larvae?

▶ What changes occur in these larvae at metamorphosis?

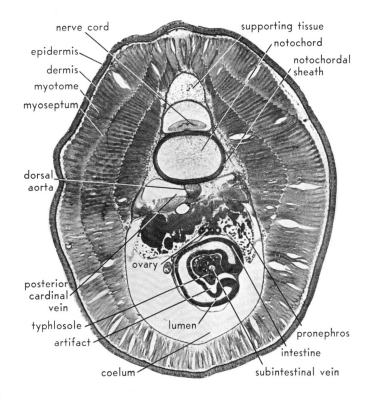

Fig. 12-8. Ammocoetes, transverse section through intestinal region.

C. Class CHONDRICHTHYES—cartilaginous fishes, sharks, and rays: *Squalus*

1—Introduction—The Class CHONDRICHTHYES, typified by the spiny dogfish, *Squalus acanthias* or *S. suckleyi,* includes skates, rays, and the relatively uncommon chimaeras or ratfish. These present-day fish are characterized by a cartilaginous skeleton and external gill slits.

The dogfish is a relatively simple vertebrate and a most useful anatomical reference. It is often studied as a generalized vertebrate because it shows the essential characteristics of the subphylum with a minimum

Fig. 12-9. Shark, external anatomy. (Photograph courtesy of Mr. Ted Hobson.)

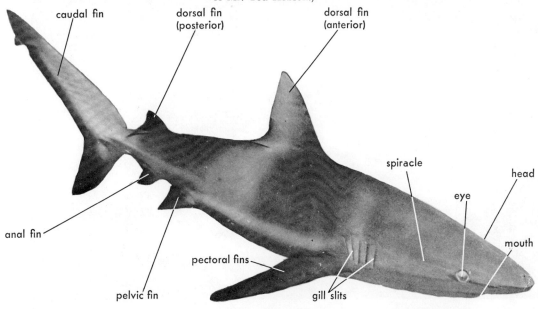

of specialized structures. A good knowledge of dogfish anatomy will serve as a basis for your introduction to all remaining vertebrate classes.

2—External anatomy (Fig. 12–9)—Examine both the dorsal and the ventral aspects of the entire animal—*head, trunk,* and *tail*. Note the streamlined shape, the fins, and the rough skin covered by scales or tiny, toothlike *dermal denticles*. These are small *placoid scales,* each of which has a projecting spine whose microscopic dentine structure is the same as that of vertebrate teeth.

Along the sides of the body is a whitish *lateral line*. This covers a sensory canal that enables the fish to feel water vibrations, equivalent to our sense of hearing. The muscle segments are also readily apparent.

▶ Can you see any resemblance between these and myotomes of Amphioxus?

Find the following head structures: *rostrum* (anterior extremity), *mouth, jaws,* and *teeth*.

▶ How are the teeth arranged?

There was once a shark—now fortunately extinct—with a 7-foot mouth gape and a sparkling array of 6-inch, triangular, slashing teeth! The structural format, however, was little different from that of your 18-inch dogfish.

Next, find the sense organs—*olfactory, visual,* and *auditory*. The paired *nostrils* are small sacs through which water circulates. The *eyes,* unblinking as in all fish, lack a movable eyelid.

▶ Why are eyelids useful chiefly to terrestrial animals?

▶ Can you find an *external ear opening*?

▶ Where is the *inner ear* and what is its function?

Next, find the *spiracle* and behind it 5 elongated *gill slits* through which respired water exits.

Identify the 2 types of fins—the *unpaired median fins* and the *paired lateral fins*. Locate the *anterior* and *posterior dorsal,* and the *caudal, pectoral,* and *pelvic* fins.

▶ Which fins are homologous to our limbs?

The heterocercal tail, asymmetrical with an extended dorsal portion, is characteristic of all sharks. It is developed to a remarkable degree in the thresher shark, where its enormously elongate lobe is used to panic and round up schools of fish.

The sex of a shark is shown by its pelvic fin. That of the male is pointed backward and modified into a *clasper* with rolled edges for sperm transfer.

▶ Hence, what type of fertilization is found in this group of sharks (in fact, in all CHONDRICHTHYES)?

Locate the *cloaca,* which is the terminus of the digestive, excretory, and genital systems.

▶ Review the above-mentioned structures and draw them on an outline of the *lateral* aspect of the dogfish.

3—Internal anatomy

a. *Digestive system* (Figs. 12-10 and 12-11). Pin your specimen out in a dissecting tray, ventral side up. Use long pins through the pectoral fin cartilages to hold it down firmly. Make a midventral incision up to the pectoral girdle, then back to

Fig. 12-10. *Squalus acanthias,* internal anatomy.

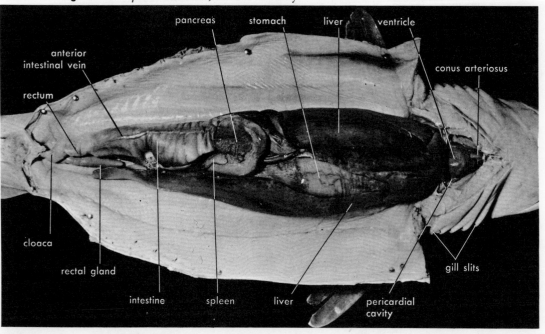

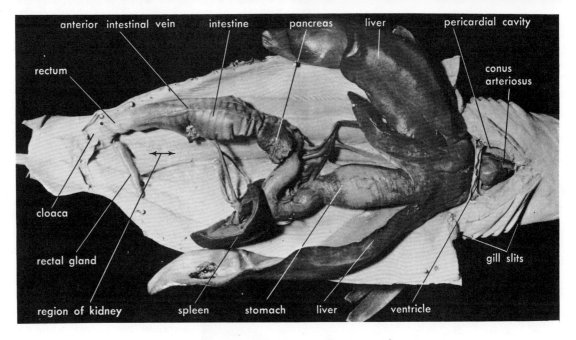

anterior intestinal vein · intestine · pancreas · liver · pericardial cavity

rectum

conus arteriosus

cloaca

rectal gland

gill slits

region of kidney · spleen · stomach · liver · ventricle

Fig. 12-11. *Squalus acanthias,* internal anatomy.

and through the pelvic girdle. Use a sharp scalpel or scissors, but be careful not to cut deeply below the skin or into the underlying muscle wall. Expose the viscera by holding back and cutting away the lateral flaps of belly skin. Pin back the pelvic fins to stretch open the cloaca. Identify: *liver, stomach (cardiac* and *pyloric* region), *spleen, pancreas, intestine, spiral valves, rectum, cloaca, urogenital papilla, testis* (or *ovary*). Look under the medial lobe of the liver for the *gall bladder* and *bile duct* (running along the *hepatic portal vein*).

Draw and identify the exposed organs, showing their normal relationships (Fig. 12-10).

Display the viscera (Fig. 12-11) by pinning back the liver lobes and by pulling stomach and spleen to one side. Then make a deep incision up the *intestine* to expose the *spiral valves* that greatly enlarge the internal surface area of this structure.

▶ What is the advantage of increase in intestinal surface?

b. *Circulatory system.*

1. The chief blood vessels serving the alimentary canal lie dorsal to it. They have to be exposed by careful dissection from the supporting mesentery. This work, which can be undertaken as a special project or by classroom demonstration, should include exposure of the *hepatic portal vein, intraintestinal, gastrointestinal,* and *posterior splenic veins.* Arteries in this area include the *hepatic, coeliac, gastric, anterior mesenteric,* and *lienogastric.*

2. A more rewarding and equally demanding dissection is that of the *ventral aorta* and *afferent*

branchial arteries. These, lying in the region of the floor of the mouth, represent the primitive pattern of anterior arterial circulation that has become greatly modified in terrestrial vertebrates. In gill-breathing aquatic vertebrates, arterial arches or branches from the aorta carry blood from the heart into *afferent* (towards) branches that lead to a capillary bed in each of the 5 gills where respiratory exchange occurs. The freshly oxygenated blood then passes from the capillaries into *efferent* (away from) branches that pass dorsally into the *dorsal aorta* and into the systemic circulation.

Dissection procedure

i. Cut through the cartilage of the pectoral girdle. Locate the *pericardial cavity.*

ii. Remove the skin from the ventral surface between the pectoral girdle and lower jaw.

iii. Cut through the superficial branchial muscles lying under the skin, pull to either side, and remove. The first *afferent branchial* artery can be seen through remaining muscle layers.

iv. Loosen the 2 anteroposterior muscles between lower jaw and heart (*coraco-mandibular* and *coraco-hyal muscles*). Cut these muscles near the heart, pull the loose ends forward, and cut them off as close to the jaw as possible.

v. Other branchial arteries are now visible. Carefully cut away the central tissue block from which various coraco muscles originate (*coraco-mandibular, coraco-hyal,* and 5 pairs of *coraco-branchials*). This will expose the coraco-branchials between the *ventral aorta* in the midline and the 5 arching *afferent branchial* arteries. Cut these muscles off as short as possible and clean away all interfering

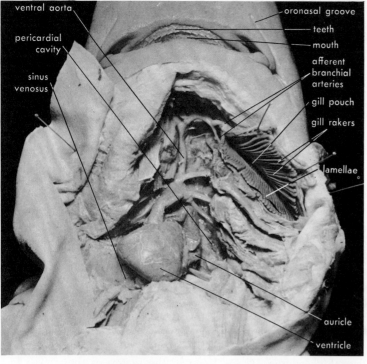

Fig. 12-12. *Squalus acanthias,* heart, afferent branchial arteries, and gill clefts.

tissues to expose the entire length of afferent branchials on at least one side.

vi. Open a gill pouch (Fig. 12-12) by cutting from the first gill slit ventrally to a point between afferents 1 and 2 (to V-shaped point of their branching from the end of the ventral aorta).

vii. Cut off the exposed gill lamellae in order to trace out the first afferent branchial artery. Re-

Fig. 12-13. *Squalus acanthias,* central nervous system, dorsal view.

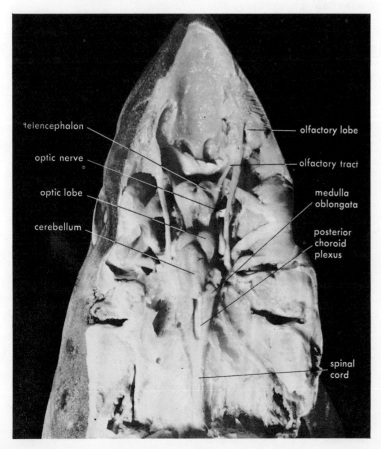

move the *gill rakers,* which arise posterior to the branchial artery. Similarly, remove the lamellae and rakers from the other gills along the same side.

viii. Complete your dissection of the entire afferent branchial system on one side and *draw* the exposed vessels. This dissection, when done with proper care, is an excellent introduction to techniques for studying vertebrate anatomy.

Additional special dissections may be attempted on afferent branchial arteries, systemic circulation, heart, inner ear, and detailed morphology of the eyes.

c. Nervous system.

1. The entire nervous system will not be exposed, but a worthwhile dissection can be made of the *brain* (Fig. 12-13), *brain stem,* and *spinal cord,* which together comprise the *central nervous system* (CNS).

Dissection procedure

i. Cut away the skin and overlying muscles from the area between and anterior to the eyes. Pull these tissues posteriorly towards the base of the head.

ii. Carefully shave away cartilage overlying the *chondrocranium,* which serves as a skull or braincase. Gradually enlarge the exposed area, keeping the scalpel horizontal so as not to damage the brain.

iii. Expose and identify the *olfactory lobes* and *telencephalon,* the *optic lobes, cerebellum, posterior choroid plexus, medulla oblongata,* and *spinal cord.*

Special dissections

i. Remove an eye and cut away the lateral facial margin of the chondrocranium in order to trace out roots of the 10 *cranial nerves.* This will require careful technique and foreknowledge of the anatomy to be encountered.

ii. Cut through the spinal cord and each cranial nerve, and lift out the brain. Identify each nerve root and the major lobes of the brain.

iii. Finally, make several sagittal cuts through the entire brain and identify the 4 *ventricles.*

▶ With what parts of the brain are the ventricles associated?

D. Class OSTEICHTHYES—bony fishes, *Perca flavescens*

1—Introduction—This class includes all bony fishes, the most varied and numerous ver-

Fig. 12-14. The perch, *Perca*, external anatomy.

tebrates. The largest group, the teleosts, include all so-called modern forms—some 29 orders of higher bony fishes. Ganoid fishes, the bowfin *Amia,* and gars are combined with teleosts to form one subclass. A second subclass contains the primitive bony fishes, the Bichir or *Polypterus,* sturgeons, and spoonbills. Both groups are combined into the Class OSTEICHTHYES by such features as a bony skeleton; cycloid, ctenoid, or ganoid scales; paired fins supported by fin rays; first gill slit not reduced to form a spiracle (as in sharks).

Our example of this class comes from the Order PERCOMORPHI, typified by the perch. These fishes all have both spiny and soft ray supports in their dorsal anal fins. They include some 20 families containing many of the best-known sport and food fishes, such as fresh-water bass and sunfish (Family Centrarchidae), fresh-water perch (Family Percidae), Cichlidae of South America and Africa, Embiotocidae or surf perches, mackerels (Scombridae), and tuna, bonito, yellow fin, and others, of the Family Thunnidae.

Our example of OSTEICHTHYES, *Perca flavescens,* the yellow perch, can be considered an adequately typical example of the higher bony fish.

2—External anatomy (Fig. 12-14)

a. Observe the laterally compressed yet gracefully streamlined shape with no neck and little flexibility along the body (nearly all propulsion is from the tail). Feel and observe the trunk and tail scales and their arrangement. Scrape off a few scales and observe them microscopically. They are *ctenoid* scales—thought to be the most advanced of the various fish scale types—in which bony elements are reduced, thus providing a protective but still flexible outer covering. Observe the grooved concentric ridges with small teeth covering the exposed part of each scale (from which the name *ctenoid* is derived).

The large flattened bones of the skull are thought to be derived from sunken enlarged scales of some ancient ancestor, perhaps an agnathid, and hence are known as *dermal bones* (a term also related to the mode of embryonic origin of these bones).

Observe the lateral line, a row of dash-shaped pits running along the side of the animal.

Various authorities consider the function of the lateral line to be sensitivity to coarser vibrations, to water pressure, to body equilibrium, or to smell. What we know about animals is still only a small fraction of what remains to be learned.

b. Next, notice the position and kinds of fins—2 unpaired *dorsal fins* with *spiny rays* supporting the anterior fin, and *soft rays* supporting the posterior fin. The caudal fin is called *homeocercal* because of its symmetry (compare with the shark's *heterocercal* tail). The paired lateral fins are somewhat differently located than in the shark—the pectorals are behind the *operculum* (the shield covering the gills), the rather small *pelvic fins* have migrated forward nearly to the

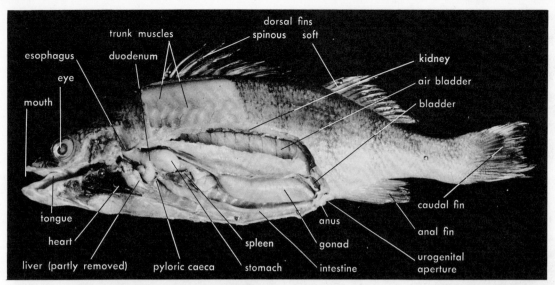

Fig. 12-15. Perch, internal anatomy, lateral view.

level of and ventral to the pectorals. In front of the anal or ventral fin is a large *anus*—not a cloaca as in the shark, since the intestinal and urogenital openings are separate.

c. Cut away the bony *operculum* from one side to expose a *gill chamber* and its 4 *gills*. Remove an individual gill to study its structure. The hard bony support is the *gill arch*, with posteriorly directed *gill filaments* (*containing which blood vessels?*). The hard anterior fingerlike projections,

Fig. 12-16. Perch anatomy, central nervous system, dorsal view.

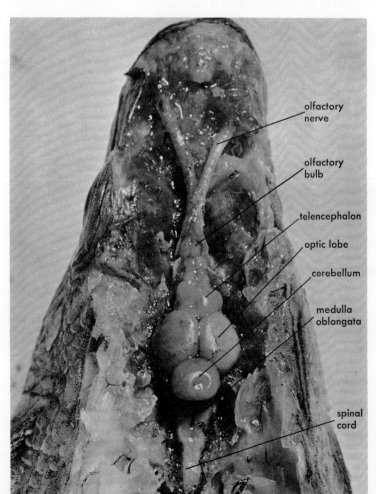

olfactory nerve

olfactory bulb

telencephalon

optic lobe

cerebellum

medulla oblongata

spinal cord

the *gill rakers*, prevent coarse material or food from passing through the gill slits. Describe the function of gill filaments.

3—Internal anatomy (Fig. 12-15).

a. The viscera of the perch, as in many teleosts, are compressed (as is the body) and shoved far forward. Expose these organs by a filletlike lateral cut to remove the wall from one side of the body. Start at the anus, cut dorsally, then toward the gills, and remove this section of body wall. Continue to cut and remove portions of flesh ventral to the gills in order to expose the heart.

b. Within the *coelom* (*abdominal* or *visceral cavity*) a large reddish *liver* is first seen. Move it aside and find a short *esophagus* posterior to the pharynx. The fingerlike continuation of the esophagus is the *stomach*. On its anterior portion are 3 stubby *pyloric caeca* directed posteriorly. Anterior to the caeca is the *duodenum*, in which digestion occurs. The coiled, posterior *ileum* (*small intestine*) is a region for absorption of digested food particles. Posteriorly, the alimentary canal enlarges to form the *large intestine*, which terminates in the *anus*.

The dorsal portion of the body cavity is filled largely with a thin-walled, extremely tough, whitish *swim bladder*. Dorsal to this, along the wall of the coelom, is the black *kidney*. Posterior portions of the body cavity are often filled with gonadal tissue, usually considerably smaller in the male than in the female.

c. The pericardial cavity, anteriorly below the gills, contains the 2-chambered *heart*. Observe the thin-walled posterior *auricle*. Anterior and ventral to it is the thick-walled *ventricle*, the true muscular pump. The portion of the heart projecting anteriorly is the *bulbus arteriosus*.

126

NOTES AND DRAWINGS

(Tear along line)

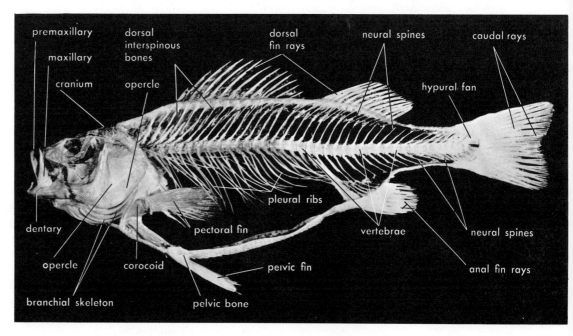

Fig. 12-17. Perch, skeletal system.

that entering posteriorly is the *sinus venosus*.

► Where is the *ventral aorta* found? The *dorsal aorta*?

► How is distribution of muscle mass related to type of swimming action?

► Can you determine the food of the perch? (Check stomach contents.)

► What else can you say about the habits of perch from the appearance of teeth, eyes, the form and length of gut, the body shape, and musculature?

4—Special projects

a. *Central nervous system.* Following the procedures used with the dogfish, expose the brain and anterior portion of the spinal cord (Fig. 12-16). Identify as many lobes and cranial nerves as possible by comparison with your previous CNS dissection.

Draw and label the exposed brain in *lateral view.*

b. *Bony skeleton* (Fig. 12-17). Using your own freshly caught specimen, prepare a demonstration preparation of an intact skeleton by one of the following methods (or another of your own choosing):

i. Burying specimen or placing it in reach of ants or flesh beetles (dermestids).

ii. Tying specimen to a fixed point on a beach where beach hoppers are abundant.

These biological methods of cleaning will produce beautiful skeleton specimens in a remarkably short time (from 6 to 24 hours).

Prepare a finished, neatly dried, and properly labeled skeletal specimen wired to a board.

CHAPTER 13

Class

Amphibia

I. INTRODUCTION

Meet *Rana pipiens*, the leopard or grass frog, Mr. Vertebrate himself. Hardly a student anywhere gets through a course in biology or zoology without examining one. As with many other representative animals, the adjective "typical" is rather like Mark Twain's explanation of the report of his death—slightly exaggerated. Perhaps the word should not be used at all. One animal is usually just as typical of the group to which it belongs as any other. Certainly every surviving animal is "specialized" in the sense that it is adapted to its environment. We commonly select representative animals by their availability. The leopard frog, for example, is one of the commonest vertebrates in the temperate zones of North America. It is also easy to raise and maintain and useful in research laboratories.

The frog's jumping for escape and a flip-out tongue for insect catching are characteristics around which natural selection and subsequent adaptation have built a rather distinctive animal. Its huge mouth, tongue construction, highly modified backbone, and unique hind legs all manifest this. Actually, an animal more representative of the amphibian evolutionary position, halfway to the dry-land vertebrates, would be one of the elongated, tailed, and less specialized salamanders (waterdogs and newts).

With this reservation in mind, we can still welcome the frog into our laboratory as a worthy vertebrate, an evolutionary intermediate between the least and most complex chordates.

► What anatomical and developmental features prove the frog's dependence on the aquatic environment?

► What features mark its independence from the aquatic environment?

► Why are amphibians considered of evolutionary significance?

II. OBSERVATIONS

A. Normal Reactions

Observe a group of living frogs. Notice their normal stance and position of the legs. Touch behind the forelegs with a needle. This stimulus sometimes causes the frog to croak. Notice the method of breathing.

► Does the chest cavity move, or the throat? How does air reach the lungs?

► What other means of respiration is available to the frog?

Touch the eyes. Note the reaction.

Turn the frog over and observe its righting reaction.

Notice the stop-and-go swimming reaction in an aquarium. Compare the function of fore and hind limbs in swimming. Describe their action. Observe the method of floating and the balancing action of the extended webbing of the hind feet. Disturb the frog and notice the speed of its emergency retreat.

Notice the location of the eyes.

▶ Of what adaptive importance is this location, and that of the nostrils as well?

▶ What is the importance of the color pattern?

These amphibians require all their protective devices in order to survive the continual predation of the large variety of animals that feed on them. Compare the rapidly moving frog and sluggish toad in this respect. The toad has skin glands that make it unpalatable to most predators. Two distinctly different evolutionary paths are illustrated by these animals.

B. Other Reactions

1—Place the frog in a screened cage or terrarium, add some living houseflies or meal worm larvae, and observe feeding reactions.

2—Apply some acetic acid with bits of filter paper to the back or sides of the animal. Note reactions.

3—Study a demonstration of the pattern of nervous responses in a *decerebrate* frog. Various degrees of destruction of the central nervous system can be tested in terms of normal attitude, swimming control, reaction to tactile stimuli, reaction to acetic acid, and righting reaction.

Decerebrate preparations can be made on slightly etherized frogs by cutting through or dissecting out the cerebrum of the brain. Frogs can also be pithed so as to destroy the brain and the anterior or the entire spinal column. These experiments demonstrate clearly the degree to which the frog's actions and responses are under local (spinal) control.

III. EXTERNAL ANATOMY
(Fig. 13-1)

A. Skin

Notice thickness and feel of the skin. Much of the frog's respiratory gas exchange occurs through

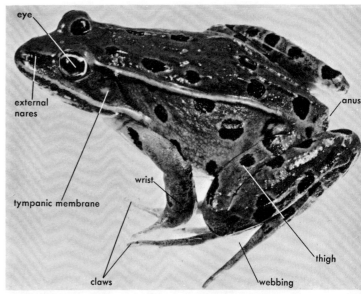

Fig. 13-1. *Rana pipiens,* external anatomy. (Photograph courtesy of Dr. John A. Moore, Columbia University.)

its moist skin surface. Contrast this with the skin of *fish, reptiles, birds,* and *mammals.*

▶ How is the amphibian's skin related to its requirement for external moisture?

Contrast the pigmentation of the dorsal and ventral surfaces.

▶ Of what adaptive significance is this difference?

B. Head

On the head, observe the *mouth, nostrils* (*external nares*), *eyes* and *eyelids,* and the *eardrum* (*tympanic membrane*) behind the eyes.

▶ Are upper and lower eyelids present?

Locate the thin third eyelid, a transparent *nictitating membrane* that protects and cleans the eye without obscuring vision.

▶ Is there a distinct neck?

The neck of some vertebrates gives the head flexibility for feeding or lateral movement.

▶ What feeding mechanism of the frog obviates the need for a flexible or extensible neck?

C. Appendages

Observe the appendages—number, position, webbing, toes, claws. Be sure to notice the lateral position of the legs (as in all amphibians). Mammal limbs, suspended directly under the trunk, provide a direct fore and aft movement, in contrast to the waddling walk of the frog. Relate this efficiency of movement to the habitats of the two classes.

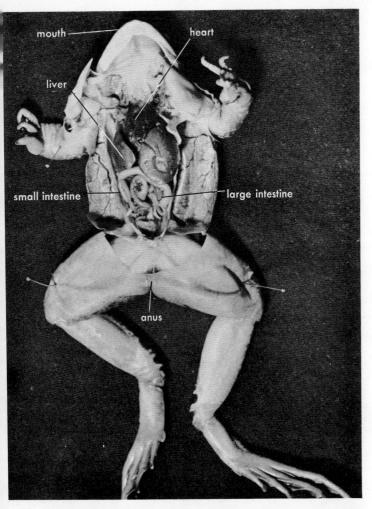

mouth

heart

liver

small intestine

large intestine

anus

Fig. 13-2. *Rana pipiens,* male, ventral view: internal anatomy.

Notice, too, that the limbs have the same general structure as our own. Find the parts corresponding to our upper and lower arm, wrist, hand, fingers, thigh, lower leg, ankle, foot, and toes.

▶ Can you locate an enlarged thumbpad?

The thumbpad, absent in females, serves as a male gripping device during copulation.

IV. INTERNAL ANATOMY
(Figs. 13-2 to 13-10)

A. Mouth

Before pinning down and dissecting your specimen, examine the mouth, opening it wide enough to observe the *esophagus* and roof and floor of the *buccal cavity.* If necessary, cut the angle of the jaws to permit a better view. In the floor of the buccal cavity is the *tongue.*

▶ Review the tongue's attachment and function.

Behind the tongue is the *pharynx* with an opening called the *glottis,* which looks like a slit on

a slightly raised circular portion of the pharynx floor. Air is carried to the lungs through this opening.

Trace the air passage from the external nares to the buccal cavity through the *internal nares* (find them!), to the pharynx, glottis, and lungs.

In the anterior roof of the mouth small *vomerine teeth* (absent in toads) can be felt. Find the teeth by rubbing the upper jaw with your finger. The teeth are named for the jaw or skull bones to which they are attached: *vomer, maxilla, premaxilla* or *mandible.*

▶ Are there any teeth on the lower jaw?

▶ What would you say is the function of these teeth?

B. Body Wall, Coelom, and Viscera (Fig. 13-2)

1—Dissection procedure—Place your freshly killed or preserved frog ventral side up in a dissecting pan with limbs pinned out.

Lift the loose skin of the belly, snip a small hole through it—not the muscles below—and cut along the midventral line from the posterior end of the trunk to the tip of the jaw. You will notice that the skin cuts easily and spaces separate it from the skin musculature. In a live frog, this space is filled with *lymph,* a colorless, intercellular body fluid. Make cuts laterally both behind the forelimbs and in front of the hind limbs, pull the skin flaps down, and pin them out. In specimens injected with colored dye or latex shortly after death, *arteries* will be red, *veins* blue. In non-injected frogs, peripheral veins are usually more conspicuous than are the arteries (which closely parallel veins throughout the circulatory system). This is caused by the passive filling of veins with blood from the tissues and draining of arteries into the tissues without further filling once the heart action has ceased.

Expose the body cavity by cutting through the ventral body wall to one side of the midline. Run the incision from the posterior end of the animal to and through bones of the shoulder girdle (Fig. 13-2). Then make lateral flaps as you did with the skin and pin them out neatly.

In cutting through the body wall you have also cut the *parietal* or *somatic peritoneum,* a thin membrane that forms the outer lining of the *coelom.* Each organ lies within the coelom and is enclosed by an extension of the inner coelomic lining, the *visceral* or *splanchnic peritoneum.* The somatic peritoneum close to the body wall and the splanchnic peritoneum around the intestine join at the *dorsal mesentery* to form the coelom in which the body organs are suspended.

2—Review of organs

a. For general orientation, make a survey of the organs exposed, naming as many as can be seen. Be careful neither to cut nor remove any of the organs. Simply displace them or search with the help of a blunt probe. *Never use scissors* once the body wall has been opened.

The anterior coelom is divided by a transverse partition, part of the pericardium that forms the *pericardial cavity* enclosing the heart.

Observe the *heart* and its major vessels. Then look on either side and posterior to the heart to find the *liver*, largest organ of the body. Note the 3 lobes (2 main lobes and a smaller medial one). Lying free between the median and right lobes is the greenish *gall bladder*, which stores *bile*.

Under the left lobe of the liver is the *stomach*. It may be considerably distended with food or quite shrunken if the animal has not recently eaten. A short, wide *esophagus* connects the mouth and stomach. The *small intestine* leads from the stomach via a *pyloric sphincter* valve into the *duodenum*, which loops forward and runs parallel to the stomach, then turns back into the remainder of the small intestine. This highly coiled tube, supported by mesenteries, enlarges to form the *large intestine* or the terminal *rectum*, which empties to the outside through the *cloaca*. Trace out the complete *digestive system* from mouth, esophagus, stomach, small and large intestine, and cloaca.

b. If your frog was sacrificed during the breeding season, its gonads will be well developed. In fact, much of the female body cavity will be filled with massed black and white eggs. Carefully remove these eggs to expose the organs. Push the intestine to one side to locate the attachment of the *ovaries* (or *testes*) to the ventral surface of the *excretory organs* or *mesonephric kidneys*, which are elongated, dark-colored structures in the mid-dorsal region. In the male, the light-colored, ovoid testes can be seen near the dorsal wall.

c. Locate the yellow *fat bodies* extending anteriorly from the excretory organs. *Adrenal (suprarenal)* glands are yellow bands across the ventral surface of the excretory organs. The term *kidney* properly applies to the typical adult structure in higher vertebrates. The frog's excretory organ is a *mesonephric kidney*, whereas those of mammals, birds, and reptiles are *metanephric kidneys*. During embryological development of higher vertebrates, the mesonephric kidney is replaced by the metanephric, or typical kidney, whereas amphibians retain the mesonephric kidney throughout their lives.

d. A few more organs still to be identified are the *spleen, pancreas, urinary bladder,* and *lungs.* The *spleen* is a deep red, spherical organ embedded in mesentery supporting the small intestine. The pinkish, diffuse, lobulated *pancreas* lies near the liver within the mesentery connecting stomach and duodenum. The thin-walled, translucent *urinary bladder* is ventral to the large intestine in the most caudal part of the coelom. The *lungs,* lying well forward and dorsally, are covered by the 2 outer lobes of the liver. A dorsal pocket of the coelom, the *pleuroperitoneal cavity,* encloses the lungs and extends along the dorsal body wall from the lungs to the junction of excretory duct and oviduct near the rectum.

e. During the present and ensuing dissections you may well observe parasitic worms—flukes, nematodes, cestodes—in the lungs, small intestine, large intestine, rectum, and bladder, or even in the mouth and Eustachian tubes. Each worm is highly specific, being adapted to a particular organ as well as host. For example, *Haematoloechus* are flukes and *Rhabdias* are nematodes found only in the lungs; *Gorgodera* and *Polystoma* are common flukes in the bladder, and *Proteocephalus,* a tapeworm in the intestine. Encysted larvae of other helminths are often seen in tissues, indicating that the frog is an intermediate host for these parasites.

► What might be their final host?

3—Digestive system—You have already identified the chief organs of the digestive system—the alimentary canal and associated digestive glands.

► Name the parts of the alimentary canal.

► Where do products of the liver enter the alimentary canal?

► Where do products of the pancreas enter the alimentary canal?

Locate again the 3 liver lobes and gall bladder. Note the 3 *cystic ducts* that carry bile from each lobe into the gall bladder. Bile reaches its final destination via the *bile duct.*

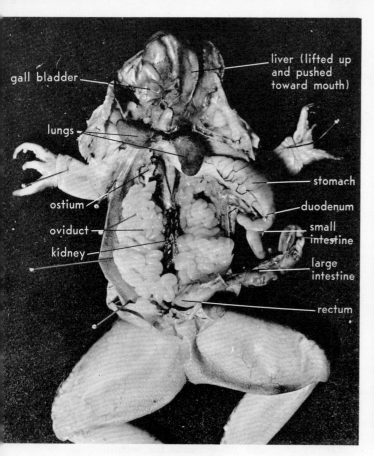

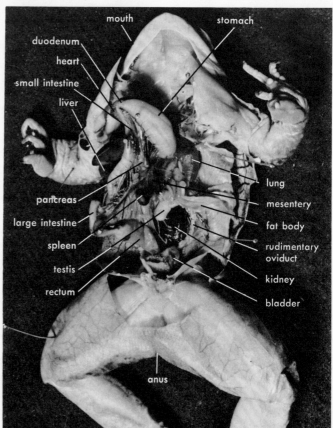

Fig. 13-3. *Rana pipiens,* female, ventral view: internal anatomy of urogenital system and digestive system.

Fig. 13-4. *Rana pipiens,* male, ventral view: internal anatomy of urogenital system and digestive system.

Trace it between stomach and duodenum to its opening halfway down the latter structure.

▶ Can you find the even finer *pancreatic ducts* emptying into the bile duct? (Look in the vicinity of the pancreas where the bile duct passes through it.)

▶ State the functions of bile and pancreatic juice.

▶ Do parts of the digestive system other than pancreas produce digestive enzymes?

▶ Name some other examples of digestive enzymes (see chart in your text).

Free the digestive system from its mesenteries; stretch it out but do not disarrange the pancreas in the first loop of the intestine. Arrange the organs so they do not obscure one another and draw the *extended* system.

Describe the sequence of steps involved, starting from a living insect picked off a leaf by a frog's tongue, to a waste parcel that passes out the cloaca.

4—Urogenital system

a. *Excretory system.* Find again the kidney, fat body, and adrenal (suprarenal) organ forming a yellow band across the kidney.

Expose the excretory system by carefully pushing the oviduct to one side (if your speci-

men is a female). Find the light-colored tubes running from the outer and posterior border of each kidney towards the rectum. Distinguish the excretory ducts from the shiny white nerves in this area and from the renal blood vessels. The ducts can be found along the dorsal surface of the enlarged caudal portion of the oviducts. The excretory ducts enter the cloaca through a papilla and a pore on its dorsal wall. Locate this connection. Find the thin-walled, bilobed bladder attached to the ventral wall of the cloaca opposite the entry of the 2 excretory ducts.

▶ How is the bladder filled and emptied?

b. *Female reproductive system* (Fig. 13-3). Find the *ovaries,* attached to the dorsal body wall by a mesentery, the *mesovarium.* They are found in a position corresponding to that of the testes in the male and have fat bodies attached near their anterior ends, also as in the male. The long white *oviducts* are coiled up posterior to the ovaries. In immature females (or females during the non-breeding season), the small lobulated ovaries near the dorsal midline bear clusters of undeveloped eggs and smaller, less deeply coiled oviducts run the length of the mid-dorsal region alongside the excretory organs. Rudimentary oviducts are also found in this location in males.

During maturation of the ovaries, the ova fill with yolk, become pigmented on one side, and burst through the thin membranous wall of the ovaries and fill the abdominal cavity. They are then passed into the openings of the oviducts. Trace the coiled oviducts of a mature female anteriorly and find the expanded, funnel-shaped openings dorsal to the lungs at the anterior extremity of the pleuroperitoneal cavity. Move the lungs to one side to locate the oviduct openings.

► Are ovaries and oviducts directly connected?

► How do eggs pass into the oviduct funnels?

► How are they passed down the tubes?

At the posterior end of each oviduct, find the expanded thin-walled organ (*ovisac*) for storage of eggs prior to laying and fertilization. It may be necessary to dissect away the dorsal mesenteries to determine the full length and size of the posterior ends of the oviducts. Note the openings of the oviducts in the dorsal wall of the rectum, which terminates in the cloaca, conveying both digestive and reproductive products to the outside. Observe that ovisacs, excretory ducts, and bladder have separate openings into the cloaca.

Individual eggs are coated with gelatinous albuminous material secreted by glands in the walls of the oviducts. At copulation, the male uses its clasping thumbpads to squeeze the sides of the female. As eggs are extruded into the water, male sperm is shed over them, and fertilization follows. A thick, transparent capsule forms from the swelling of the gelatinous layer around each egg as it enters the water. Extruded eggs thus form a compact mass in which the individual fertilized eggs (zygotes) proceed into the early stages of development.

c. *Male reproductive system* (Fig. 13-4). Male gonads consist of 2 light-colored, bean-shaped *testes* along the dorsal body wall suspended from the anterior end of the excretory organs by a mesentery, the *mesorchium*. Sperm ducts (*vasa efferentia*) carry seminal fluid through many fine white tubules that cross the mesorchium from the testes and enter the inner border of each kidney. These tubules lead into the collecting tubules of the kidneys, which carry the sperm into the excretory ducts. Therefore, the mesonephric duct of the male frog serves as a *vas deferens*, conducting sperm as well as urine to the cloaca. It is thus often termed a urogenital

duct. A *seminal vesicle* is attached to the outer side of each urogenital duct near its junction at the dorsal wall of the rectum. Sperm is stored in these vesicles prior to copulation.

► Is there a rudimentary female oviduct in your male frog? Though not functional, it corresponds in structure to that of the female.

5—Circulatory system (Figs. 13-5 and 13-6)

a. *Arterial circulation.* Remove the alimentary canal, then the reproductive system, bladder, and fat bodies, but do not damage major blood vessels, nerves, or excretory organs.

Expose the *heart* in its protected ventral position in the pectoral girdle and within 2 folds of the *pericardium* (Fig. 13-5) that surrounds it. Note the single, heavily muscled posterior chamber of the heart, the *ventricle*, and 2 thinner-walled, dark-red anterior *atria* that lie on either side of a large bifurcated vessel anterior to the heart, the *conus* (or *truncus*) *arteriosus*. The latter is branched into 2 heavy walled arterial vessels that in turn are divided into the principal arteries (carrying blood *away* from the heart).

► How does the frog heart compare with that of the fish you studied?

Recall that in the fish *all* blood from the heart has to pass through the gill capillaries to be aerated prior to circulating through the rest of the body. But in the frog and all air-breathing vertebrates a new structure is involved—the *lungs.* Distinct vessels carry deoxygenated blood from heart to lungs, and aerated blood back to the heart, which then pumps this blood out to the systemic vessels and to all parts of the body. Instead of 1 circulation, we have 2—pulmonary and systemic. In the frog an incomplete separation of these 2 circulations exists, as the 3-chambered heart does not completely separate blood to be pumped into the lungs from that returning from the lungs and destined to be pumped into the body circulation. In mammals, however, this evolutionary development is complete, with a 4-chambered heart that segregates oxygenated blood from deoxygenated, and ensures the efficient separation and operation of this double circulatory system.

Trace the conus arteriosus forward and observe the symmetrical division into major arteries. Three branches lead from each of the 2 primary divisions, or aortae, of the conus arteriosus. These are the 3 principal *arterial arches* on

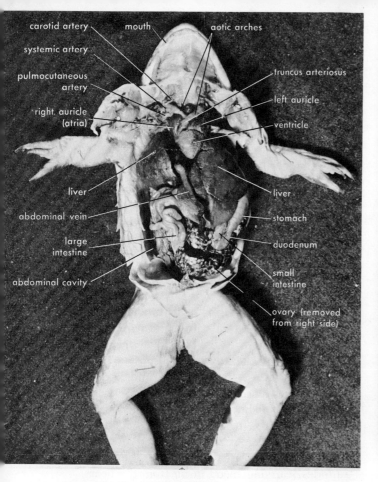

Fig. 13-5. *Rana pipiens,* female, ventral view: circulatory, digestive, and reproductive systems.

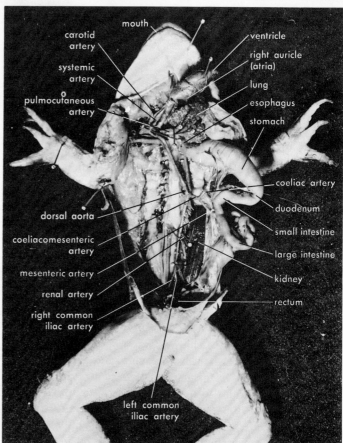

Fig. 13-6. *Rana pipiens,* female, ventral view: circulatory and digestive systems.

each side of the body: *carotid, systemic,* and *pulmocutaneous.* The most posterior branch, the *pulmocutaneous artery,* supplies blood to the lungs via the *pulmonary artery;* its dorso-lateral branch, the *cutaneous artery* to the skin, also serves as part of the respiratory system. The middle branch is the *systemic artery* that passes laterally, arches dorsally, continues caudally, fuses with the corresponding partner systemic artery near the sixth vertebra, and continues posteriorly as the single *dorsal aorta.* The most anterior of the 3 branches is the *carotid artery* that sends blood to the head. Each carotid branches almost immediately into an *external* and *internal carotid.* Find the systemic artery again, and locate its largest branch, the *subclavian artery,* which supplies the foreleg. Continue posteriorly to the united dorsal aorta, which sends a large branch ventrally from the point of junction of the 2 systemic arteries to the digestive tract—the *coeliacomesenteric artery* that, as its name implies, passes to the alimentary canal via the dorsal mesenteries (branching into a *coeliac artery* to the stomach, pancreas, and liver, and a *mesenteric* to the small intestine, rectum, cloaca, and spleen). Next, find the many *renal arteries,* which branch from the dorsal aorta near the mid-dorsal line and pass to each kidney, and small *lumbar arteries* that pass to body wall muscles. Free the margin of the kidney to find the entrance point of these arteries.

▶ How many renal arteries pass into each kidney?

The most anterior of these arteries is the *genital (spermatic* or *ovarian)* that passes to testes or ovaries.

At its terminus, the dorsal aorta divides into 2 *iliac arteries,* each of which passes into a hind leg as the *sciatic artery* that subdivides into smaller arteries (Fig. 13-6).

Show these major vessels and divisions in a diagrammatic outline.

b. *Venous circulation.* Veins, as you know, return deoxygenated blood from the capillaries to the heart. These vessels merge into successively larger vessels, from venules to veins, which are thin-walled tubes through which the blood flows in a steady stream rather than in high-pressure spurts as in the thick-walled arteries. Backflow is prevented in veins by small valves located at regular intervals. All venous blood of the body (except blood from the lungs) flows into the *sinus venosus*, the triangular, thin-walled sac on the dorsal side of the heart. Blood from the lungs returns via the *pulmonary veins,* which lead directly into the *left atrium.* Blood collected into the sinus venosus passes into the *right atrium* via the *sinoatrial aperture,* a valvelike opening that prevents backflow into the sinus venosus when the right atrium contracts. The 2 atria pump blood into the single *ventricle,* backflow again being prevented by a complex series of valves that also permit the major propulsive effort—contraction of the ventricle—to send blood spurting into the conus arteriosus and into the pulmonary and systemic arterial circulation.

Many major veins will have been damaged or removed in your dissection, but the general pattern should still be discernible. Work out and identify as many of the following veins as you can find, supplementing your search with the illustrations and demonstration dissections available for class use. Three main veins carry the blood from all parts of the body into the sinus venosus—these are the 3 *vena cavae.* Two *anterior vena cavae* (or *precaval veins*) convey blood from the head, forelegs, and forebody into the anterior connections of the sinus venosus, and a single *posterior vena cava* (or *postcaval vein*) carries blood from the hinder parts of the body into a single large medial vessel that empties into the posterior apex of the sinus venosus triangle.

Three large veins join in each brachial area, near the arterial arches, to form the anterior vena cavae that drain into the sinus venosus. As with the 3 arterial arches, we shall consider the 3 branches of the vena cavae individually, posteriormost first. The latter is the *subclavian vein* from the forelimb, where it is formed from the *brachial vein* in the basal part of the forelimb, and a large *musculocutaneous vein* that drains the skin and body wall muscles. This vein carries oxygenated blood from the skin and enables the frog to respire through its skin while the animal is immersed and cannot use its lungs. The middle vessel that joins the vena cava is the *innominate vein,* also formed by 2 tributaries: the *internal jugular* (passing dorsally near the angle of the jaw, it drains brain and head), and the *subscapular vein,* a small vessel from the dorsal surface of arm and shoulder. Most anterior of the 3 vessels is the *external jugular vein,* which drains the lower jaw and buccal cavity floor (via *mandibular* and *lingual*

veins). The single posterior vena cava (in contrast to the paired posterior cardinal sinuses of the dogfish) is formed from a series of paired branches from the kidneys, the *renal veins.* These veins should be compared with the similarly branched renal arteries that supply blood to the kidneys. The posterior vena cava runs anteriorly (ventral to the dorsal aorta and dorsal to stomach and liver), passing to the right of the coeliacomesenteric artery. It is joined by a pair of *hepatic veins* from the 2 main lobes of the liver, then enters the sinus venosus. Near the anterior end of the kidneys the gonadal veins (*ovarian* or *spermatic*) join the vena cava.

Blood returns from the large hind legs principally through 2 major vessels, the *femorals.* Find them on the outer margin of the legs, near the surface. Trace a femoral vein forward to its division into 2 branches near the pelvic girdle. The inner branch from each femoral, the *pelvic vein,* passes ventrally. Near the ventral body wall the pelvics join and continue anteriorly along the ventral mid-body wall as the single *anterior abdominal vein.* You first noted this vessel in the frog when you made the initial abdominal incision. Small vessels join the anterior abdominal, draining the body wall musculature. Just behind the heart the vessel turns dorsally and branches into the left and right lobes of the liver. These branches become part of the *hepatic portal* system. Other contributors to the hepatic portals are the *gastric vein* from the stomach, *intestinal* from large and small intestines, and *splenic* from the spleen. On an intact specimen you can locate the main hepatic portal in the mesenteries, parallel to the bile duct.

Return now to the 2 branches of each femoral vein, the pelvic branch having just been traced. The more dorsal branch is the *renal portal vein.* The *sciatic vein* from the inner dorsal surface of each hindleg joins the corresponding renal portal vein. The combined vessel then passes forward to the outer edge of each kidney, sending small veins into the organ. These veins divide into venules and capillaries to produce a capillary bed, the *renal portal system.* The blood flowing through this bed emerges into renal veins that form the posterior vena cava as already described.

Note that all the blood from the femorals passes into one of two portal systems—directly into the renal portals or into the hepatic portals. via pelvic and anterior abdominal veins.

► What is the definition of a portal system?

► What is its primary function in kidney and liver respectively?

► Can you suggest why portal systems tend to reduce the efficiency of the circulatory system? (Might this account for loss of the renal portals in mammals?)

c. *Capillary circulation.* A fine means to appreciate the fantastic number and branchings of the circulatory system is to observe capillaries in the toe webbing of a living frog. Study such a demonstration closely, noting the regular movements of blood cells (can you detect the pulse?), the arteries, arterioles, and capillaries. Many of the latter are fine enough to allow just a single individual blood cell to squeeze by at a time. This represents a considerable difference from the rate of movement in the dorsal aorta! The frog's toe webbing is a thin membrane in which circulation can be seen, and all tissues and *every living cell* is sustained by such intimate and constant association with a capillary bed. We therefore emphasize that the capillaries are the structural basis of the operation of the circulatory system, enabling the individual cells to be nourished and sustained. Be sure to notice that all these vessels still form a single *closed system* (*as opposed to what other type and in what groups?*).

► How can you distinguish veins from arteries in the frog webbing?

► Can you locate branched *lymph vessels* between the capillaries in the frog membrane?

d. *Lymphatic system.* Lymph, though part of the circulatory system, is very different in appearance and function from the blood in arteries and veins. It is colorless, contains few cells, no red blood cells, and is found outside of the blood vessels, bathing individual body cells. It is therefore an intercellular fluid, the actual vehicle conveying oxygen from capillaries into the cells and CO_2 from cells to capillaries. Dissolved food products, cellular wastes, in fact all materials exchanged between cells and blood are carried by lymph. Lymph flowing into the veins becomes part of the supporting fluid or *plasma* of the blood.

The lymphatic fluid has its own circulatory channels and vessels and joins the bloodstream at junction points with certain major veins. Spaces among cells enable lymph to flow through regular channels. In the frog these are well developed, and seen as *subcutaneous lymph spaces* between skin and body wall. These connected spaces actually carry the lymph through fine *lymph capillaries* and lymph *vessels* propelled by 2 pairs of *lymph hearts* that pump the fluid into the venous system. An anterior pair is located near the third vertebra, pumping into the *vertebral vein* (a tributary of the internal jugular). The posterior lymph hearts lie near the end of the vertebral column and pump into the iliac veins. Semilunar valves prevent backflow into the lymph channels. These hearts beat independently of one another and the true heart. Details of this system cannot be studied here, but its functional importance must be clear in order to follow the general conception and unity of the complete circulatory system.

6—Respiratory system—Remove the heart of your frog, being careful to avoid damage to the *lungs.* Trace the lungs anteriorly to their entrance from the *larynx,* dissecting away any obstructing tissue.

Review the other parts of the respiratory system: *external nares, nasal canals, internal nares, glottis.*

► What is the function of the Eustachian tubes, which pass into the middle ear from the roof of the mouth (near the juncture of the jaws)?

Make a complete dissection of the respiratory system by raising the stump of the bisected esophagus and cutting the corners of the mouth to remove intact the esophagus, lungs, lower jaw, and floor of the mouth. Cut through the glottis to expose the larynx, a small, boxlike cavity supported by 2 pairs of ringlike cartilages. Stretched longitudinally across the larynx are a pair of elastic bands, the *vocal cords.* Air passing through a slit between the cords sets them into vibration, producing the characteristic resonant croaking of the frog.

Cut through the larynx, the paired *bronchi,* and into the attached lung. Notice the lung's pleated inner surface, which greatly enlarges the total surface area.

► Of what advantage is this enlargement?

Review how air passes into and out of the lungs, including the related role of the circulatory system.

► How is the skin also involved as an essential respiratory organ in amphibians?

► Did you find parasites in the lungs?

► Was there evidence of damage to the lungs?

► What does such damage imply about physiological balance between these parasites and their host?

7—Nervous system

a. *Sense organs.*

1. *Eye*—remove both eyes carefully from their sockets. Cut around the eyelids, sever the muscles that hold the eye in position, and cut the optic nerve behind the eyeball.

Identify the *upper* and *lower eyelids* and the inner or *nictitating membrane;* the smooth *conjunctiva,* underlying the eyelids; and the *cornea,* transparent surface of the eyeball. Behind the *cornea* find the pigmented *iris diaphragm* with its central oval opening, the *pupil.* Continuous with the cornea is the *sclera,* a tough white membrane covering the back of the eyeball. Locate the white *optic nerve* passing posteriorly through the eyeball and socket.

► To what part of the brain does this nerve connect?

► What is the function of the structures named above?

Cut a vertical section through each eye (use a new razor blade); make one cut along the antero-posterior axis, the other perpendicular to the first.

In front of the *lens* is the *anterior cavity* (with fluid *aqueous humor*). The lens, behind the iris, is transparent in a living specimen and forms a flattened sphere. Behind the lens is the *posterior cavity,* with gelatinous *vitreous humor.*

Inside the sclera lining the back of the eyeball is the *retina,* the true photosensitive organ. Between the 2 coats is the blackened, vascular *choroid coat.*

When stimulated, the light-sensitive retinal cells transmit impulses along the optic nerves. These impulses are interpreted in the higher brain centers as vision. It is believed that each retinal nerve fiber stimulates a discrete cell in the visual center so that the retinal pattern of stimulation is copied in the visual center of the brain. Photographs from the retina of the frog have actually been made, showing a "developed" image reproducing the pattern of light that stimulated the retina. A dark-adapted frog, briefly exposed to a light through a window, was quickly sacrificed. Its retina was removed in the dark, and the cells stimulated formed a pattern of a window with cross markings and shade exactly as it actually appeared.

2. *Ear*—expose the ear by carefully removing the skin covering 1 of the 2 tympanic membranes of the eardrum. Open the cavity into the middle ear by cutting around the membrane. Find the *columella,* a slender bone that is connected from the center of the tympanic membrane to the opening of the inner ear (the *fenestra ovalis*). This bone conducts sound vibrations from the tympanic membrane to highly sensitive cell endings (*organ of Corti* cells) that transmit stimuli to delicate nerve endings of the *auditory nerve* in the inner ear. The auditory nerves in turn transmit impulses according to the pattern of stimuli and the result is interpreted in the brain as sound.

The *Eustachian tube* connects the mouth cavity with the middle ear and serves to equalize the air pressure on the 2 sides of each tympanic membrane, thus ensuring a constant tautness of the membrane, essential for proper auditory reception. Locate the tube by careful probing. Review in laboratory models, charts, or your text the functions of the *middle* and *inner* ear in shark, frog, and man.

► What are the relationships between the sense of *balance* or *equilibrium* and *sound perception?*

b. *Spinal nerves.* On the dorsal wall of the pleuroperitoneal cavity are the shiny white or yellowish cords you probably have already seen. Ten pairs of these spinal nerves pass out from the vertebrae, the largest being the second pair paralleling the subclavian arteries. This relatively small number is a reflection of the frog's reduced number of vertebrae and loss of the tail. Trace one of these nerves as far as possible out into the front leg, separating the muscles where necessary. The first 3 nerves have interconnecting branches that form a *brachial plexus;* the next 3 are small and innervate the back muscles. The 7th, 8th, and 9th have many interconnections, forming a *sciatic plexus* from which a single large *sciatic nerve* passes into each hind leg, where it is seen on the inner dorsal side embedded among the muscles and near the sciatic vein. Trace one of these out into a leg along with the sciatic artery and sciatic vein that accompany it.

Ventral to the spinal nerves and parallel to the spinal cord are the *sympathetic trunks,* a pair of chains of ganglia, connected by lengthwise fibers, one on each side of the cord. This is part of the *autonomic nervous system,* by which various organs, smooth muscles, and involuntary bodily reactions are controlled. A *ramus communicans* connects each ganglion to a nearby spinal nerve. The ganglia in turn innervate various visceral organs, glands, and blood vessels via fibers that unite in *plexuses,* then connect to

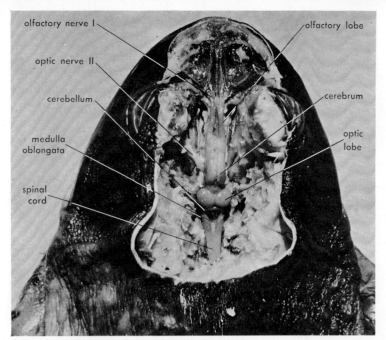

Fig. 13-7. *Rana pipiens,* dorsal view: central nervous system.

Labels on figure: olfactory nerve I, optic nerve II, cerebellum, medulla oblongata, spinal cord, olfactory lobe, cerebrum, optic lobe

the target organs. Search for some of these trunks and nerves (keep your specimen under water, and use a hand lens or dissecting microscope). Observe that the two sympathetic trunks are in close association with the systemic arteries, approach each other where the arteries merge, and then run parallel to the dorsal aorta. Usually the chains are covered by a large layer of black pigment cells.

c. *Central nervous system:* the brain (Fig. 13-7) and spinal cord.

1. *Dissection.* Expose the brain of your specimen by making careful cuts anteriorly from the base of the skull (point of attachment of first vertebra). Remove bits of the dorsal skull plate, using only the points of your scissors and fine forceps. Expose the entire intact brain with its covering of protective *membranes*.

Similarly, expose the spinal cord by cutting posteriorly through the dorsal parts of each vertebra. Pull the exposed vertebra apart to view the cord.

2. *Anatomy of the brain.* Remove the covering membranes and blood vessels. Note the abundant blood supply to the brain. Identify the following major parts of the brain (Fig. 13-7).

i. *cerebrum* (two *cerebral hemispheres*), or forebrain, with the *olfactory lobes* extending anteriorly. Find the *olfactory* or *first cranial nerves* extending from the olfactory lobes to the nasal cavities.

ii. *diencephalon,* a small medial structure of the midbrain covered by a thin vascular roof called the *anterior choroid plexus.* On its dorsal sur-

face arises a small *pineal stalk,* ending in the *pineal body.* Ventrally, the *optic chiasma, infundibular lobe,* and *pituitary body* are found.

iii. *optic lobes,* swollen lateral lobes, characterize the dorsal surface of the midbrain.

iv. *medulla oblongata,* the hindbrain, roofed over by another thin vascular coat, the *posterior choroid plexus.* The medulla is ventral, and continuous with the spinal cord. It marks the base of the brain.

v. *cerebellum,* highly crenulated thin ridge of tissue running dorsally across the anterior border of the medulla.

The brain is actually a hollow structure, consisting of *ventricles* (cavities) within the portions noted above and all connected with one another. The *lateral* or 1st and 2nd ventricles lie in the cerebral hemispheres; the diencephalon contains the 3rd ventricle, followed by the optic ventricles of the optic lobes, and then the medulla oblongata, the 4th ventricle. The *foramina of Monroe* connects the first 2 ventricles to the third, and the latter leads to the 4th by the *iter* or *aqueduct of Sylvius.* The same passage leads to the optic ventricles.

3. *Cranial nerves.* The 10 structurally specialized *cranial nerves,* possibly derived from spinal nerves, each innervate specific structures, as discerned by tracing their pattern of embryological development. An important evolutionary assumption therefore follows: If specific muscles in two different vertebrates are innervated by the same cranial nerve, these structures are probably homologous—in spite of extreme functional differences of the muscles in the adult stage of the animals being compared. Particularly useful in this study of vertebrate relationships are the *olfactory* (I), *optic* (II), *trigeminal* (V), *auditory* (VIII), and *vagus* (X) nerves.

Draw the intact CNS from the dissection you have completed. Then remove the brain and cord intact by lifting them out gingerly. Cut away nerve roots or membranes that block the removal.

Place the dissected CNS in a syracuse dish and study it from all views to check your drawing and earlier observations.

Keen observers may locate the *optic chiasma* (ventral crossing of optic nerves under the diencephalon); the *infundibular lobe,* posterior to the chiasma; and the *pituitary body* or *hypophysis* connected to the infundibulum, but often left adhering to the floor of the cranium when the brain is raised. Locate the *pineal body* as well.

Make thin dorsal slices, then a careful

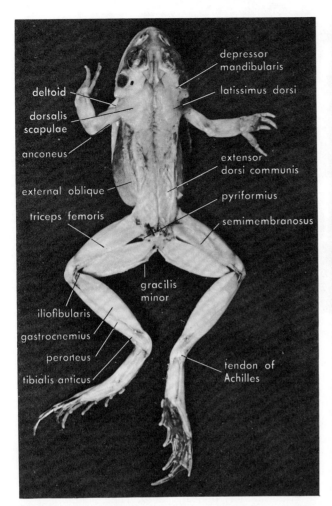

Fig. 13-8. *Rana pipiens,* dorsal view: musculature system.

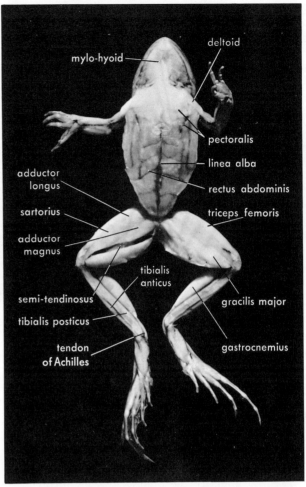

Fig. 13-9. *Rana pipiens,* ventral view: musculature system.

sagittal section to help you visualize the position and interconnections of the ventricles.

8—Muscular system (Figs. 13-8 and 13-9)—
Our review of the muscular system of the hind leg (perhaps the only remaining intact part of your frog) is intended as a sample of the organization and function of the system. Use the leg not dissected for the sciatic nerve branches.

Muscles are in opposing units called *flexors* and *extensors.* Together these are under exquisitely delicate nerve control and give balanced or opposed movements in which groups of flexors and extensors coordinate precisely.

Skin one of the legs and separate the individual muscles with a blunt probe.

Find the *gastrocnemius,* the large calf muscle attached to the *Achilles* tendon.

Determine its *origin* or base of attachment to an immobile structure, and *insertion* or point moved by the contraction.

Find muscles that oppose movement of the gastrocnemius.

▶ Are they flexors or extensors? Of what structures?

Along with the gastrocnemius and tendon of Achilles, the lower leg or *shank* has in dorsal view the *peroneus* muscle, which originates on the femur, inserts on the tibiofibula, and extends the leg. The *tibialis anticus,* also originating on the femur and inserting on the long tarsal bones, extends the leg and flexes the foot.

▶ What is the action of the gastrocnemius? Of the tendon of Achilles?

The upper leg or *thigh* has several large muscles as seen in dorsal view: the *vastus externus, pyriformis,* and *semimembranosus.* In ventral view one can add the *sartorius, triceps femoris, adductor magnus,* and *gracilis major.*

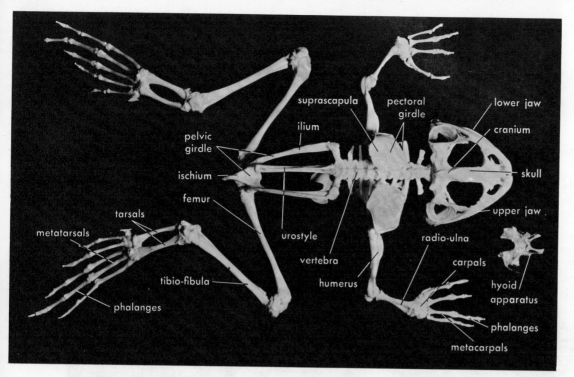

Fig. 13-10. *Rana catesbeiana*, dorsal view: skeletal system.

With the help of Figs. 13-8 and 13-9 identify as many of these muscles as possible. Then prepare a *chart* showing each muscle you have identified, its *origin, insertion,* and *action.* Remove the muscles as needed to establish these facts.

► Which of these muscles can properly be termed paired or opposed?

Identify the precise muscles involved in the swimming action of the hind leg, that is, in extension and withdrawal of the leg.

► How does the frog jump?

9—Skeletal system (Fig. 13-10)—Examine a prepared skeletal mount of a bullfrog to see relationships of the different bones. Study the photograph (Fig. 13-10) and charts or drawings available. Learn the principal bones and compare them with those of the shark, cat, and man.

Identify from a mounted specimen as many of the following bones as you can: *skull, cranium, upper* and *lower jaw* (individual bones of the skull need not be learned except as a special assignment), *pectoral girdle, scapula, suprascapula, sternum, vertebrae, urostyle, humerus, radio-ulna, carpals* (6), *metacarpals, phalanges* (fingers), *pelvic girdle, ilium, ischium, pubis, femur, tibio-fibula, tarsals (calcaneum, astragalus,* plus several smaller bones), *metatarsals, phalanges* (toes), *clavicle,* and *coracoid.*

Make a chart listing the corresponding bones from the *shark, frog, cat,* and *man.*

► What are the essential differences among the 4 skeletal systems?

► Would you classify these differences as fundamental structural ones or as adaptive modifications from a common structural archetype? Defend your position with specific examples.

► What unusual skeletal specializations are found in the frog?

NOTES AND DRAWINGS

(Tear along line)

CHAPTER 14

Class

Mammalia

I. INTRODUCTION

Why are mammals said to be "highest" among living things? In other words, what characteristics permit us to rate mammals (and of course ourselves) as an evolutionary peak? Is it because mammals are the most specialized, numerous, large, or widely distributed animals? Or would you say that none of these factors can adequately explain their success?

Authorities agree that we must look elsewhere for a key to understanding the obviously successful evolution of mammals. One must examine physiological, neurological, and reproductive factors especially carefully. Specialization, or improvement of these systems in mammals, has made possible a remarkable degree of plasticity and adaptability to a wide range of external conditions, while retaining a highly efficient constancy of the internal environment. Structural and functional stabilizing adjustments have been developed, which are summarized in the word *homeostasis*, which means a dynamically balanced, self-regulating system of internal controls —the original feedback control, a principle now widely used in self-regulating computing machines.

Chief among the evolutionary developments leading to homeostasis are internal temperature regulation and a prolonged, protected incubation and training period for the young. The foremost innovation is temperature control (warm-bloodedness or *homeothermy*) aided by body insulation of hair, fat, and elaborate peripheral vasomotor controls. In birds the insulating material is feathers, but the result is much the same. Temperature regulation is associated with many physiological and anatomical controls to retain an internal temperature of 37°C, the most efficient level for most physiological processes. Among the evolutionary developments that ensure this are rapid and efficient circulation of blood; various cooling and heating devices such as sweating, governed by precise circulatory and metabolic controls; increased biochemical activity of individual cells; and highly developed hormonal and neurological controls.

The cold-blooded (*poikilothermic*) vertebrates—fish, amphibians, reptiles—have developed behavioral reaction patterns to control their body temperatures to some degree. Among reptiles particularly, basking in the sun, hiding underground, and other such behavior permit marked temperature control. But these are external rather than automatic internal controls as is typical of homeothermic animals.

The second primary evolutionary step is development of means to protect the young and permit long periods of early development and, later, of training. *Intra-uterine development* of the embryo is followed by varying periods of nourishment of newborn young by maternal mammary glands and by parental protection and training. This extended development facilitates learning and permits further growth and specialization of the central nervous system, chiefly the brain—the most important coordinating center of all. Highly organized and essentially transformed, the brain most clearly separates mammals from reptiles and amphibians as well as from birds. The latter possess a similarly highly developed homeothermic system, but physical demands of flight may have prevented the development of as heavy or complex a brain in birds as in higher mammals—though birds are more intelligent than the phrase "flying feathered reptiles" implies. Intelligence permits improved behavioral response to environmental demands and, most important, the ability to *vary* these responses, to adjust, and to change as a result of experience and learning. The ultimate expression of this is the capacity to modify the environment—best seen in man, of course. Man has even escaped to considerable degree the rigors of natural selection. Whether or not he has truly escaped natural selection and substituted his own is a question that inescapably faces us today and will grow increasingly critical in the future.

Whether by physiological ability to withstand climatic and other environmental extremes, or by patterns of behavior, intelligence, or learning employed to avoid or vary them, mammals as a group are less temperature dependent than are reptiles and amphibians and, hence, are less restricted geographically. *Individual* mammalian species or groups may, of course, be highly restricted in distribution, having become adapted to a set of specialized conditions (for example, monkeys to the tropics, Koala bears to certain Australian *Eucalyptus* trees, the Okapi to deepest Congo rainforests). Yet, as a *class*, mammals retain an extraordinary capacity to withstand a great variety of conditions, as witnessed by their vast distribution and numbers. Some, notably man, certain rodents, many domestic animals, mountain lions, deer, coyotes, and others, demonstrate as *species* this capacity to flourish in many climates and environments.

Along with their capacity to respond and to cope with the environment generally, mammals also have become highly specialized morphologically, thus becoming adapted to specific ways of life and restricted habitats. To appreciate mammalian types of adaptation, it is convenient to review mammalian *orders*, since each order represents a fairly distinct pattern. Some 26 orders are recognized among living groups of higher (*placental*) mammals. More primitive mammals comprise 2 other orders usually placed in a distinct subclass or infraclass, the *monotremes* (egg-laying mammals, the echidna and duck-billed platypus) and the *marsupials* (kangaroo, oppossum, and other pouched mammals). More familiar orders of placental mammals include the following 10 major groups that should be learned: INSECTIVORA (shrews, moles), CHIROPTERA (bats), PRIMATES (lemurs, tarsiers, monkeys, apes, man), RODENTIA (rodents), LAGOMORPHA (rabbits, hares), CETACEA (whales, porpoises), CARNIVORA (dogs, cats, weasels, and the like), PROBOSCIDEA (elephants), PERISSODACTYLA (odd-toed hoofed mammals such as horses, zebras, rhinoceroses), and ARTIODACTYLA (even-toed hoofed mammals—pigs, hippos, camels, deer, giraffes, goats, cattle, buffaloes).

► What families are included in the Order PRIMATES? In the CARNIVORA?

► What distinctive adaptations enable each of these 10 orders to survive in a particular habitat?

Probably no terrestrial vertebrates are more abundant or more wide-ranging, rugged, adaptable, and prolific (all distinct criteria of biological success) than *Rattus norvegicus* and *Rattus rattus*, the common rats. Aside from specialized teeth (*and what mammals do not have specialized dentition?*) the rat can be thought of as a fairly generalized representative mammal, as nearly fitting the term "typical" of an entire class as one might find.

II. EXTERNAL ANATOMY—RATTUS

Carefully examine your specimen to observe the general body shape, elongate tapering head, thick neck, heavy body, and long scaly tail. Then observe its external features more closely. Rodents are characterized by long, gnawing, continually growing incisor teeth that must be worn down as rapidly as they grow. This wearing process removes the *dentine* surface on the inner face more than it does the harder outer *enamel*.

► What is the result of this differential wearing?

► What types of teeth are found in the rat?

► How many are there?

► How are types of teeth and food habits correlated?

The *vibrissae* (whiskers) project laterally from the snout. These tactile hairs are considerably

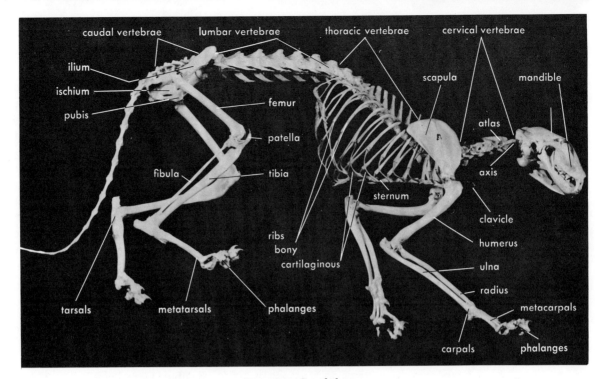

Fig. 14-1. Cat skeleton.

wider than the animal. In a fraction of a second the rat can tell whether the hole he is diving into is large enough to accommodate his body! Almost any information discernable by touch reaches the rat through his vibrissae.

Notice the *mouth*, its anteroventral position, cleft upper lip, and the elongated lower lip. Examine the external *nares (to what do they connect?)*, the *eyes*, and *eyelids*.

In the anterior corner of the eye is a vestigial skin fold, the *plica semilunaris*, apparently homologous to the extra eyelid or nictitating membrane of birds and reptiles.

The *pinna*, or cartilaginous concha of the outer ear, directs sound waves into the ear opening (*external auditory meatus*) and assists in determination of the direction or location of the sound source.

Find the *anus* below the base of the tail. In the male, the *scrotum*, which contains the *testes*, will be seen near the anus. During the season of reproductive activity, the testes descend from the abdominal cavity into the scrotum, which becomes quite conspicuous. At other times, or in immature males, the scrotum is reduced and testes are withdrawn into the body cavity. This external location when testes are spermatogenically active is related to the poor tolerance of spermatozoa for normal body temperature. Male gametes are inactivated at 37°C or higher, and the scrotal sac is a mammalian adaptation providing a lower temperature for them. Just anterior to the scrotum is the opening of the male urogenital system terminating in the *penis*, which is usually withdrawn into a skin covering, the *prepuce*. In the female, there are 3 openings: (1) *anus*, (2) *vag-*

inal opening in front of the anus, and (3) *urinary opening* on the tip of a papillate structure in front of the vagina.

Check the feet of your specimen. All digits except the thumb, or *pollex* of the forefoot, end in claws. Pads, or *plantar tubercles*, protect the bottom of the feet and provide a gripping surface for walking or climbing—a useful combination with claws. Notice the occasional bristles between the epidermal scales of the tail.

▶ What is the function of the tail?

III. INTERNAL ANATOMY

A. Skeletal System—Cat (*Felis domesticus*)

The vertebrate skeleton conforms to a uniform pattern, although still showing highly varied adaptations in different groups. A 2-inch shrew has as many neck vertebrae as a 17-foot giraffe, yet there is quite a difference between the two.

We can learn the vertebrate skeleton pattern from any example, although the cat (Fig. 14-1), a representative carnivore, is especially useful because of its availability and the absence of extreme skeletal specialization such as is found in the frog (Fig. 13-10). However, the frog skeleton still can be used—especially that of the very large bullfrog (*Rana catesbeiana*). The marked differences between frog and cat should be noted (ribs, sternum, forearm, tarsals, pelvis, vertebrae) with reference to specialization for jumping in the frog. Study an articulated bullfrog on demonstration and available charts and text illustrations. Review movements of the bones and their remarkable efficiency and multiple utility, serving for support, muscle attachment, nerve protection, blood cell manufacture, and various other aspects both structural and functional.

Using specimens provided for you, name and work out movements and attachments of the cat bones and processes listed below (Fig. 14-1):

a. Skull (Which bones form the jaw? the cranium? the face?)
  1. premaxilla
  2. maxilla
  3. nasal
  4. lacrimal
  5. frontal
  6. jugal
    i. zygomatic process
  7. parietal
  8. squamosal
    i. zygomatic process of squamosal
  9. pterygoid
  10. palatine
  11. occipital
  12. sphenoid complex (how many bones?)
  13. nasal aperture
  14. internal choanae
  15. foramen magnum
  16. tympanic bulla
  17. external auditory meatus
  18. mandible
  19. teeth (Compare the *type, number,* and *form* of teeth of the cat, rat, and man. What does this tell us of their food habits and probable body structure?)
    i. incisors (number?)
    ii. canines (number?)
    iii. premolars (number?)
    iv. molars (number?)

b. Thoracic cage
  1. ribs (How do they articulate dorsally? ventrally?)
    i. true ribs
    ii. floating ribs
  2. sternum (Is it all bone?)
c. Pectoral girdle (1 and 2 below) and anterior appendages (3 to 8 below)
  1. scapula
    i. spine
    ii. acromion process
    iii. coracoid process
    iv. glenoid fossa (articulating with what?)
  2. clavicle
  3. humerus
  4. ulna
    i. olecranon process (another name for this structure?)
  5. radius
  6. carpals (how many?)
  7. metacarpals (how many?)
  8. phalanges
d. Pelvic girdle (articulating with which vertebrae?) and posterior appendages (2 to 8 below)
  1. innominate—consisting of 3 fused elements (i to iii)
    i. ilium
    ii. ischium

    iii. pubis
    iv. obturator foramen
    v. acetabulum (formed from which bones? function?)
  2. femur
    i. head
    ii. shaft
    iii. greater trochanter
    iv. lesser trochantter
  3. patella (another name?)
  4. tibia } corresponding to which
  5. fibula } arm bones?
  6. tarsals
    i. calcanium
  7. metatarsals (common name?)
  8. phalanges (common name?)
e. Vertebrae (How many in the cat? elephant? whale?)
  1. cervical
    i. axis
    ii. atlas
  2. thoracic—Identify the following parts:
    i. neural spine
    ii. neural arch
    iii. neural canal
    iv. transverse processes
    v. pre- and postzygapophyses
  3. lumbar } How are
  4. sacral } they distin-
  5. caudal } guished?

B. Muscular System

Our review of muscles will have to be a selected sampling to demonstrate attachments and actions of a few typical groups. In vertebrates, *skeletal* or *striated* (voluntary) muscles are attached to other muscles or to bones either directly or by *tendons* (nonelastic cords of connective tissue). A good example is the *Achilles tendon* between heel bone and gastrocnemius.

► What happens when this tendon is cut (hamstringing)?

Muscles can only contract. Controlled movement of a limb must therefore be handled by 2 or more pairs of *opposed* muscles, each of which performs a specific contracting function. The muscle that straightens or extends a limb or part is an *extensor;* the opposing muscle, which bends it, is a *flexor.* The degree of tension between the two—*tonus*—is a state of partial contraction. The balance of muscle tensions maintains the body's position and permits controlled movement. Muscles can also be classed into *abductors* (moving a part *away* from the median line), *adductors* (moving it *toward* the midline).

The complexity of muscle attachments and use of tendons to economize the serious space problem—there simply isn't room enough on our bones for all our muscles—emphasizes the advantage of arthropods in this respect. Having an exoskeleton, arthropods live inside their skeleton, lack tendons, and utilize the entire outer body wall for muscle attachment. This represents about 10 times the space (surface) relative to size that vertebrates have.

Each muscle has its own separate point of attachment, the *origin* (point or area of attachment to the less movable or more stable base) and *insertion* (point of attachment to the part being moved).

We shall examine a group of easily exposed muscles of the upper arm and shoulder of the rat. The skin should be pulled away from the arm and shoulder, fascia removed, and muscles separated by probing with the blunt side of your scalpel. Separate the muscles, but don't cut them—leave their origin and insertion intact for review.

Remember this is a sample, the value of which is to give practice in gross dissection and to teach you the appearance and antagonistic actions of a group of muscles—a lesson in organization. It is *not* intended as a blind memory session. For each muscle listed below, work out the *origin, insertion,* and *action.* Isolate each muscle as much as possible without damaging it. Review your dissection and have your teaching assistant check it and test your knowledge of origin, insertion, and action. Try to imagine the opposing muscles at work, then answer these questions:

► What muscles does the rat use to lift its front leg?

► What arm and shoulder muscles contribute the primary motions in throwing a baseball?

	ORIGIN	INSERTION	ACTION
1. *pectoralis major* (triangular shape)	sternum (anterior half)	humerus	?
2. *pectoralis minor*	sternum (posterior half)	?	?
3. *sternomastoids* (straplike muscles on ventral surface of the neck)	sternum	mastoid of skull	?
4. *acromiodeltoid* (large flat muscle across the back and shoulders)	clavicle and acromion process (lumbar vertebrae and fascia)	humerus	?
5. *trapezius* (3 thin muscle sheets covering neck and anterior back)			
(a) *spinotrapezius*	dorsal spines of thoracic vertebrae	spine of scapula	?
(b) *acromiotrapezius*	cervical and thoracic vertebrae	spine and acromion process of scapula	
6. *triceps brachii*			
(a) *long* head of t.b.	scapula	olecranon process	extensors
(b) *lateral* head of t.b.	?	olecranon process	extensors
(c) *medial* head of t.b.	?	olecranon process	extensors

NOTE

The triceps, which are particularly adapted to quadrupedal gait, are very poorly developed in humans. The longest muscles of the quadruped forelimb lie on the posterior side of the upper arm. The 3 heads noted above have the same action but are so distinct as to be practically separate muscles.

7. *biceps brachii brachialis* (lies lateral to the biceps and acts with it)	glenoid fossa	forearm	?

C. Digestive System

1—Mouth and esophagus—Examine the mouth and the muscular tongue attached to the floor of the mouth cavity. Anterior to this attachment is a more loosely connected portion of the tongue, held by a vertical *frenular fold.* The roof of the mouth is formed by the anterior *hard palate* and posterior *soft palate.*

Above the latter is the *nasopharynx.* Into this large cavity the *posterior nares* pass, as do *auditory tubes* that enter the nasopharynx through longitudinal openings near the junction of the dorsal and lateral walls of the *pharynx* and the posterior border of the soft palate.

The pharynx in turn connects with the *esophagus* posterior to the *glottis,* the valve-

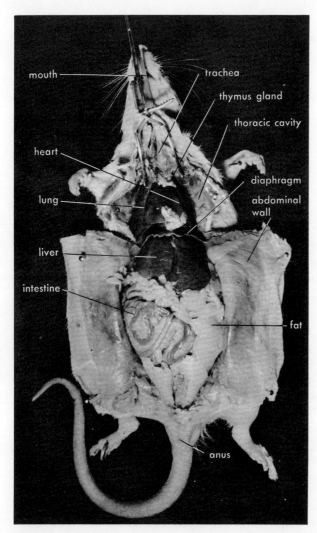

Fig. 14-2. Rat, female, internal anatomy.

like action of which keeps food from entering the *trachea* (windpipe). This latter structure, ventrally located in the neck (feel it from the outside), contains the *larynx* (voice box). The glottis is covered by the *epiglottis*, which is raised when air passes into or out of the larynx but is bent backward over the glottis and trachea while food is being swallowed.

2—Dissection procedure (Figs. 14-2 to 14-6) —Lay the animal on its back and make a medioventral abdominal incision, from pelvis to diaphragm. Cut laterally through the body wall near pelvis and diaphragm to form flaps that can be pinned back to expose the viscera (Fig. 14–2). Remove abdominal fat deposits but do not disturb the alimentary canal.

3—Structures exposed—Locate first the curved *stomach* that consists of 2 portions— the thin-walled, large *cardiac* sac on the left side, and the opaque, thicker-walled *pyloric*

sac on the right. The esophagus empties into the cardiac sac. The food passes into the pyloric sac and then into the anterior part of the intestine (*duodenum*) via a muscular fibrous ring, the *pyloric sphincter*. Find this valve as an externally visible groove.

Insert a flexible probe into the mouth. Locate the route of the esophagus through the neck, thoracic cavity, and diaphragm (before it terminates at the cardiac sac of the stomach).

Trace out the coiled *small intestine* supported by mesenteries containing numerous blood vessels. Do not damage these structures; simply follow them. The *duodenum*, *jejunum*, and *ileum*, successive divisions of the small intestine, are inseparable externally. The ileum empties into a saclike *caecum*, which in man is reduced to the vestigial *vermiform appendix*. The caecum, which is particularly well developed in herbivores, may function as a storage organ for the bulk of ingested food, for bacterial fermentation, or as a special absorptive structure. Digestion of cellulose and other plant materials is particularly difficult, and herbivores characteristically possess a long intestine and large caecum, whereas carnivores do not.

Trace out the large intestine, which starts at the *ileocaecal junction*, to the *ascending colon*. Bulbous objects inside the terminal portion or *descending colon* are fecal pellets. Waste passes through the colon, out a short *rectum* (near and within the pelvis), and finally outside via the *anus*, guarded by an *anal sphincter muscle*.

Observe the large, multilobed brown *liver*. This largest of all the organs produces, among numerous other substances, *bile*, which enters the duodenum through the *bile duct* found in the *hepatoduodenal mesentery*. The rat lacks a bile storage organ or *gall bladder*, which is present in the mouse and many other animals including man. Find the point near the pyloric sphincter where the bile duct joins the duodenum.

The *pancreas*, lighter in color than the liver, is a rather diffuse organ in the first (duodenal) loop of the small intestine. Its large dorsal lobe can be seen near the pyloric sac. Pancreatic juice with a number of digestive enzymes flows through many small pancreatic ducts, which enter the bile duct, and passes into the gut through the latter tube. (Look near the dorsal surface of the pancreas for the pancreatic ducts.)

Find the dark red, spherical *spleen*, posterior to the greater (outside) curve of the stomach. This organ, functionally a part of the circulatory system, is a major phagocytic and white-blood-cell-forming center.

Trace a food bolus from mouth to anus, reviewing all major structures passed along the way.

D. Respiratory System

1—Trachea and bronchi—If possible, study a mammal skull cut in median saggital section. Observe the complex passages in the *nares* leading to the *pharynx*.

Dissect away the neck muscles of the rat to show the ringed *trachea*, the *glottis*, *epiglottis*, *larynx*, and *pharynx*. Review relationships of these parts and the passage of air through each.

▶ How is air prevented from being sucked into the esophagus when food is swallowed, or food prevented from passing into the trachea?

On the outer ventral surface of the trachea, near the attachment of the larynx, is the H-shaped *thyroid gland*, an essential endocrine organ.

Dissect out the larynx and epiglottis; separate them from the pharynx. Slit the larynx ventrally and study the *vocal cords*, a pair of dorsoventral folds in the lateral walls.

Trace the trachea into the thoracic cavity. Note its division into 2 *primary bronchi*. These bronchial tubes enter the lungs and divide repeatedly into *secondary* and *tertiary bronchi* and thence into still smaller *bronchioles*. They ultimately branch into the smallest units of the lung—innumerable, microscopic, bulb-shaped termini of the smallest bronchioles, the *alveoli*, each of which is supplied by an equally small knot of capillaries connected to pulmonary venules and arterioles. Gas exchange occurs by diffusion through capillary walls into and from the extremely thin-walled alveoli—some three-fourths of a billion of them in man, with a surface area of over 1000 square feet.

2—Thoracic cage and lungs—In the thoracic cage, the lungs lie in 2 distinct *pleural cavities* lined by a fine membrane forming a *pulmonary pleura* over the lungs and a *parietal pleura* over the inner surface of the thoracic wall.

Review the mechanism of breathing— the role of the diaphragm, thoracic cage and intercostal muscles, the pleural cavities, and relative pressures inside and outside the pulmonary cavity and the highly elastic lungs.

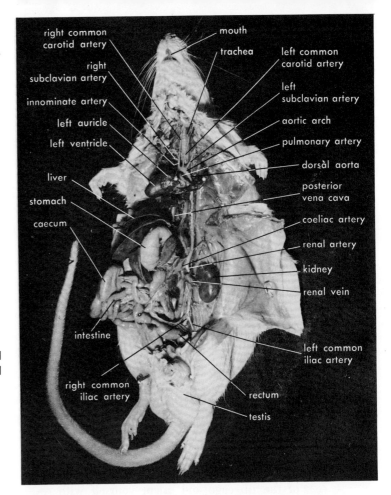

Fig. 14-3. Rat, male, internal anatomy: digestive and circulatory systems.

E. Circulatory System (Fig. 14-3)

1—Introduction—By far the largest number of vessels with the greatest total blood-holding capacity will not even be seen in this exercise. For the complete system we must include not only the heart and its major vessels, but miles of fine *capillaries* and *lymph channels* in which the real work of circulation and exchange of gases, nutrients, and waste materials is performed with each individual cell. The heart is the vital pump, as we well know. *Arteries* and *veins* are the principal conduits, functioning primarily to get the blood to and from the tissues. Allowing blood to flow to individual cells is the job of capillaries. These minute ducts, only one cell thick, form a vast interconnecting network between arteries and veins and their respective branches. Blood from arteries passes through successively smaller branches, the *arterioles*, before entering the capillary bed. Gases, nutrients, and wastes diffuse through capillary walls, and pass via intercellular lymph to and from each cell.

Red blood cells serve as vehicles for carrying oxygen to the intercellular fluids and carbon dioxide from them. Only under accidental conditions (shock or hemorrhage) do red blood cells pass through capillary walls. Capillaries converge into larger ducts, *venules,* which carry the deoxygenated blood into veins and eventually back to the heart.

2—Dissection and orientation—Injected animals showing red dye or latex in the arteries and blue material in the veins should be used for this exercise. Continue the abdominal incision through the skin to the throat. Pull back the cut skin with your fingers to expose the thoracic musculature. Carefully insert your scissors and cut through the thoracic cage and body wall, continuing to cut towards the throat. Use short strokes with the point of your scissors to avoid digging into the heart and lungs. Continue the cut through the center of the clavicle until you see the trachea and esophagus as it enters the thorax. Bend the forelimbs back, snapping them at joints if necessary. Carefully use your fingers and blunt probe to free the membranes from the rib cage and remove bits of fascia and clots of latex that obstruct your view. Look for injected blood vessels as they enter the thorax and expose them carefully. Pin back the walls of the rib cage and orient yourself with respect to exposed structures.

Locate: *rib cage* and *sternum; diaphragm* (wall of muscular tissue separating thoracic and abdominal divisions of the coelom); *pericardium* (membrane surrounding heart); and on either side of the *pericardial cavity* surrounding the heart, a *pleural cavity,* each surrounding a lung.

▶ Which lung is the larger?

▶ Is this uniform in other students' dissections?

The *mediastinal septum,* a membrane between the pericardium and the floor of the thorax, runs from the diaphragm to the anterior wall of the thoracic cavity. See if any remnants of this membrane have escaped destruction. The *mediastinum* is actually the space between the pleural cavities in which the heart, the major vessels, the trachea, and the esophagus are situated.

▶ Describe the function of the *diaphragm muscle.*

Now you can explore the heart and great vessels of the cardiopulmonary circulation. Remove the double layer of pericardium surrounding the heart. The pericardial cavity is the space between the 2 layers of pericardium. First note the triangular shape of the heart with its pointed posterior apex. The small, thin-walled pair of anterior chambers,

atria or *auricles,* appear as flaplike structures on the heart, being collapsed since they lack sufficient musculature to be held rigid. Actually, the left ventricle comprises most of the heart tissue, the right ventricle being much smaller. The 4 chambers, separated by *interauricular* and *interventricular septa,* permit a distinct *double circulation* (pulmonary and systemic) with complete separation of oxygenated and deoxygenated blood.

▶ How does this compare with the circulatory pattern in the frog?

▶ Why is the mammalian pattern said to be more efficient?

▶ Is this efficiency related to homeothermy and the high metabolic rate of mammals?

Clear away any fat or tissue interfering with your view of the major blood vessels. Notice the *thymus gland,* a mass of fatty tissue anterior to the heart. This endocrine gland is best developed in young mammals and regresses after maturity.

3—Pulmonary circulation—Find the *pulmonary artery,* which arises from the right ventricle and then divides to form *right* and *left* pulmonary arteries to the lungs. Newly oxygenated blood returns from each lung via *right* and *left pulmonary veins* into the single *pulmonary vein* that empties into the left auricle. (Notice that discrimination between artery and vein is based upon *direction of blood flow* to or from the heart.) From the left auricle, blood is pumped into the left ventricle at the same time that the right auricle is filling the right ventricle for another spurt of blood into the pulmonary artery. Simultaneous contraction of the 2 ventricles is perfectly timed with their state of filling and sends blood into the pulmonary circulation from the right ventricle and systemic circulation from the massive left ventricle. Backflow on the right side of the heart (into right auricle when the right ventricle contracts) is prevented by the 3-flapped *tricuspid valve.* On the left side the same function is performed by the *bicuspid* (or *mitral*) valve. *Semilunar valves,* 3 between right ventricle and pulmonary artery and 3 between left ventricle and aorta, prevent backflow into the ventricles after their contraction or *systole* (*diastole* being the relaxation phase of the heartbeat).

4—Major arteries—The *aorta,* a large, thick-walled whitish vessel, passes forward diagonally to the right, then arches dorsally to the left side after it leaves the left ventricle. This is the unpaired *aortic arch* from which 5 important branches arise (note that there is no corresponding *right* arch as in the frog). First of these branches is the *innominate artery*, massive but very short, actually the stem of the aorta that gives rise to the second and third major branches, the large *right subclavian* to the right foreleg and the somewhat smaller *right common carotid artery* that runs along the right side of the trachea. The latter vessel later divides into the *right external* and *right internal carotid* arteries.

The fourth principal branch from the arch is the *left common carotid artery*, which also runs along the trachea, the left side, then forms the *left external* and *left internal carotids*. The *left subclavian artery* is the last trunk, leading anteriorly, passing into the left foreleg (*brachial artery*) after giving off a branch to the neck and skull (*vertebral artery*) and another to the ventral wall of the thorax (*internal mammary artery*). Similar branching of the *right subclavian* occurs.

At the base of the aorta, *coronary arteries* branch. These are the vital arteries supplying the muscles of the heart itself.

The dorsal arch then curves dorsally towards the vertebral line where it penetrates the diaphragm and forms the main systemic trunk, the *dorsal aorta*. In birds, it is the *right* aortic arch that persists rather than the left as in mammals.

Move the viscera to one side and follow the dorsal aorta caudad as it branches into its principal arteries (Fig. 14-3). First, find the *coeliac artery*, whose 3 branches supply blood to the stomach, liver, and spleen. Next is the *anterior mesenteric artery*, slightly posterior to the coeliac. Its various branches supply the pancreas, the small intestine (remember the many red blood vessels in the intestinal mesenteries?), the cecum, and the large intestine. Locate the large *renal arteries*, coming off at different levels, one to each kidney, followed by branches to the gonads that are called either *ovarian* or *spermatic arteries*. Near the genital arteries are small *iliolumbars*, which send blood to the dorsal body wall musculature.

Near the caudal end of the aorta is the unpaired *posterior mesenteric artery*, which supplies the large intestine and rectum. This artery often forms confluent branches (anastomoses) with branches of the anterior mesenteric artery.

Finally, the dorsal aorta ends in a bifurcation to form the *right* and *left common iliac arteries*. These in turn send branches dorsally to the back, and then divide into *external iliac arteries* to the thighs, and *internal iliac arteries* to the pelvic areas, and a small single *caudal artery* to the tail.

5—Major veins—Notice that most arteries are paralleled by similar veins that return deoxygenated blood to the heart. Starting with the major veins in the neck, find the *right* (or *left*) *external jugular*, the principal vessel at the side of the neck. It is formed from the *anterior* and *posterior facial veins* near the corner of each jaw. Look along the margin of the trachea for the small *internal jugular*, which joins the external jugular and the *subclavian* from the foreleg to form the *anterior vena cava*. The *left subclavian* receives the principal vessel of lymph circulation, the *thoracic lymph duct*, near the junction of the left subclavian and left internal jugular. *Anterior intercostals* and *internal mammary veins* join the anterior vena cavae (right and left) before the latter enter the right auricle. The *azygos vein* joins the right anterior vena cava near its entrance into the right auricle. It is an asymmetric vessel, bringing blood from posterior intercostal tissues, passing to the right of the mid-dorsal line. It is thought to be a remaining portion of the posterior cardinal system as studied in the dogfish, just as the anterior vena cavae (or precavae) developed from the anterior cardinal veins.

All posterior circulation passes into the right atrium via the single *posterior vena cava*, derived from the right posterior cardinal vein. Try to determine the successive blood vessels feeding into the posterior vena cava by dissecting back and working out the source of the major veins supplying blood to it. Find the *hepatic veins* (*how many?*) entering the posterior vena cava when the latter becomes embedded in the liver near the diaphragm, where it receives the *phrenic veins*.

The short but large paired *renal veins* enter the vena cava at different levels, corresponding to the position of each kidney.

▶ Where do the *left ovarian* (or *left spermatic*) vein and the *right ovarian* (or *right spermatic*) vein join the blood flow returning to the heart?

Observe that in the posterior trunk the vena cava is dorsal to the dorsal aorta, opposite to the condition in the thoracic region.

Similar to the branching of the arterial system, a pair of *iliolumbar veins* drains the dorsal body wall and joins the posterior vena cava caudad to the gonadal veins. The vena cava in turn begins at the junction of the *common iliac veins*, each of which is formed from an *internal iliac* from the dorsal side of the hind limb and from an *external iliac vein*

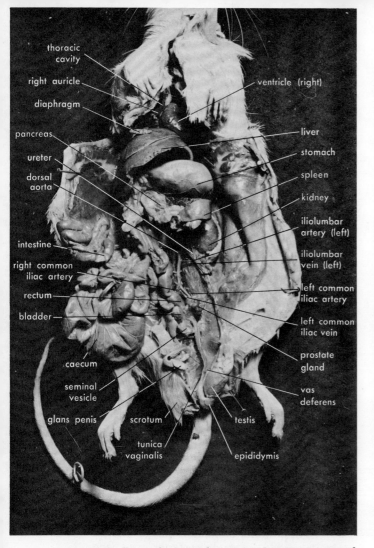

Fig. 14-4. Rat, male, internal anatomy: digestive, urogenital, and circulatory systems.

Labels for Fig. 14-4: thoracic cavity, right auricle, diaphragm, pancreas, ureter, dorsal aorta, intestine, right common iliac artery, rectum, bladder, caecum, seminal vesicle, glans penis, scrotum, tunica vaginalis, ventricle (right), liver, stomach, spleen, kidney, iliolumbar artery (left), iliolumbar vein (left), left common iliac artery, left common iliac vein, prostate gland, vas deferens, testis, epididymis

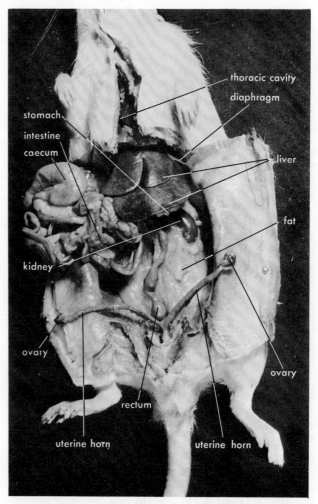

Fig. 14-5. Rat, female, digestive and urogenital systems.

Labels for Fig. 14-5: stomach, intestine, caecum, kidney, ovary, uterine horn, rectum, thoracic cavity, diaphragm, liver, fat, ovary, uterine horn

formed from the *femoral* and other vessels on the inner margin of the legs.

6—Hepatic portals (dyed yellow in triply injected animals)—This important set of veins carries food-laden blood from the digestive tract to the liver where its load of dissolved food materials can be exchanged and physiologically processed, passing from innumerable capillaries to the liver cells. The *hepatic portal* is formed from 4 vessels: the *lienogastric* (from stomach and spleen), *duodenal* (from duodenum), *anterior mesenteric* (from small intestine, colon, and caecum), and *posterior mesenteric* (from the rectum). The hepatic portal vein can be seen in the supporting mesenteries parallel to the bile duct. The portal capillaries recombine into venules and veins, and then enter the posterior vena cava from hepatic veins, as you have already observed. Note that no renal portal system is found in mammals.

► How would you explain the advantage of such a loss?

F. Urogenital System (Figs. 14-4 and 14-5)

The U-G system, as this is called, is considered a combined unit since its component parts are closely related embryologically and evolutionarily. In the mammalian male reproductive system, tubules and ducts (Wolffian ducts) of the mesonephric kidney are utilized, whereas ducts corresponding to female or Müllerian ducts disappear or remain vestigial (Fig. 14-4).

In females, on the other hand, the Müllerian ducts give rise to oviducts and uterus, and the mesonephric or Wolffian ducts and tubules disappear (Fig. 14-5).

1—Kidney (external)—Kidneys are filters of the circulatory system. They are bean-shaped organs covered with peritoneum ventrally and attached dorsally to the wall of the peritoneal cavity. It is best to think of them not only as waste-removing organs but as organs that control the essential balance between body salts and water and remove nitrogenous wastes such as urea, nonvolatile foreign substances, and either excess salt or excess water.

Three developmental types of kidneys occur in vertebrates: the *pronephros* (seen in adults only in certain primitive fishes); the *mesonephros* (in adult cyclostomes, most fishes, and amphibians); and finally, the *metanephric* kidney of all adult reptiles, birds, and mammals. The embryological sequence of these 3 kidney types, especially development of the mesonephric kidney, shows a close relationship between gonads and adult kidneys, despite their anatomical separation.

Examine again the kidneys of your rat. Note that the right one is not in line with the left but extends forward into the right lobe of the liver. Along with the ureter, the renal artery enters and the renal vein leaves at the medial margin (*hilus*) of each kidney. Filtration of blood from specialized capillaries or *glomeruli,* excretion of excess salts or water, and removal of other materials occur in the many tubules in the kidney. Each is enmeshed in capillaries from the renal arteries, which then pass their blood into the renal veins. Waste fluid, or *urine,* passes from the tubules to a larger duct, the *ureter,* which carries this fluid from kidney to bladder. The bladder, a distensible, thin-walled sac, is attached by a strong ligament to the ventral body wall. Two ureters join the bladder, which drains its contents to the outside via the single *urethra.* In the male the urethra is a urogenital duct, as in the male frog, since it carries either urine or seminal fluids.

Locate the *adrenals,* small oval structures at the anterior end of each kidney (Fig. 14-3). These important endocrine glands produce adrenalin (or epinephrine) and numerous other hormones.

2—Kidney (internal)—Remove one kidney and cut it lengthwise to expose the hilus, and view the major divisions. Observe the funnel-shaped ureter that opens in the hilus to form the internal *pelvis* of the kidney. Next, observe the pelvis closely and see how it is divided into sections, each of which is a *calyx* (plural: *calyces*).

The kidney tissue, enclosed by a connective tissue *capsule,* is divided into outer *cortex* and inner *medulla.* Observe the numerous fine lines in the medulla converging towards the hilus and forming triangular *renal pyramids,* the outer layers of which show radial *medullary rays.* These striations are actually *collecting tubules,* each an important portion of the *nephron,* basic functional unit of the kidney. Examine these units in tissue

slices or prepared slides under a dissecting microscope. Darker radial striations and scattered dots in the cortical region consist largely of *renal corpuscles;* the other striations are the *tubules.*

Prepared slides should be consulted for histological details of this complex and remarkable organ. Renal corpuscles consist of a *glomerulus* or knot of capillaries, enclosed by *Bowman's capsule,* the bulbous origin of each tubule, surrounded by a fine capillary net.

► How do these corpuscles function in filtering blood?

Find the *proximal* and *distal convoluted tubules* in your slide preparation. (In cross section, the lumen of the distal tubules has a characteristic star shape, proximal tubules a circular shape.) Locate the *loops of Henle,* which function chiefly for water resorption. With the aid of laboratory models and charts, review the organization and function of the entire nephron: the glomerulus, Bowman's capsule, capillaries, and tubule.

3—Male genital system (Fig. 14-4)—Observe again the large *scrotum* containing the *testes* and *sperm ducts.* The ventral groove between the testes marks the *septum scroti,* and coincides with an internal partition between them. Slit the scrotum ventrally, and observe the overlying sac, the *tunica vaginalis,* formed of connective tissue in which the testes appear to be suspended. Remove the tunica carefully. The next layer or sac exposed is the *tunica albuginea,* and under it a highly twisted mass of *seminiferous tubules.* Remove a few tubules and study microscopically a teased out preparation.

► Can you find bundles of spermatozoa within the tubules?

The *epididymis* is a tubular storage system in which spermatozoa are retained after formation in the seminiferous tubules. This compact structure, closely adherent to the wall of the testes, is divided into an anterior or head portion (*caput epididymis*); a slender mid-portion or body along the dorsal surface of the testes (*corpus epididymis*); and a tail portion (*cauda epididymis*) spreading over the posterior (caudal) end of the testes. Find the large *vas deferens,* which collects the spermatozoa from the epididymis and passes anteriorly into the body cavity. This duct, along with the associated blood vessels and a nerve, comprises the spermatic cord. Trace out this cord into the penis.

► Where does the cord join the urethra?

Retrace the path of spermatozoa from testis to penis.

In man and most mammals, testes remain in the scrotum permanently descended from the body cavity. In rodents, insectivores, bats, and marsupials, this descent occurs periodically before each breeding season, after which the testes are withdrawn into the body cavity by the *cremaster muscle.*

Next, examine the male intromittent organ, the *penis*, through which spermatozoa and accompanying seminal fluids are transferred to the vagina during copulation (coitus). Insert the point of your scissors into the external opening of the penis and cut the skin back to the length of the structure. Clear away the *prepuce* (foreskin) that covers it. The penis is directed posteriorly in rodents, whereas in most mammals it projects cephalad. Remove the muscle and connective tissue, and locate the spongy, erectile tissue that fills with blood to give the penis rigidity during copulation. Along the ventral surface are 2 *corpora cavernosa penis* that lie dorsally when blood fills the organ causing it to be directed anteriorly. A single *cavernosum urethra* lies in a groove between the 2 corpora cavernosa. Notice that the cavernosum urethra ends in an enlarged head, or *glans penis*, within the prepuce. The urethra passes from the bladder through the cavernosum urethra and to the outside via the urethra opening in the glans.

The remainder of the male genitalia, semen-producing and sperm-storing glands, lie in the pelvic area of the body cavity. Two irregularly shaped or curved and rather large *seminal vesicles*, and 2 pairs of smaller *prostate glands* lie in the same vicinity, one pair dorsal and the other ventral to the spermatic cord.

4—Female genital system (14-5)—The vagina, the external orifice of the female genitalia opens anterior to the anus. Anterior to the vagina, the urethra opens separately through a papillate structure at the base of which is the *clitoris,* an erectile structure homologous to, though less well developed than, the male penis and lacking an opening.

The rest of the female U-G system is internal, near the kidneys. First find 2 round, pea-sized *ovaries*, each invested in a capsule, the *bursa ovarica*, merging with the special ovarian mesentery, the *mesovarium.*

▶ Where is this mesentery attached?

The *oviduct* forms a tight coil at one end of the mesovarium. The proximal opening within the bursa ovarica receives an egg freed by rupture of an *ovarian follicle* and passes it by ciliary action into the *funnel* or proximal end of the oviduct. In other mammals the funnel lies free in the peritoneum and sweeps in the eggs, but in the rat the connection is much closer, as the funnel of the oviduct lies within the bursa of the ovary.

The egg passes down the tightly convoluted tubule of the oviduct and enters one horn of the uterus.

▶ What happens to the egg from this point?

Notice that the uterus consists largely of the horns. In fact, there is no single uterus (*corpus uterus*). In the rat, the horns open separately into the vagina. This development of the horns rather than the body of the uterus is an adaptation for multiple births.

▶ How does this compare with the human uterus? With that of the dog? The horse?

G. Central Nervous System (Fig. 14-6)

Our review of the nervous system will be restricted to an examination of the *brain* and its associated *cranial nerves.* This is the most specialized and distinct part of the nervous system, and, in fact,

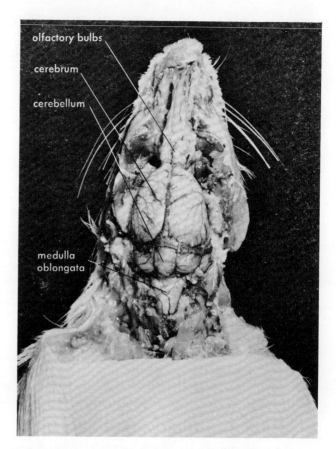

olfactory bulbs
cerebrum
cerebellum
medulla oblongata

Fig. 14-6. Rat, central nervous system, dorsal view.

NOTES AND DRAWINGS

(Tear along line)

the part that appears to be of the greatest evolutionary significance throughout the Class **MAMMALIA.**

Dissection of the skull requires care, skill, patience, and complete control of your tools to avoid damaging the delicate structures within. In fact, this dissection will be considered a laboratory exercise in technique, for which you will receive a special grade. A minimum of instruction is included here to give you greater opportunity to break into and successfully enter the vault of the cranium. The prize is the brain and the roots of the cranial nerves, delivered intact.

A good point of entry into the braincase is the mid-dorsal *sagittal suture*. With a careful puncture as a start and judicious use of the scalpel firmly held flat so as to shave thin portions off the skull roof, you can enlarge the hole, chipping away small pieces of bone to expose the dorsal surface of the brain. Learn to control the pressure of your instrument so you can direct considerable force and leverage with complete control and reasonable freedom from a fatal slip into the brain.

First you will observe the 2 membranes, *dura mater* and *pia mater*. Expose the *medulla oblongata, cerebellum, cerebrum,* and *olfactory bulbs* in posterioanterior succession. Break through the occipital portion of the skull and expose the vertebral column. The *atlas*, lying against the base of the skull, serves as a convenient marker for separation of the brain from the spinal or vertebral column with its *spinal cord.*

Individual vertebrae can be separated from one another and shoved posteriorly to expose the anterior portion of the cord; or parallel dorsal cuts can be made through the vertebrae to expose the cord below.

With care and sufficient luck you can expose the brain from olfactory bulbs to the anterior spinal cord (Fig. 14-6). Call your instructor to check your dissection before proceeding further.

Next, sever the spinal cord posterior to the medulla and very carefully remove the intact brain from the skull. Work up from the cord, using the stump of the cord as a lever. Concern yourself primarily with the cranial nerves, so as to prevent pulling them from the brain. To facilitate later identification of these nerves, each cut should be as far from the brain as possible. Be particularly cautious with the olfactory lobes, the most difficult part to remove intact. Place the isolated brain in water and identify each of the 12 cranial nerves, the *optic chiasma*, the *pineal* and *pituitary bodies,* and the major divisions and chief subdivisions of the brain. The latter include *frontal* and *temporal lobes* of the cerebral hemispheres, *Sylvian fissure, corpus callosum* (transverse sheet between the hemispheres), *hippocampus* (floor of lateral ventricles), and *choroid plexus* (vascular cover of the third ventricle). In the midbrain find the *corpora quadrigemina* (2 divisions of each optic lobe, seen posterior to the pineal body on the dorsomedial surface), and *crura cerebri* (swellings on ventral surface of midbrain). In the hindbrain find the medulla oblongata, which tapers into the spinal cord; find also the cerebellum, dorsal outgrowth of the medulla, with its dorsomedial lobe, the *vermis*, and two lateral, irregularly convoluted lobes, the *flocculi.*

Study illustrations or sections of the brain to locate the major *commissures* (groups of fibers connecting one side of the brain to the other), the ventricles (including the third and fourth or *lateral* ventricles), and their connecting openings.

▶ How does the rat brain differ in relative size and development of its major divisions from that of man?

CHAPTER 15

Cytology and

Histology

I. INTRODUCTION

► What defines a cell? A tissue? An organ? An individual?

► Is an animal truly dead so long as some of its constituent cells continue to live?

► What controls cell division?

► What determines differentiation of cells and tissues in an animal when each of its cells has precisely the same genetic constitution?

► What determines developmental patterns, controls their integration, and stops the process when completed?

These questions, which become progressively more difficult to answer as one moves up the levels of structural and integrative complexities, are some of the most troublesome and basic queries in biology. The more we learn, the more complex and puzzling becomes the entire animal, whether hydra or man. In fact, pat answers for even the simplest of these questions won't do any longer. We know enough to realize that the single cell is not simple, that it does not necessarily consist of a standard cytoplasmic packet surrounding a central nucleus. For example:

► Is a virus a cell?

► How do multinucleate cells like the amoeba *Pelomyxa* or vertebrate striated muscle cells defy the generally accepted definition of a cell?

►Do you consider the parenchyma of flatworms to be cellular?

► If a cell is a *unit* of structure and function, what is a protozoan?

► Is the extremely resistant, practically inert spore of the botulism bacteria a cell?

As you examine each level of structural organization, you will discover exceptions, conflicting definitions, new interpretations, and new concepts. Study of form and function of subunits of cells, intact cells, and their combination into larger units represents one of the most active and productive areas of contemporary biological research. New approaches are yielding new tools, techniques, and conclusions. New conclusions, of course, mean disagreements, from which arise new syntheses and, ultimately, greater understanding.

Before commencing a detailed comparison of specialized vertebrate cells and their function, consider the questions posed above, define terms, and review the structure of a diagrammatic cell. Then study the outline of basic cell types given in Section III below.

The following definitions are basic and generally accepted, but do not allow them to rule out peripheral definitions or marginal exceptions. This attitude should make it easier to face new ideas and to abandon cherished interpretations memorized from this or other texts.

II. DEFINITIONS

1—*Cytology*—study of cells, their structure and function.

2—*Histology*—study of tissues, their structure and function.

Comparative studies involving physiology and anatomy are included in both cytology and histology. Many new techniques are now utilized to investigate ultrastructure and functioning of the most minute components.

▶ **What is the chief tool for study of ultrastructure?**

Protein synthesis, gene action, developmental processes, comparative physiology, and structure and action of intact tissues are other areas of active contemporary research in cytology and histology.

3—*Cell*—the smallest living integral unit, characterized by growth at some stage and metabolism throughout its life.

4—*Tissue*—a group of coordinated cells with one or several common structural and functional specializations.

5—*Organ*—a complex of tissues forming a functional unit, usually of a stable structural organization.

6—*Organism*—a highly organized unit that is living and is capable of growth, differentiation, assimilation, metabolism, reproductive constancy, and integrated response to its environment.

Return to the initial questions in the introduction.

▶ **How would you answer them now?**
▶ **Are you satisfied with these answers?**

Review in your text the structural diagrams of a "typical" plant and animal cell. Such cells are considered to be nonspecialized, though capable to some degree of all essential cellular functions, including *reproduction, metabolism, contractility,* and *conductivity.* Cells specialized for one or more of these 4 functions can form different tissues or organs, each of which performs a specific activity in the intact organism (example: germ cell, liver cell,

muscle cell, and nerve cell). Our study of tissues is essentially an examination of their constituent cells that show one of the above 4 essential characteristics to the near-exclusion of the others. Our study of organs is, in turn, a review of their tissues. Study of the specialized modifications of tissue function and structure in each organ is reserved for later courses in physiology and anatomy.

In review, remember that organs and tissues consist of cells that appear to be strikingly different, yet in basic respects have the same organization. Such cells have developed marked specialization of *one* of the fundamental activities common in some degree to *all* living cells.

Examine your slides with these purposes in mind: (1) to learn a few generalized and specialized cell types, (2) to identify examples of tissues or organs composed of these cells, (3) to integrate this information into an appreciation of the *organism* as a harmoniously functioning balance, whether in one or many cells, (4) to provide a background to current research probings into genetic control mechanisms, differentiation, embryogenesis, and overall control processes in the intact organism, and (5) an added aim—to gain an appreciation for the painstaking steps needed to reduce an organ or tissue to minute, stained cross sections permanently affixed to a slide. Review with your instructor the steps of microtechnique—killing, fixing, embedding, sectioning, staining, clearing and mounting tissues, each with associated periods of hydration, dehydration, and other chemical treatments. *Respect* your slides and the patience and skill required to make them.

III. OUTLINE OF BASIC TISSUE TYPES; EXAMPLES FROM VERTEBRATE TISSUES

A. Epithelium (covering or lining tissue)

Cell arrangement of the 3 types listed below may be *simple* (platelike), *stratified* (layered), or *pseudostratified* (irregularly layered), and have cilia or other specialized outgrowths.

1—*Squamous epithelium*—forms lining of blood vessels (Fig. 15-1), peritoneum (Fig. 15-2), and epidermis (Fig. 15-3).
2—*Columnar epithelium*—found in lining of digestive tract, mucous membranes, excretory ducts, and trachea.
3—*Cuboidal epithelium*—glandular tissue.

B. Blood and Lymph (vascular and intercellular tissues; liquid matrix and supported cellular elements)

1—Blood—circulating vascular fluid with various formed elements or blood cells.

a. *red blood cells* (RBCs or *erythrocytes*)—circular, biconcave discs, non-nucleated in mammals, contain hemoglobin that carries oxygen or carbon dioxide to and from cells.
b. *white blood cells* (WBCs or *leucocytes*)—nucleated, amoeboid corpuscles of blood, lymph, pus, and tissues; included are *lymphocytes, monocytes, eosinophiles, basophiles,* and *heterophiles,* certain of which ingest and destroy harmful elements, foreign substances, or cellular debris of the organism.
c. *blood platelets*—small, colorless discs that play a role in blood clotting; occur only in mammals.
d. *plasma*—intercellular fluid supporting blood, including clotting elements but not cells.
e. *serum*—intercellular and blood fluid, *without* clotting elements or cells.

2—Lymph—transparent intercellular or lymphatic vessel fluid, includes white blood cells, chiefly lymphocytes.

C. Connective Tissue (supportive tissue)

These are various cells embedded in a matrix of fibrous or mucoidal substances that bind together and support body structures. Types of connective tissues are:

1—Loose connective tissue—differentiated by type of intercellular fibers: *collagenous* (white) or *elastic* (yellow). Loose connective tissue may contain such cells as *fibroblasts, macrophages, lymphoid wandering cells, mast cells, eosinophiles, plasma cells, pigment cells, fat cells,* and *undifferentiated cells.*

2—Dense connective tissue—chiefly in skin and in submucous layer of intestine. Fibers are thick, compactly woven collagenous bundles. Cells are difficult to identify but probably the same as those in loose connective tissues.

Examples of connective tissues are the following:

1—Regular connective tissue—collagen bundles arranged in a definite manner.

a. *tendon*—connects muscle to bone or muscle.
b. *ligament*—less regular form than tendon, a tough fibrous band between bones or supporting viscera.

2—Special connective tissue

a. *mucous connective tissue*—found in embryos.
b. *elastic tissue*—found in vocal cords, arteries (Fig. 15-1).
c. *reticular tissue*—in spleen, liver.
d. *adipose tissue* (fat) (Fig. 15-3).
e. *specialized pigment tissue*—in sclera of the eye.

3—Cartilage—specialized fibrous connective tissue in skeleton of embryo and joints of adults (Fig. 15-4).

a. *hyaline cartilage*—in embryo and adult joints (Fig. 15-6).
b. *fibrocartilage*—in intervertebral discs.

4—Bone—calcified fibrous connective tissue with cells connected by thin protoplasmic strands (Fig. 15-5).

D. Muscle Tissue (contractile tissue)

1—Striated muscle—voluntary, forms skeletal muscle; made up of long, cylindrical, multinucleate fibers with characteristic cross striations; nuclei lie outside fibrils (Fig. 15-8).

2—Smooth muscle—involuntary, chiefly in internal organs, principally, the digestive tract, hence also called *visceral* muscle; long, spindle-shaped, mononucleate fibers (Fig. 15-7).

3—Cardiac muscle—involuntary heart muscle made of striated fibers that branch and anastomose to form a single interconnected network; nuclei interior, fibers with *intercalated discs* (function uncertain) (Fig. 15-9).

E. Nerve Tissue

This is composed of *neurons,* cells that are highly specialized for irritability and conduction (Fig. 15-10), and of *neuroglia* or nerve-supporting cells.

Nervous tissue should be thought of as a closely coordinated single system with specialized units.

1—Central nervous system (CNS)—brain and spinal cord.

2—Peripheral nervous system—nerve tissue outside CNS.

3—Autonomic nervous system—formed from 2 chains of ganglia found along spinal cord and scattered among body tissues; concerned chiefly with regulation of visceral activity and divided into 2 units, named for location of ganglia, with balanced (opposed) function. It is a portion of the peripheral nervous system.

a. *sympathetic nervous system* (or *thoracolumbar* n.s.).

b. *parasympathetic nervous system* (or *craniosacral* n.s.).

▶ How do the 2 major divisions of the autonomic nervous system function in relation to one another?

▶ What chemicals are intimately associated with the functioning of each?

F. Other Specialized Cells

There are other specialized cells which are of interest but cannot be considered as distinct tissues. These are the *reproductive cells—egg cells* and *spermatozoa.*

▶ Why are these not properly classed as tissues?

IV. LABORATORY INSTRUCTIONS

A. Stained Slides

Study as many examples of stained tissue preparations as are available. Certain slides will be studied at your desk, others at demonstration microscopes.[1] Refer to your text and charts for comparative material and detailed discussion of more specialized cell and tissue types, checking them against the outline in the preceding section.

Learn to judge differences in your slide preparations due to the angle of cut of microtome knife, the intensity of stain, or factors such as shrinkage or pressure resulting from the technique employed. *Be particularly careful to locate portions of tissues that demonstrate representative cells.* Consult your instructor to be certain you have judged correctly. From available slides *select, draw,* and *label* (1) a "typical" cell and (2) a few cells characteristic of each of the 5 basic tissue types described in Section III (A through E).

Select good examples and draw grouped cells

---

[1] Proper use of the microscope is of utmost importance. Review the discussion of control of illumination in Chapter 1. Use low-level illumination with the low-power objective, especially for living material. Glare masks the image, whereas reduced illumination (controlled by closing down iris diaphragm or lowering the condenser) enhances outlines and brings out tissue pockets or folds that are entirely lost in the scattered rays of brighter light.

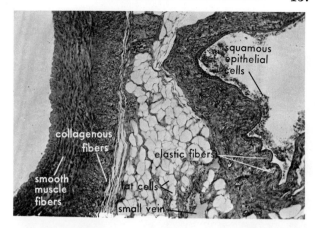

Fig. 15-1. Squamous epithelial cells of the blood vessel. (Copyright by General Biological Supply House, Inc., Chicago.)

showing sufficient detail to illustrate their specialized characteristics. State the *specific* slide you used, the magnification, portion of organ or tissue drawn, and type of tissue illustrated.

The following are examples of prepared slides that are usually available.

1—Liver cross section—useful for structure of a typical cell. Select a cell showing *cell membrane, cytoplasmic granules, mitochondria, vacuoles* or other inclusions, *nucleus, nuclear membrane, chromatin.*

2—Cartilage—Note the *hyaline matrix,* with embedded *chondrocytes* (cells).

▶ Can you find the collagen fibers?

Fig. 15-2. Squamous epithelial cells of the peritoneum. (Copyright by General Biological Supply House, Inc., Chicago.)

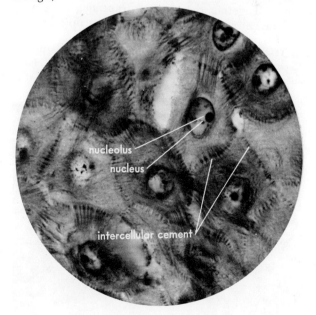

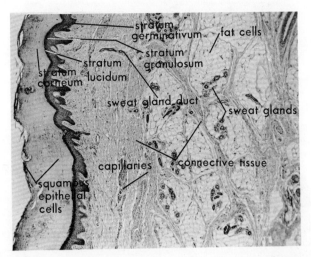

Fig. 15-3. Squamous epithelial cells of the epidermis. (Copyright by General Biological Supply House, Inc., Chicago.)

▶ Distinguish between white fibers of hyaline cartilage and wavy fibers of elastic cartilage (Figs. 15-2 and 15-5).

3—Bone (Fig. 15-5)—Study a transverse section from a long bone. Living cells are absent, as the slide was made from specially ground dried bone. This method of preparation fills all cell spaces and canals with fine powder causing them to appear as black areas or thin black lines. The outermost cover is *periosteum*, a fibroelastic sheath that surrounds the outer bone surface. Below this are concentric bone layers, *circumferential lamellae*, parallel to the outer surface. *Concentric lamellae* surround each central pore (*Haversian canal*), once a cavity for blood vessels. *Interstitial lamellae* fill the space between Haversian canals. Together they form a *Haversian system*. Bone cells (*osteocytes*) originally occupied the

Fig. 15-4. Cartilage, a specialized fibrous connective tissue. (Copyright by General Biological Supply House, Inc., Chicago.)

spaces between adjacent lamellae, but only lens-shaped spaces (lacunae) remain in your prepared specimen. *Bone cell processes* once served as intercellular bridges, passed through *canaliculi*, and connected different portions of living bone. All that remains are microscopic radiating lines of canaliculi. The large central *marrow cavity* connects with bone tissue by a *subperiosteal lymph space*. Note also that *Haversian canaliculi* radiate from each central canal. Specially prepared sections of decalcified bone, stained to show the cells, may be available and should be examined in conjunction with the ground dried bone preparations.

4—Skin (integument) (Fig. 15-3)—Rat or human skin is generally used. Study the successive layers with their associated cell types:

a. *epidermis*

1. *stratum corneum*—outermost or "horny" layer of *keratin* (main constituent of bone, hair, nails).

2. *stratum lucidum*—thin, translucent band, best seen in thickened skin of palm or sole.

3. *stratum granulosum*—flattened cells.

▶ How many layers comprise this stratum?

The dark stain is from *keratohyalin*, the same substance that forms keratin in the stratum corneum.

4. *stratum germinativum*—basal layer.

▶ What cell types can you find in this layer?

Fig. 15-5. Bone, a calcified fibrous connective tissue. (Copyright by General Biological Supply House, Inc., Chicago.)

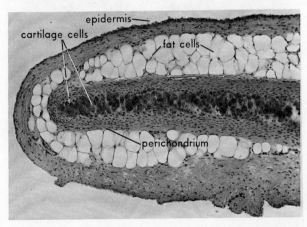

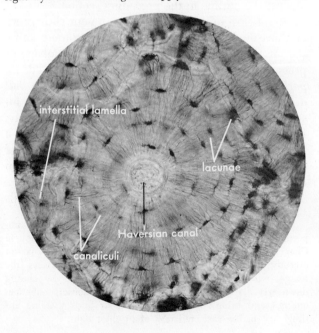

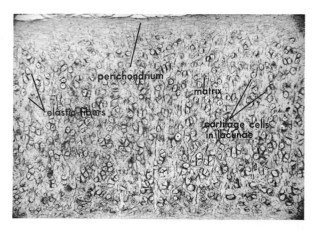

Fig. 15-6. Hyaline elastic cartilage. (Copyright by General Biological Supply House, Inc., Chicago.)

b. *dermis (corium)*—connective tissue with blood vessels, nerves, dermal glands; matrix of wavy collagenous fibers. Projections or *papillae* extend from the dermis into the lower epidermis.

Embedded in the skin are *hair follicles,* consisting of epithelial cells (*inner root sheath* and *outer root sheath*) and a connective tissue cover, or *theca.* The *hair shaft* arises from the center of the follicle.

Note the associated blood vessels and nerves in the hair papilla. With each hair is a delicate smooth muscle, the *arrectores pilorum* (which in man produces "goose pimples"), and a *sebaceous gland* usually connected with a follicle.

The gland secretes *sebum,* an oily substance that maintains the pliable structure of hair.

c. *sweat glands*—coiled tubular glands connected to the surface by a *sweat pore.* (These glands are absent in the rat, present in man.)

► Where are sweat glands found in the dog?

5—Blood—Study stained slides of frog or rat blood. Compare with fresh preparations. Notice the presence and large size of a *nucleus* in the frog erythrocytes.

► How many types of leucocytes can you identify?

6—Muscle (Figs. 15-7 to 15-9)—Study examples of striated, smooth, and cardiac muscle fibers.

► What stains were used on your slide?
► What does each type of stain show?

7—Nerve

a. *brain*—Cellular structures are made visible by a special *Golgi stain,* a silver impregnation process for brain cells that stains nerve cells black. Find different types of supporting or *glial* cells.

► What nerve cell types can you locate?

b. *spinal cord*—Locate the central, dense, cellular *gray matter,* and lighter outer *white matter,* containing few cells and many fibers. Find the *motor*

Fig. 15-7. Smooth muscle. Dark, oval elements represent the nuclei; the longer elements are the muscle fibers. (Copyright by General Biological Supply House, Inc., Chicago.)

Fig. 15-8. Striated muscle showing the multinucleate fibers with characteristic cross striations. (Copyright by General Biological Supply House, Inc., Chicago.)

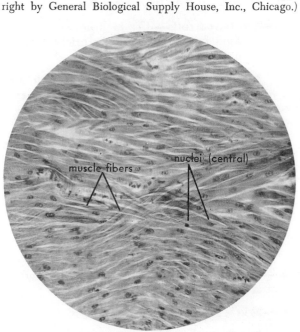

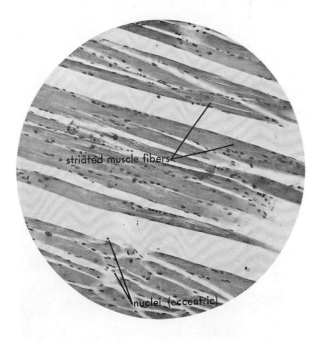

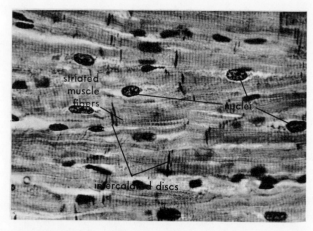

Fig. 15-9 Cardiac striated muscle showing interior nuclei, cross striations, anastomosing network of fibers, and intercalated discs. (Copyright by General Biological Supply House, Inc., Chicago.)

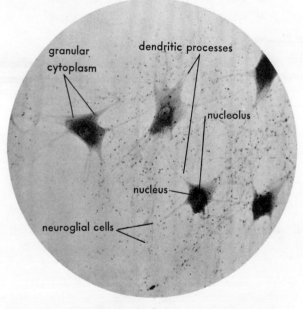

Fig. 15-10. Nervous tissue of the spinal cord showing five nerve cells and numerous neuroglia cells (small dark dots). (Copyright by General Biological Supply House, Inc., Chicago.)

Fig. 15-11. Ciliated epithelium isolated from frog mouth. (Copyright by General Biological Supply House, Inc., Chicago.)

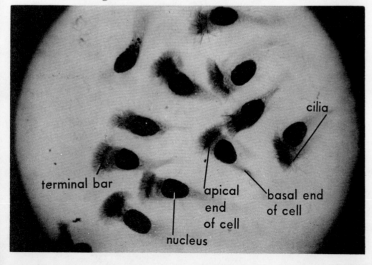

cells, very large cells at each corner of the base of the "butterfly"—a trapezoid formed by gray matter, named for its appearance in cross section. Study the *cell body* of a motor cell under high power (Fig. 15-10). Locate its large nucleus, nucleolus, granular cytoplasm, and processes.

▶ **What accounts for the difference between "white" and "gray" matter?**

Define: nerve, nerve cell body, dendrite, axon, motor cell, internuncial cell. Find an example of each in your slide.

B. Fresh Material

Study as many as possible of the living or fresh tissues listed below. Use small bits of tissue in order to get well-flattened preparations under the coverslip. Place the sample on your slide in a drop or two of 0.7 percent saline; if necessary, macerate it with needles to separate the cells before applying the cover. Thick or bulky samples are useless, as you are looking for *cell types,* not organ anatomy. Fresh blood samples can be smeared directly across a clean slide with the edge of another slide (see your instructor for details). They should be stained in Wright's or Giemsa's stain, or examined directly in a drop of saline.

From available material select representatives of the 5 basic types described in Section III. As you did with the stained preparations, select and *draw* an example of each.

Types of living material readily available (mostly from fresh frog tissue) are the following:

1—Red blood cells—Use high power to examine blood from human (finger prick), frog (heart puncture or cut toe), or rat (tip of tail).

▶ **How do the red cells of these animals compare with respect to cell size and shape, and presence of nucleus?**

▶ **Can you find any white cells?**

▶ **What happens to blood cells in saline that is too concentrated? Too dilute?**

2—Inner cheek scrapings—Use a toothpick to scrape the lining of your cheek. Mix contents in a drop of saline and examine.

▶ **What cell types do you find?**

▶ **What did you expect to find?**

3—Cartilage (Figs. 15-4 and 15-6)—Find matrix with embedded chondrocytes.

4—Skin (Fig. 15-3)

▶ **What cell types can you identify?**

NOTES AND DRAWINGS

(Tear along line)

5—Ciliated epithelium (Fig. 15-11)—Scrapings from roof of mouth of freshly killed frog will show movement of cilia under high power.

6—Muscle—Preserved or fresh tissues from frog or rat are generally used.

a. *striated (skeletal) muscle* (Fig. 15-8)—Macerate a small bit of elongate tissue from leg muscle, teasing it lengthwise to separate fibers. Find the *sarcolemma* (muscle membrane), *nuclei,* and *fibrils* with their transverse striations (hence: striated muscle).

b. *heart muscle* (Fig. 15-9)—Find the branches and anastomoses, and intercalated discs (dark bands).

c. *smooth (visceral) muscle* (Fig. 15-7)—Small sections of intestinal wall soaked in chloral hydrate are easiest to study. Find the tapering, elongate smooth muscle fibers, best seen at the edge of your preparation. Vital stains can be used to sharpen details and to accentuate the nuclei.

7—Nerve—Study carefully a portion of nerve from a freshly killed frog. Place in saline on your slide; separate the minute longitudinal fibers with your needles. Note that the nerve consists of a number of discrete nerve fibers, each of which is actually a *nerve cell process,* either an *axon* or *dendrite.*

▶ What is the difference between these types of nerve cell processes?

Under high power, study an axon and find its central, transparent *axis cylinder,* surrounded by the *myelin (medullary) sheath* and then the *neurilemma,* thin outermost membrane of the fiber.

▶ Which nerve fibers *lack* the myelin sheath?

8—Reproductive cells

a. *spermatozoa*—Male gametes can be studied from freshly excised testes of the frog, rat, or any other available animal in its breeding cycle.

Among invertebrates, the seminal vesicle of an earthworm, or the testis of *Ascaris* or various echinoderms are all excellent sources. Study a *diluted* sample in saline under high power and find the numerous actively moving spermatozoa.

▶ How do they move? Find the *head* (shape?) and *tail* (relative length?).

▶ Can you find developing *spermatids?*

▶ Are any other cells visible? Compare morphology of frog and *Ascaris* sperm.

b. *eggs*—Starfish or sea urchin ovaries are convenient as the eggs are small; the frog egg is good for low-power study. Note size and form of the *membrane,* the granular nature of the cytoplasm, and the large nucleus.

▶ Can you locate a *nucleolus?* A *polar body?* Define each.

C. Study of Organs—Complexes of Integrated Tissues

A more intensive study of vertebrate physiology than is possible here is needed to relate the activity of specific tissues with the functions of each organ. Yet a review of tissue constituents of organs will help show the sequence of organizational levels from cell, to tissue, to organ, to organ system, and to intact living organism. Among organs usually available in stained sections are the following: *liver, pancreas, kidney, esophagus, stomach, intestine, testis, ovary, lung, trachea, spinal cord,* and *brain.* Some of these have already been studied for details of cell or tissue types. Review examples given to you for tissue arrangement so as to develop a general concept of the construction of these organs.

Select *3* preparations of different organs; *draw* an outline of the entire structure, *label* the basic layers, and show *tissue and cellular detail* in a small pie-shaped portion.

CHAPTER 16

Cell

Division

I. INTRODUCTION

The life cycle of all sexually reproducing organisms consists of 2 basic steps: (1) gametogenesis and fertilization, and (2) differentiation, growth, and maturation.

Step 1 involves random *separation* and *recombination* of hereditary material (namely, genes and chromosomes).

Step 2 is operation of the genetic code from the sperm and egg in a newly fertilized egg (*zygote*) to produce an individual with characteristics of both parents. Expression of the inherited message continues throughout differentiation of cells, tissues, and organs, during later growth, and in the fully mature organism.

Mitosis, cell division of body (somatic) cells, is the chief means for orderly growth. This remarkable mechanism precisely apportions the nuclear substance of 1 cell into 2 daughter cells. The result is a continual and exact duplication of the essential nuclear control machinery, not once but billions of times. Some two and a half trillion cells are said to comprise the human body. The nuclear constitution of each somatic cell is identical to that of the zygote.

▶ How many mitotic generations would you estimate have occurred in *your* development from the zygote stage?

One primary purpose in this review of cell division is to recognize the mitotic mechanism for the incredible device it is—a means to convey genetic information imparted by sperm and egg into a zygote and thence to every living cell in the body, no matter how many or how specialized. So long as cells of an organism retain their nuclear apparatus intact, they remain genetically identical.

▶ Can you think of any cells that lose their nuclear constitution in the course of maturation?

A more restricted and specialized type of cell division occurs in the gonads when sexual cells (*gametes*) are formed. Gametes possess *half* the normal chromosome complement—1 chromosome from each pair—and thus are said to be *haploid* (1 set, or onefold). Somatic cells, in contrast, have 2 complete chromosome sets in their nuclei, and therefore are called *diploid. Meiosis,* the process by which haploid cells are produced from diploid ones in the gonads, is another example of precision cellular mechanics. A part of *gametogenesis* (gamete production), meiosis actually consists of 2 phases, 2 closely integrated divisions that produce 4 haploid nuclei from 1 diploid nucleus. As with mitosis, it is the steps of nuclear division that interest us. Details of nuclear rearrangement show the procedure of chromosomal reduction from diploidy to haploidy and tell us something of the genetic significance of these events. Maturation of the gametes—production of 4 mature spermatozoa or 1 egg and 3 polar cells—completes the processes of *spermatogenesis* or *oögenesis* following each meiotic (reduction) division.

The genetic shuffling referred to in step 1 occurs (1) in the separation of each chromosome pair at meiosis and (2) in the recombining of 2 chromosome sets when sperm and egg nuclei fuse in fertilization. Any one of the millions of sperms produced has as good a chance as any other to fertilize a particular egg. Another, perhaps greater source of random mixing occurs *within* each chromosome pair just before its separation at the reduction division. This is the process of *crossing over* between parts of each chromosome pair during the 4-thread or *tetrad* stage of the first meiotic division. Crossing over permits reciprocal exchange between corresponding portions of members of a tetrad. Hence, after meiosis, a gamete could possess a different array of genes in each chromosome than that found in the original mother cell of the sperm or egg.

Review these concepts carefully to make certain that you understand not only the steps in meiosis but also their significance. Though meiosis and fertilization are random processes, they are really highly complex, magnificently regularized mechanisms that ensure different gene combinations during successive generations. *This continual source of variation by genetic recombination is the raw material on which natural selection can act during the course of evolution.*

► What, then, is the *biological significance* of separate sexes?

Throughout this exercise, keep in mind the role of cells or processes being studied in relation to the total life cycle of the organism. Be able to distinguish between *meiosis, fertilization, differentiation, mitosis, embryology, growth,* and *maturation.* Know the definition of each term and its relationship to the others. Know when and where each occurs during an animal's lifetime.

Terms employed in describing cell division define useful—if arbitrary—stages of a continuous process: *interphase, prophase, metaphase, anaphase,* and *telophase.*

► Diagram each stage for both meiosis and mitosis.

► Distinguish between the two processes in terms of *essential details, overall differences,* and *basic biological significance* of those differences.

II. MITOSIS

A. Materials

Numerous organisms are useful to illustrate the mitotic stages. Large numbers of dividing cells are seen in slides of onion root tip (Figs. 16-1 to 16-3), hyacinth root tip, salamander larva epithelium, *Ascaris* developmental stages, and whitefish embryo (Figs. 16-4 to 16-9). Note that these are all rapidly growing, hence rapidly dividing regions or organisms.

B. Instructions

Examine slides showing various stages of division. Remember that the stages of mitosis are employed only to describe the continuing division process and to help us to study successive changes undergone by chromosomes, nucleus, and cytoplasm. Chromatin material will be stained black by a nuclear stain, usually *hematoxylin;* cytoplasm will probably appear gray (reddish if stained with *eosin,* a cytoplasmic counterstain).

Laboratory diagrams and models should be studied to help you visualize mitosis as a three-dimensional process.

1—Interphase (Figs. 16-1 to 16-3)—During this nondividing stage, chromosomes are metabolically most active. They are uncoiled, giving the nucleus an irregular network appearance once thought to indicate that the chromosomes literally broke apart during interphase. Recent studies have proven that the individual chromosomes, though extremely long during their unwound active period, retain their individual integrity at all times. Find the *cell membrane, nuclear membrane,* and *centrosome* (small sphere near nucleus, with a dark granule, the *centriole*). Note the vacuolated cytoplasm.

2—Prophase (Figs. 16-1 to 16-5)—This stage marks the onset of nuclear reorganization prior to division. It is characterized by centrosome division and gradual thickening of individual chromosomes owing to coiling of the strands. Actually, each chromosome consists of 2 identical halves, called *chromatids.*[1] These

---

[1] Do not confuse *chromatids,* the precisely identical halves of each chromosome thread, with *chromosome pair,* 2 distinct and separate *homologous chromosomes* carrying corresponding genetic units. One member of each homologous chromosome pair can be traced to the sperm, the other to the egg of the original zygote.

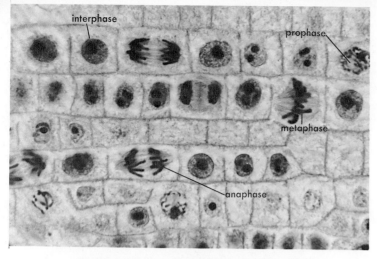

Fig. 16-1. Various mitotic phases in the onion root tip. (Copyright by General Biological Supply House, Inc., Chicago.)

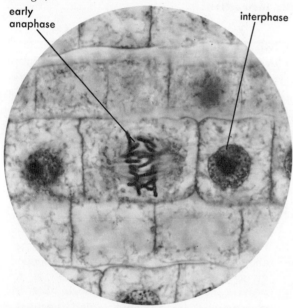

Fig. 16-2. Onion root tip, early anaphase. (Copyright by General Biological Supply House, Inc., Chicago.)

Fig. 16-3. Onion root tip, interphase, anaphase, and telophase. (Copyright by General Biological Supply House, Inc., Chicago.)

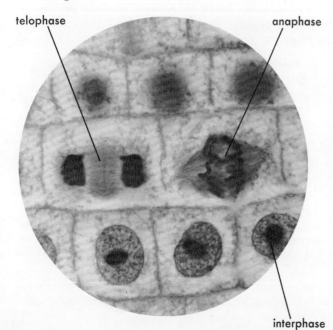

halves separate during later phases. The divided centrioles move to opposite ends of the cell to form poles towards which the daughter nuclei will later move.

3—Metaphase (Figs. 16-1, 16-4, 16-6, and 16-7)—This stage is marked by alignment of separate chromosomes along the center of the cell (*equatorial plate*) accompanied by dissolution of the nuclear membrane and appearance of *astral rays*[2] or fibers around each centriole. *Individual chromosomes in this stage are not paired,* but align themselves separately on the equatorial plate. Each chromosome, however, retains its 2 halves or chromatids. Look for *spindle fibers* between each chromosome and its centriole. The point of spindle fiber attachment on the chromosome is the *centromere.*

4—Anaphase (Figs. 16-1 to 16-4 and 16-8 and 16-9)—The centromeres split, 1 division product remaining attached to the chromatid of each chromosome. The chromatids first separate; after separation they then begin a rapid migration toward opposite poles. (The speed and precision of this step can best be appreciated by observing it in a time-lapse motion picture.) The chromatids assume a sharply angular shape—usually a V. The point of the angle marks the centromere, and it is this which leads the movement toward one of the centrioles. This movement may be caused by contraction and pulling of the spindle fibers, causing each centromere, and in turn the attached chromatid, to be drawn towards the centrioles. It may also be due to mutual repulsion of the division products of each centromere. The result, however explained, is a cluster of chromatids assembled in 2 groups, one around each centriole. Note that the 2 chromatids of each chromosome always move to opposite poles, assuring *equal division of the nuclear material.* The chromatids can now be considered separate chromosomes and the 2 chromosome clusters daughter nuclei, each with a set of precisely similar genetic material.

5—Telophase (Fig. 10-3)—Each daughter nucleus becomes enclosed in a new nuclear membrane. The chromosomes uncoil and appear again as chromatin networks. New centrosomes appear. Cytoplasmic separation occurs in plants as an ingrowth of a distinct plate or cell wall. In animals it results from an unfolding of cytoplasm between the nuclei and a gradual pinching apart of the daughter cells.

[2] Absent in plant cells.

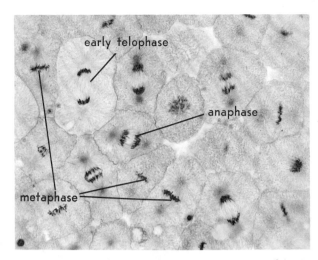

Fig. 16-4. Whitefish mitosis showing various mitotic figures. (Copyright by General Biological Supply House, Inc., Chicago.)

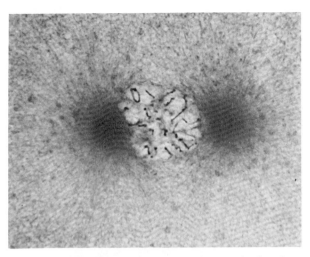

Fig. 16-5. Whitefish, early prophase. (Copyright by General Biological Supply House, Inc., Chicago.)

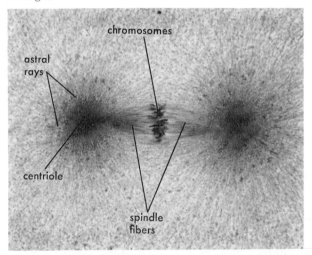

Fig. 16-6. Whitefish metaphase. (Copyright by General Biological Supply House, Inc., Chicago.)

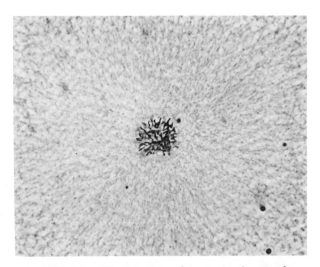

Fig. 16-7. Whitefish mitosis, polar view of metaphase. (Copyright by General Biological Supply House, Inc., Chicago.)

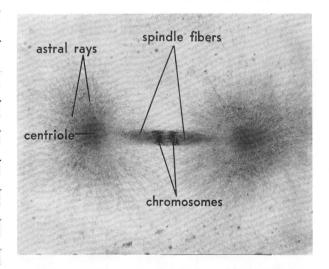

Fig. 16-8. Whitefish mitosis, anaphase. (Copyright by General Biological Supply House, Inc., Chicago.)

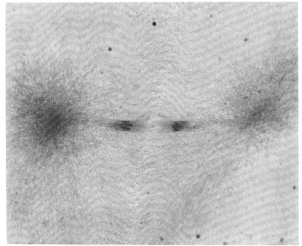

Fig. 16-9. Whitefish mitosis, late anaphase. (Copyright by General Biological Supply House, Inc., Chicago.)

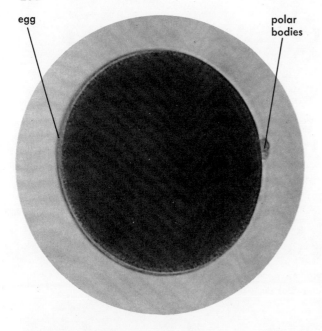

egg　　　　　　　　　　　polar bodies

Fig. 16-10. Starfish polar body formation. (Copyright by General Biological Supply House, Inc., Chicago.)

Find as many of the above stages as possible in both *polar* view (looking down on the metaphase plate so that chromosomes are viewed arranged in a circle or in a central cluster) and in *lateral* view (showing both centrioles).

Draw each stage, including both an early and late prophase, selecting the view that shows each stage to best advantage. Label parts referred to in the above discussion, designate view shown, magnification, and other pertinent details.

▶ Where in the body does mitosis ordinarily occur?

▶ What is meant by the statement, "*Unpaired chromosomes appear on the equatorial plate, yet each is actually doubled*"?

▶ How is exact equality of partition ensured?

III. MEIOSIS

A. Introduction

Meiosis is not only a precision means of producing variability, but of producing *balanced variability* so that each gamete has a complete chromosome set, hence a complete gene set. Nothing in nature is more precise—millions of sperms or eggs, each with 1 representative of every single genetic factor common to that species. Think of the effect if the method were slightly *less* exact, some sperm re-

ceiving extra genes for one structure, missing a few for another!

Our purpose in this exercise is to review the steps by which this precise division takes place and to understand the biological significance of the result.

Thoroughly familiarize yourself with diagrams of meiosis by which germ cells are produced in ovaries and testes.

Note that in egg formation, the meiotic process results in *1 egg* and *3 polar bodies* (Fig. 16-10); the latter are essentially nuclei lacking cytoplasm. The single egg carries most of the cytoplasm of the other 3 cells, an apparent adaptation to the nutritive needs of the egg and early zygote.

Sperms, however, are little more than tailed, haploid nuclei with very little cytoplasm. All 4 cells derived from the 2 meiotic divisions of a sperm mother cell become mature spermatozoa. Hence, 4 times as many sperm result from the same number of mother cells as in the case of eggs. Yet, the basic process of meiosis is identical in each case, and should be studied chiefly from the standpoint of chromosomal changes resulting in the formation of haploid gametes.

▶ What is the function of meiosis?

▶ How is meiosis related to reproduction in general and to sexual reproduction in particular?

▶ How is meiosis related to fertilization? To mitosis?

B. Procedure

Your material showing spermatogenesis probably will be taken from the testis of a salamander, frog, or grasshopper.

Each lobe of the frog testis usually contains material at an approximately equal stage of development. Look for mature gametes near the opening of the sperm duct and for developing ones at the opposite end. In the grasshopper, testes are slender *lobes,* each with its own duct. Lobes are subdivided into *lobules,* each with progressively more advanced gamete maturation from the tip of the lobule to the sperm duct, where mature sperm are found.

For oögenesis, developing eggs of the nematode *Ascaris* are particularly favored demonstration material. This organism has very few chromosomes (only two pairs in the species generally used in these studies, *Ascaris megalocephala,* a parasite of horses). Successive stages of meiosis can therefore readily be followed with eggs of this species.

For orientation, examine under low power a prepared slide of testicular material showing sper-

NOTES AND DRAWINGS

(Tear along line)

matogenesis, and of ovarian material illustrating oögenesis. In each, attempt to find the characteristic stages of meiotic divisions summarized below.

Examine the stages later under high-dry or oil immersion for maximum detail.

Draw each stage using selected examples from your slide. Be prepared to explain the genetic significance of each stage you have drawn.

First meiotic division (reductional division)

Prophase. This, the longest portion of the full division sequence, is divided into a number of substages. Basically, it is the time when chromosomes coil and shorten and the 2 separate chromosomes of each *homologous pair* come together. This is termed *synapsis*, or *pairing*. As in mitosis, each chromosome has 1 *centromere* and 2 *chromatids*. The synaptic pair thus forms a group (*tetrad*) of 4 chromatids. It is at this stage that the important process of *crossing over* occurs. As in mitosis, the centriole divides, separates, and marks the poles of the dividing cell.

Metaphase. The nuclear membrane breaks, tetrads start to separate, *asters* form around the centrioles, and the process of chromosome separation, the *true reduction phase*, begins.

Anaphase. Continuation of the above —each chromosome (still consisting of its *2 chromatids*) moves towards one of the 2 centrioles, 1 chromosome from each pair going to opposite poles.

Telophase. End of division 1 of meiosis, with precisely half the chromosome number in each daughter cell. Yet each chromosome still consists of its 2 chromatids, tied together by a single centromere.

Second meiotic division (equatorial division)

This division occurs without a preceding interphase, as a direct continuation of the first division. Each daughter cell of division 1 undergoes a rapid, mitotic type of division. The chromosomes line up, each consisting, as noted above, of 2 chromatids connected by a single centromere.

Metaphase. The centromeres split, allowing separation of chromatids towards opposite poles.

Anaphase. Chromatids pull apart rapidly, centromeres first, and form 2 groups, one around each centriole. A new nuclear membrane forms around each cluster.

Telophase. The final division sequence, cytoplasmic separation. Each haploid nucleus now contains only single-stranded, distinct chromosomes—*1 thread from each tetrad* (original pair of homologous chromosomes).

These stages are followed by completion of the gametogenic process, production of mature spermatozoa or eggs. In the male, 4 haploid *spermatids* are the products of meiosis of a diploid mother *spermatogonium*. Each spermatid elongates, develops a tail, and becomes the rapidly motile, fully developed *spermatozoan* (sperm). In the female, corresponding stages are 4 haploid *oötids*, meiotic products of 1 diploid *oögonium*. However, only 1 viable egg results. The 3 *polar bodies*, seen on the egg surface, are the nuclei of 3 oötids whose cytoplasm was absorbed by the fourth oötid that became the mature egg.

▶ Can you see the adaptive importance of this?

Fertilization is the consummation of the sexual process, in which 2 mature nuclei of opposite sex fuse within the egg and form a single nucleus. The product becomes a diploid zygote and the process of development of a new, diploid individual begins with the first cleavage division.

▶ What type of cell division follows zygote formation?

In some organisms, fertilization may occur before completion of oögenesis. In these cases sperm entry stimulates rapid completion of the developmental process and nuclear fusion follows. The formation of the fusion (diploid) nucleus stimulates an entire sequence of physiological events that result in *development, growth, maturation,* and, ultimately, a new individual.

▶ What might be the result in the next generation if meiosis failed and *diploid* gametes were formed?

▶ Does this actually occur in nature?

▶ How is meiosis related to genetic variability? To evolution?

I. INTRODUCTION

A. General Considerations

Differentiation and embryo development and growth, summarized in the term *embryology*, embody a wondrous sequence of change. Our objectives during this laboratory period are not only to see some of the earliest stages of development, but also to become familiar with the evolutionary significance of the patterns disclosed. Both living and stained material will be used to observe cleavage stages and cell and tissue differentiation. Advanced embryological stages, best seen in stained whole mounts or tissue serial sections, will be studied in a later course in embryology. If time and facilities permit, however, you will enjoy observing later developmental sequences in frog larvae or chick eggs, both of which are easily maintained in the laboratory through their full embryological period.

Fertilization, cleavage, and blastula and gastrula formation can be observed in a number of marine invertebrates. Echinoderm embryos are especially good to work with owing to lack of yolk, shells, and membranes, and consequent ease of study. Their early pattern of development, especially cleavage and gastrulation, is both dramatic and diagrammatically simple. For inland laboratories, frog eggs or those of any other amphibian collected during the breeding season are suitable. These vertebrates demonstrate the embryological process through metamorphosis and to development of the adult organism. Chick embryos are also excellent under the specialized conditions of a yolk-laden egg enclosed in special membranes within a calcified shell. Fixed preparations of mammals may also be used; these are often the 6, 12, and 20 mm stages of pig embryos or even various stages of calf development. Comparative material helps to illustrate broadly similar patterns of development in widely differing vertebrates.

B. Early Developmental Stages

Descriptions of the stages listed below are based on *Pisaster ochraceus*, the common Pacific sea star.

1—Unfertilized egg (Fig. 17-1)—The female gamete is recognizable by its large nucleus (at this stage termed a pronucleus or *germinal vesicle*), by its *nucleolus*, and by the surrounding *cell membrane*. The *animal hemisphere* is the portion with least yolk; the *vegetal hemisphere* (not vegetable, please) has the greatest amount of yolk.

CHAPTER **17**

Embryology

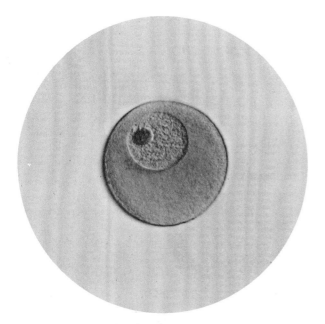

Fig. **17-1.** An unfertilized sea star ovum showing the nucleus and nucleolus. (Copyright by General Biological Supply House, Inc., Chicago.)

2—Fertilized egg (zygote)—Immediately after sperm entry, a remarkable series of physical and physiological changes commences. Sudden alteration of the egg surface prevents entry of other sperm; then follows rapid formation of a *fertilization membrane* extruded under an outer jelly layer. The sperm head penetrates the egg cytoplasm and its nuclear material forms a *male pronucleus* that fuses with the *female pronucleus* to form the *fertilization nucleus.*

3—Cleavage—The early mitoses following zygote formation, *before any increase in size occurs,* constitute the cleavage stage. Furrows or cleavage planes can be seen in the cytoplasm. The resulting cells are blastomeres. During this initial phase of differentiation cleavage divides the zygote into smaller units, establishes the basic symmetry, and blocks out future zones of specialized growth. Certain materials responsible for later differentiation appear to be passed to various blastomeres during cleavage.

a. *2-cell stage* (Fig. 17-2). The first cleavage is by several times the slowest; it divides the zygote into equal meridional halves with the furrow passing through the animal and vegetal pole. This division establishes the primary bilateral symmetry.
b. *4-cell stage* (Fig. 17-3). The second cleavage plane, also meridional but at right angles to the

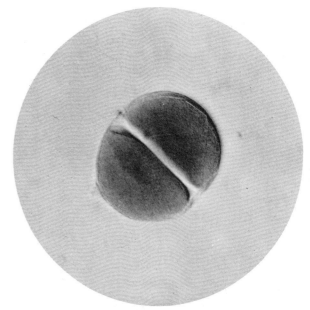

Fig. **17-2.** Two-cell stage of the sea star. The egg has divided by mitosis into two cells, with the cells remaining in contact with each other. (Copyright by General Biological Supply House, Inc., Chicago.)

first, produces 4 equal blastomeres, like quarters of an orange.
c. *8-cell stage* (Fig. 17-3). The third cleavage is equatorial, passing slightly above the equator and perpendicular to the other 2 cleavages. At this stage the yolk apparently slows division in the

Fig. **17-3.** The 8-cell stage of the sea star results in two tiers of cells, one on top of the other. However, the division is not quite equal, with the result that the upper cells are smaller than those in the lower tier. (Copyright by General Biological Supply House, Inc., Chicago.)

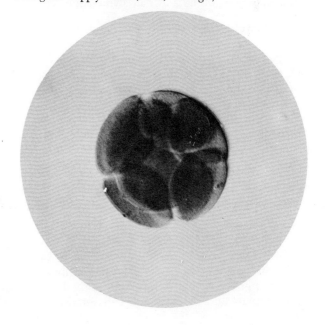

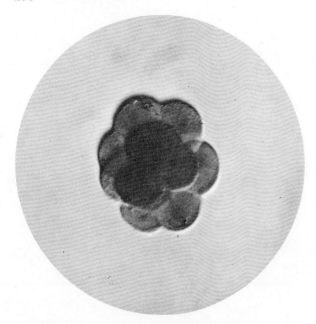

Fig. 17-4. The 16-cell stage of the sea star results in a solid ball of cells. (Copyright by General Biological Supply House, Inc., Chicago.)

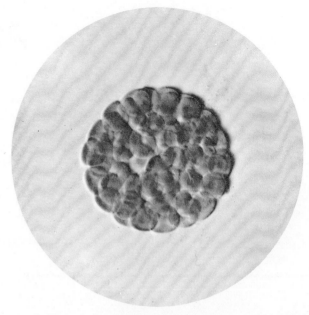

Fig. 17-5. Sea star zygote, later cleavage stage. (Copyright by General Biological Supply House, Inc., Chicago.)

vegetal hemisphere and tends to permit more rapid cleavage in the animal hemisphere. The smaller animal cells, *micromeres,* possess little yolk. Vegetal cells, laden with yolk, are macromeres.

d. *16-cell stage* (Fig. 17-4). No definite cell arrangement can be seen, only a solid ball of cells, the *morula.*

e. *32-cell and subsequent stages* (Fig. 17-5). Continuation of mitoses forms a single-layered, hollow sphere of ciliated cells. This stage initiates the larval phase, when the organism leaves the fertilization membrane and can swim about freely.

4—Blastula (Fig. 17-6)—This is the single layered sphere of about 1000 ciliated cells arranged around a central *segmentation cavity* or *blastocoel.* Cleavage is now complete and *blastulation* has occurred. The blastula is still approximately the size of the original egg, hence the blastomeres necessarily have become progressively smaller as cleavage continued.

▶ How does the genetic constitution of the blastomeres compare with that of the zygote? Of the original egg?

5—Gastrula (Figs. 17-7 to 17-9)—This is the change from a *1*-layered to a *2*-layered embryo by differential growth and movement of cells in *gastrulation.* The 2-layered embryo forms after the vegetal hemisphere of the blastula flattens and the flattened cells gradually

move into the blastocoel (*invagination*). Rapid cell division causes rolling in of cells (*epiboly*) at the margin of the depression. Together, these changes produce the 2-layered gastrula. Though it varies widely in different groups, gastrulation is the first step in the formation of the *primary germ layers* (*ectoderm, mesoderm, endoderm*). In most animals, gastrulation is rather strikingly modified from the simple echinoderm pattern, chiefly because yolky portions of the larva slow down and interfere

Fig. 17-6. Sea star blastula. (Copyright by General Biological Supply House, Inc., Chicago.)

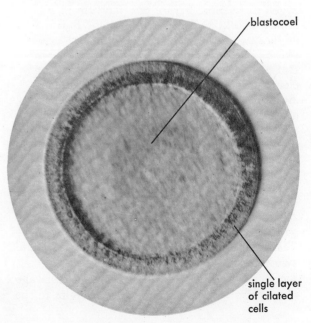

blastocoel

single layer of ciliated cells

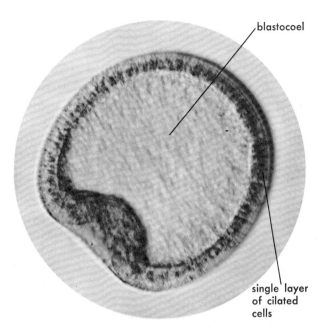

Fig. 17-7. Early gastrula stage of the sea star. (Copyright by General Biological Supply House, Inc., Chicago.)

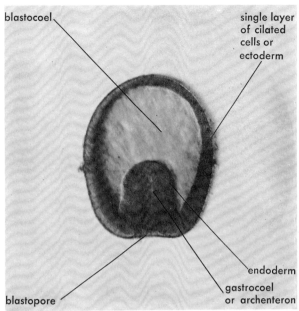

Fig. 17-8. Sea star gastrula showing blastopore and beginning of gastrocoel cavity. (Copyright by General Biological Supply House, Inc., Chicago.)

with the process. In a hen's egg, for example, the gastrula is a tiny island of tissue floating on a huge, dense yolk. But the end results are similar, whether cells sink in, roll in at the blastocoel margin, or simply move independently into the cavity and re-form as an inner layer.

As the inner layer forms it gradually eliminates the old blastocoel and forms a new cavity, the *gastrocoel* (or *archenteron*, meaning "primitive gut"). The external opening of the blastocoel is the *blastopore*—posterior end of the larva, future *anus* in echinoderms, and *neurenteric canal* in vertebrates.

The new embryo now changes rapidly. It elongates along the blastopore axis and begins to develop the important middle layer of the body, the mesoderm. The external cell layer, ectoderm, forms the body covering and most of the nervous system. The endoderm or inner layer, formed from cells that have invaginated into the blastocoel, eventually becomes the gut lining. In echinoderms, hemichordates, and primitive chordates such as Amphioxus, a pair of *enterocoels* (literally, gut pockets) bulge out from the roof of the gut and form *coelomic pouches* that gradually fill the space between ectoderm and endoderm. These pouches then separate from the gut and grow to form mesoderm tissue sheets that in turn form the *coelom*. Where the sheets join above and below the gut along the dorsal and ventral axes of the embryo, they form a double-walled *mesentery*. The bulk of body substance in eucoelomates develops from

mesoderm and is formed in close association with the mesodermal linings and coelom.

C. Evolutionary Considerations

The coelom has been discussed as a format for complexity and a highly efficient mode of animal organization. Coelomic construction, in fact, helps define "higher animals." All bilaterally symmetrical animals (Grade **BILATERIA**) are grouped on the

Fig. 17-9. Late gastrula stage of the sea star. (Copyright by General Biological Supply House, Inc., Chicago.)

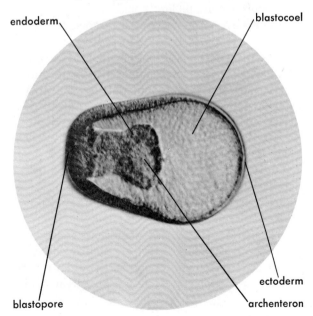

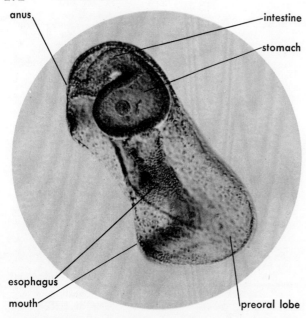

anus   intestine
stomach
esophagus
mouth
preoral lobe

Fig. 17-10. The swimming dipleurula larva of the sea star. (Copyright by General Biological Supply House, Inc., Chicago.)

basis of their coelom, whether absent, partial, or complete (that is, the Levels **ACOELOMATA, PSEUDOCOELOEMATA,** and **EUCOELOMATA**; review Chapter 6 (p. 43) for discussion of these categories).

    The majority of animals are eucoelomates, as we have seen. Embryological study of the coelom, however, shows that it develops by 2 clearly distinct methods. This distinction, along with *manner of cleavage of the zygote* and common possession of a particular *type of larva,* separates the Level **EUCO-ELOEMATA** into 2 large groups of phyla—the Superphylum **ENTEROCOELA** (sometimes termed the "echinoderm-chordate line") and the Superphylum **SCHIZOCOELA** (the "annelid-arthropod line").

    The enterocoel type of mesoderm and coelom formation is considered to be of sufficient evolutionary as well as structural significance to indicate a fundamental hereditary relationship among animals developing in this manner. The Superphylum **ENTEROCOELA** therefore was erected to include the Phyla **POGONOPHORA, CHAETOGNATHA, ECHINODERMATA, HEMICHORDATA,** and **CHORDATA** (in spite of great modifications in higher chordates). *Radial* (as opposed to *spiral*) cleavage of the embryo and common possession of a *dipleurula* swimming larva also link these groups. The dipleurula larvae of certain echinoderms and acorn worms (hemichordates) are similar enough to have been mistaken one for another—yet they develop into adults so different as to be placed in distinct phyla.

► What does this indicate about the usefulness of characteristics expressed *early* in development as indicators of fundamental relationship?

    A totally different pattern of mesoderm and coelom formation characterizes the other huge group of higher organisms, the annelid-mollusk-arthropod complex forming the Superphylum **SCHIZOCOELA.** In these animals, mesoderm forms as *paired bands* growing from specific cells in the blastopore area; zygote cleavage is *spiral,* not radial; and a *trochophore* larva is formed. The mesodermal bands later split to form the coelom. This process, *schizocoely* (split-coelom), shows many interesting differences from the enterocoel pattern. The substances that later form mesoderm cells of schizocoels become differentiated far sooner than in enterocoels. In certain annelids and mollusks, future mesoderm cytoplasm can even be located within the *egg.* Coelom and mesoderm formation, combined with the distinctly different type of cleavage and larval form, mark the 2 groups as genetically far separated. This, in turn, implies origin of the embryological patterns *after* separation of the 2 lines from a still earlier common ancestor.

    Though it appears much the same as a final product, the coelom of enterocoels and of schizocoels is formed by such distinct embryological steps that the similarity is thought to be an evolutionary *convergence* (similarity of 2 structures or animals derived from different evolutionary antecedents).

► Can you think of any other example of convergence?

    Embryological patterns are significant in telling us how individual animals develop, and are also useful in defining relationships so ancient that traces of them are no longer apparent in the adult organism. The *adult* animal generally demonstrates more recent or specialized structures acquired later in evolution.

► *Explain* or *rephrase* each of the following embryological generalities so that their meanings are clear to you.

    1. Between *distantly* related animals (having separated from a common ancestor far back in time), developmental patterns show similarities chiefly in the *earliest* stages. Between *closely* related animals the pattern is similar throughout, diverging only late in development (*compare:* embryological sequence or *ontogeny* of man and chicken with that of man and ape).

    2. An eye-catching statement, "Ontogeny recapitulates phylogeny" (development of an individ-

ual repeats the evolution of its race), was once considered a biological maxim. A more accurate, modern version would be, "Ontogeny repeats *embryological stages* in phylogeny."

II. *LABORATORY INSTRUCTIONS*

A. Sea stars

1—Patiria, the bat sea star, is sexually ripe at any time of the year. Laid out on moistened paper toweling, it will readily extrude eggs (orange) or sperm (whitish). Other sea stars or echinoderms should be collected only when sexually active. Dissect out the gonads to assure an abundance of viable eggs and sperms. Wash eggs several times in fresh sea water in *clean* finger bowls. To a fairly large suspension of such eggs, add a drop or two of *diluted* testicular material (containing many millions of sperm). *Adding too heavy a sperm suspension will inhibit* proper development by causing polyspermy (fertilization by more than 1 sperm per egg) and arrested or abnormal cleavage.

At 15-minute intervals, pipette out a few eggs (with a clean pipette—the eggs are sensitive to minute amounts of impurities) and examine microscopically. Keep accurate notes of observations, including a time schedule of important embryological changes.

Find and *draw* good examples of the following stages from your own or other students' living material or from stained slides.

a. *Unfertilized egg.*

b. *Fertilized egg (zygote).* Show jelly layer, fertilization membrane, nuclear changes.

c. *2-, 4-, 8-, 16-cell stages.* At normal room temperature these should appear in 3 or 4 hours.

d. *Blastula.* Draw an optical section (cross section visible when you focus on the center of the organism). Show blastocoel, micromeres, and macromeres.

e. *Gastrula.* Find early stages of invagination. Draw an optical section.

f. *Advanced gastrula.* Draw an optical section showing outpockets of coelomic pouches.

g. *Bipinnaria and brachiolaria larvae.* Examine these interesting larvae; compare them with *dipleurula* larva.

2—Frog or salamander

a. *Procedure.* Spring or early summer are the best times to collect breeding frogs. Ovulation may be artificially induced at other times of the year by injecting ground hypophysis material, containing the hormones stimulating sexual development, into the female body cavity. (The hypophysis is a small endocrine gland that can be dissected out from the ventral surface of the brain.) After ovulation, which generally occurs 24 to 48 hours after injection, eggs may be squeezed from the ripe female and covered with a diluted suspension of sperm from the ground-up testis of a male frog.

Fertilized eggs should be kept in a shallow dish, well lighted, and in *fresh, regularly changed* pond water. If proper care is taken to change the water daily and feed the developing tadpoles with bits of bread crumbs or yeast, they can be maintained throughout their developmental period. Normal feeding habits will be observed by placing tadpoles in a fresh-water aquarium where they can feed on algae. Record stages of development, temperature (try varying it on different groups of tadpoles), and types of food consumed. If possible, follow the entire metamorphosis and turn in a careful report on this special project.

b. *Stages to study and draw* (stained or living material).

1. *Zygote.*

2. *2-, 4-, 8-, and 12- or 16-cell stage.* Show cleavage furrows, location of resulting cells and disposition of pigment. Be sure to notice size of cells in advanced stages of cleavage, and relationship between cell size and cleavage rate (cell number) at the animal and vegetal hemispheres.

3. *Early blastula* (32 cells). Note blastocoel and gradual incorporation of yolk into vegetal cells. If stained sections are available, study these for a better idea of relationships between blastocoel, embryonic hemispheres, and individual cells.

Fixed, unmounted specimens can be cut in half under a dissecting microscope or hand lens and examined.

4. *Gastrula.* Locate a crescent-shaped slit between the pigmented animal and nonpigmented vegetal cells. Pigmented cells cover more than half of the sphere, owing to their more rapid division. Continued rapid division and downward migration cause these cells to cover most of the larva. A *germ ring*, originally an equatorial belt of cells, marks the margin of the advancing movement of animal hemisphere cells. As these cells shift in position, the vegetal hemisphere cells move into the blastocoel and overgrowth of animal hemisphere cells continues. Eventually the germ ring encircles the remaining external yolk cells and marks the blastopore. Continued growth of pigmented cells reduces the ring to a *yolk-plug*, then to a minute opening. As gastrulation is completed, the embryo rotates 90° in its jelly envelopes, causing the true dorsal surface to be uppermost.

Draw a vegetal view of a frog gastrula, showing the blastopore slit; then draw a later stage in which the slit has become a yolk-plug.

The dorsal margin or lip of the germ ring (the crescentic slit mentioned earlier) is of particular interest. This is the *dorsal lip of the blastopore*—a key center of organization of the embryo—where the *primary organizer*—a diffusible chemical responsible for onset of a chain of chemically induced differentiation—is produced. The first structure to be differentiated from invaginating cells which form the *archenteron roof* (*chordamesoderm*) is the *notochord*. This marks the mid-dorsal region of the embryo, an area of intense activity and rapid differentiation. Gastrulation in the frog is a distinct modification from enterocoelic pouches as in echinoderms and Amphioxus. It is, however, similar to the above process, since mesoderm is formed from particular archenteron roof cells and later separated out as a double tissue sheet to form the coelom.

Each step in differentiation follows a preceding stimulus that in turn induces another stage in this extraordinary series of sequential changes. The total process is especially remarkable when we realize that throughout the rapid, highly integrated development, the embryo must utilize food, respire, and metabolize as an independent functioning organism enclosed within its protective jelly envelopes. The corresponding echinoderm dipleurula and the annelid trochophore are actually free-swimming organisms at this stage.

► What would the chick embryo look like at the corresponding stage? The human embryo?

5. *Later stages.*

i. Stained section of a *late gastrula*. Locate the blastopore, reduced blastocoel, gastrocoel (archenteron), remaining yolk cells, and primary germ layers. The mesoderm is starting to form notochord from the roof of the archenteron at this stage.

ii. *Neural fold stage.* Find mesoderm, notochord, and *neural plate* (or neural *fold*, depending on the stage).

► Which are the anterior, posterior, dorsal, ventral axes?

► Where is the anus? Mouth? Brain?

iii. *Neural tube stage.* Note fusion of the neural folds.

► What do they form?

Find the *mesodermal somites*.

► What will they produce?

Review the overall sequence of stages to this point.

► What major changes are yet to occur in the developing tadpole?

Further observations can be made through stages of tadpole growth and metamorphosis (leg and mouth formation in the young adult, disappearance of the tail and operculum). Tadpoles should be maintained in aquaria and watched carefully over a long period of time. Periodic examination of sacrificed specimens will show changes in both external and internal anatomy and provide ample material for additional study by interested students.

NOTES AND DRAWINGS

(Tear along line)

CHAPTER 18

Genetics

I. INTRODUCTION

In the preceding sections we reviewed the series of changes in the life cycle of an organism from a fertilized egg of one generation to production of a fertilized egg in the next generation. *Cell division, differentiation, growth, gametogenesis,* and *fertilization* are all parts of this process.

In this course it has been necessary to study aspects of the cell cycle one at a time in a rather piecemeal fashion. But relationships of the processes and their applicability to every living thing always must be kept in mind. Now near the end of our review, we should be able to integrate these different concepts into an overall appreciation of both the variations and the uniformities of organic life.

The significance of life cycle stages in terms of genetic recombination and variation, mechanics of inheritance, chromosome structure, and gene action all fall within the scope of *genetics,* the study of heredity.

Genetics is rapidly becoming one of the theoretical underpins of all biological knowledge. It no longer is simply a quantitative study of inheritance of specific characters, such as eye or hair color (*classical genetics*). During the past few years, investigations on transmission of traits have expanded to include control mechanisms in development (*developmental genetics*) and hereditary direction of the physiological action of the whole organism (*physiological genetics*). All cellular activities, including functioning of adult cells, tissues, and organs, reflect the results of *gene action*. Another aspect of this wide-ranging science is the development of special statistical techniques for study of evolutionary processes and species formation (*population genetics*). Still more recently, genetics has helped to probe the very heart of life itself: the structure of the gene and manner in which its "coded" messages are conveyed from nucleus to cytoplasm. Such research is far from finished. Every question answered raises many more that could not previously even have been asked. Each answer adds to our understanding and throws exploratory light into still deeper recesses of vast unknown areas of biology.

This laboratory period can illustrate only a few basic principles of the gene and of the chromosomal theory of inheritance, but these form the base on which the science of genetics is built. Chief among these principles is the *quantitative* and *statistical* (or *unitary*) nature of transmission of inherited traits.

Hereditary transmission of genetic factors through successive generations without "blending" or dilution is the so-called First Postulate of Mendel: *the nonmixing of hereditary factors or genes* (termed *alleles* by early workers). Nearly 100 years after its discovery, this principle is still the foundation of modern genetics.

Many organisms can serve equally well as tools for study of genetic principles. Work with viruses, bacteria, molds, protozoa, worms, fruit flies, wasps, corn, peas, rats, mice, man, and many other organisms has contributed knowledge on the subject. Smaller and relatively simpler organisms have the advantage of ease of handling, rapid life cycle, and fairly easily identified characteristics by which individuals or populations differ and through which results can be gauged.

Drosophila melanogaster, the common fruit fly, is the most famous of all genetic tools. More of its hereditary pattern is known than of any other living creature, including man. Research techniques have been carefully worked out and many identifiable traits or "marker genes" are available for study. Marker genes are actually *mutations*—permanent, inherited differences from the so-called normal expression of some trait. These mutations usually result from exposure of fruit flies of earlier generations to x-rays. All life cycle stages of the fly can be x-rayed and any change produced is permanent (hereditary) *if these changes happen to involve appropriate reproductive rather than somatic cells.*

Mutant stocks have been carefully bred, catalogued, studied, and compared with original or "wild type" flies over the course of 60 years. Crosses between normal and mutant flies are followed in terms of number and proportions of progeny showing mutant or normal traits. Large numbers of offspring are raised and experimental crosses are repeated many times to give statistical validity to conclusions reached. Essential for these experiments are the procedures originated in the brilliantly lucid studies of Mendel during the last century, as valid today as then:

1—Maintenance of parent stocks pure *(homozygous)* for both normal and mutant expression of each particular character.

2—Controlled crossing between these parental stocks.

3—Accurate counts of all progeny; statistical evaluation of these counts and determination of ratios of classes of offspring showing the mutation.

Results expected under the particular theory being tested are compared statistically with results actually obtained. New theories are proposed or views developed as to the probable manner of transmission of the trait, based on interpretation of the proportions of progeny found expressing the marker. From such experiments, and many others considerably more complex, the current concepts of hereditary transmission of specific chromosomes and genes have been developed. This imposing body of knowledge has been verified and advanced by innumerable experiments. The history of its development is one of the most brilliant and exciting chapters of modern biology.

II. LABORATORY INSTRUCTIONS

A. Introduction

The original parents of an experimental cross, one pure for the marker trait and the other for its normal expression, are called the P_1 generation (first parental). Their offspring are the F_1 (first filial) generation, and *their* offspring, the F_2 generation.

▶ Review Mendel's original experiments described in your text. Note how he initiated the procedure of testing hereditary concepts by using selected *individual* traits and parents previously bred out and tested as pure for the expression of these traits. Then observe how he simplified the results by formulating ratios, and from these derived an hypothesis. Using his hypothesis, Mendel predicted the outcome of a different cross, then tested it by making the cross and comparing ratios actually found with those he had predicted. Ultimately, he derived his famous 2 postulates: (1) *nonmixing of alleles* (which established the concept of discrete hereditary units or *genes*) and (2) *random reassortment of alleles* (which later were applied to the statistically random separation of *chromosomes* at meiosis and recombination at fertilization).

▶ What would you say were the most important contributions and truly novel aspects of Mendel's approach?

▶ How does his work illustrate the scientific method?

B. Procedures in *Drosophila* Genetics

Stock cultures of various mutant strains as well as normal wild-type *Drosophila* are maintained in cotton-plugged milk bottles or smaller shell vials. These contain agar medium with an appropriate nutrient base and added yeast. Larval flies, or maggots, feed on bacteria growing in the yeast. Later the larvae pupate and emerge as adult flies. The total life cycle takes about 2 weeks, depending on temperature.

Crosses are made by placing a male and a previously unmated female in a freshly prepared culture bottle, which is labeled and stored until eggs are laid (usually on paper toweling in the bottle). The parents are later removed and, after emergence, the F_1 adults are removed, etherized, and examined individually under a dissecting microscope for the trait being studied. Results are tallied and F_1 parents selected for the next cross if another is needed. The resulting F_2 generation is similarly handled. Females for the F_1 cross must be freshly emerged from their pupal cases to ensure virginity and properly controlled experimental mating (or they are subjected to a brief period of high temperature to kill sperm from an earlier insemination).

In order to undertake these experiments, a few simple but essential techniques must be carefully learned. Your teaching assistant will demonstrate and explain the following procedures.

1—Opening and stoppering the culture bottles; "shaking the flies down."

2—Transfer of flies to an empty bottle and etherization (not too much ether if you expect to use the flies again).

3—Handling of flies with a fine brush; arranging them for ratio counts and microscopic examination on a glass plate.

Besides the mechanics of handling flies, labeling bottles, transferring, etherizing, and counting, you must know the following thoroughly.

1—The life cycle; appearance of larvae at various growth stages; difference between pupae and empty pupal cases; sex of adults (distinguished at a glance).

2—Difference between newly emerged and older adults for selection of virgin females.

3—Appearance of normal and mutant traits.

4—Methods of collecting and listing data, statistical procedures, determination of experimental results, and calculation of predicted results.

C. Study of Flies

1—Study a living example of each stage of the *Drosophila* life cycle under low power.

a. *egg.* Note size, shape, 2 posterior projections.
b. *larva.* Note segmentation, means of locomotion, black chitinous jaws on head, and respiratory spiracles posteriorly.

c. *pupa.* Observe pigmented *puparium* (pupal case from preceding larval molt) containing metamorphosing last stage larva; locate eyes, folded wings, legs, and anterior, hornlike spiracles; observe empty pupal case.
d. *adult.* Draw a dorsal view of *each* sex, showing major external structures.

2—Observe culture bottles containing flies at different stages of development. Progressive changes in the medium and markings on the glass made by the crawling larvae help indicate the phases of life cycle present.

3—Obtain a fly culture for practice in etherizing and handling flies.

4—Examine microscopically as many examples of mutant stocks as are available.

▶ How many progeny can a single pair of normal *Drosophila* produce?
▶ Where is *Drosophila* found in nature?
▶ Are mutant types commonly found in nature? If not, why not?

D. Genetics Experiments

1—**Monohybrid or 1-factor cross** (illustrating which law of Mendel?).

a. **Autosomal mutation.** You will be given a culture of flies showing an autosomal mutation (mutation on a chromosome *other* than the X or Y sex chromosomes) and another bottle of flies with normal expression of this trait.

1. Study examples of your flies to identify the mutation clearly so as to distinguish it from the normal expression of this gene.
2. In a culture bottle with fresh medium, place a virgin mutant female and normal male.
3. In a second bottle, make the *reciprocal* cross (virgin normal ♀ × mutant ♂).
4. Label each bottle with your name and date and show the proper symbols for the cross and generation.
5. Remove and destroy P_1 flies from each bottle after 5 to 7 days to ensure sufficient time for egg laying.
6. When adults start to emerge in each bottle, select a freshly emerged female and a male for your F_1 cross. As you are running 2 experiments concurrently, keep the data for each separate.

▶ Must a virgin female F_1 parent be used?
▶ Why can you select parents at random in both your experiments?

Prepare your F_1 crosses as you did the P_1, using a properly labeled new culture bottle or tube for each. Remove and destroy F_1 parents after 5 to 7 days.

7. Collect remaining adult F_1 progeny as they appear over the course of several more days. Etherize and examine them, separate into appropriate *classes* (male, female, mutant, normal), and count members of each class.

Record your results on a data sheet in tabular form, showing all classes of progeny, and both *observed* and *predicted* ratios of these classes. The predicted ratio is to be calculated or determined from the hypothesis of mode of inheritance that you are testing.

8. Repeat the steps of number 7 above for the progeny of your F_1 crosses (F_2). Keep results of the original reciprocal crosses separate so they can be compared later.

Large samples are important for these counts, so collect as many F_2 as time allows (but do not allow time for F_3 to emerge).

▶ Why are large samples necessary?

9. Calculate results and summarize data for each experiment. Compare observed with predicted results.

▶ Are the differences statistically valid?

▶ What differences can you detect between the reciprocal crosses?

▶ What conclusion do you draw from this?

10. Prepare a report summarizing both your experiments including *objectives, methods, data* and *observations, results,* and *conclusions.* Include the proper notation to represent the crosses and their products.

Discuss briefly the genetic significance of the difference between mutations arising in *autosomal* and *sex chromosomes.*

2—Sex-linked monohybrid cross—Repeat the procedures described above with a *sex-linked* mutation (one located on the X or sex chromosome). White-eye in *Drosophila* is a widely used example and one used to establish some of the basic premises of the gene theory.

Be sure to make reciprocal crosses as you did in the autosomal experiment. Prepare a report on your sex-linked crosses. Include the hypothesis you are testing and a statistical comparison between ratios expected and ratios found. Divide your report, as you did the previous one, into *objectives, method, data* (tabulated counts and necessary calculations), *observations, results,* and *conclusions.*

In your conclusions include answers to the questions below and account for experimental discrepancies from predicted results. It may be of interest to add to your data those of other student teams to increase your statistical sample.

▶ Will enlargement of your sample enhance the validity of your results?

▶ How do results of your reciprocal sex-linked crosses compare?

▶ How do the sex-linked and autosomal results compare?

▶ How do you explain the differences observed?

▶ What general principle is illustrated by these crosses?

▶ What principle is demonstrated by a cross involving 2 distinct mutations (a *dihybrid* cross)?

▶ Why would Mendel's postulates be difficult to discern if 3 different mutations (a *trihybrid* cross) were used? Observe how this points up the significance of Mendel's use of the simplest possible cases, the 1- and 2-factor crosses.

▶ How would you be able to explain the results of a tri- and a multiple-factor cross?

Similarly illuminating experiments can be performed using other material such as corn seedlings, bacterial cultures, bacterial viruses, or mice.

The relevance and importance of genetic principles are confirmed by their universality of application.

NOTES AND DRAWINGS

(Tear along line)

Appendix

A. Student Equipment

It is recommended that each student provide the following materials unless otherwise directed by the instructor.

Laboratory notebook
Drawing paper
Drawing pencil (4H)
Sandpaper pad for sharpening pencil
Eraser, soft rubber
Ruler, celluloid, millimeters-inches (6 inches long)
Set of dissecting instruments:
  Scalpel
  Scissors, straight, medium point
  Scissors, heavy
  Forceps, straight, milled tip (5 inches long)
  Forceps, curved, milled tips, about 5 inches long
  Dissecting needles, in handles
  Probe
  Medicine droppers (pipette)
  Instrument case
Safety razor blades
Microscope slides, glass
Microscope coverglasses, No. 1 (22 mm), square or circular
Package of ordinary pins

B. Reference Tables

Equivalent values are all shown on one horizontal line (for example, 0.305 m = 304.8 mm = 12. in. = 1. ft = 0.333 yd). Standard abbreviations are shown in parentheses.

Linear Measure

METRIC				UNITED STATES AND BRITISH			
Kilometers (km)	Meters (m)	Millimeters (mm)	Microns (μ)	Inches (in)	Feet (ft)	Yards (yd)	Miles (mi)
1.	1000.				3280.8	1093.6	0.621
	1.	1000.		39.37	3.281	1.093	
	0.001	1.	1000.	0.039			
	0.025	25.4		1.	0.082		
	0.305	304.8		12.	1.	0.333	
	0.914	914.4		36.	3.	1.	
1.61	1609.3				5280.	1760.	1.

Fluid Measure

METRIC		U.S. STANDARD			
Liters (l)	Milliliters or cubic centimeters (ml or cc)	Fluid drams (fl dr)	Fluid ounces (fl oz)	Quarts (qt)	Gallons (gal)
1.	1000.	270.5	33.8	1.056	0.264
0.001	1.	0.271	0.034		
0.004	3.69	1. (60 minims)	0.125		0.001
0.029	29.6	8.	1.	0.0625	0.008
0.946	946.3	256.	32.	1. (2 pints)	0.25
3.78	3785.3	1024.	128.	4.	1. (231 cu in.)

Weight

METRIC			AVOIRDUPOIS		
Kilograms (kg)	Grams (g)	Milligrams (mg)	Grains (gr)	Ounces (oz)	Pounds (lb)
1.	1000.		15,432.	35.27	2.204
0.001	1.	1000.	15.43	0.35	
	0.001	1.	0.015		
	0.065	65.	1.		
0.028	28.35		437.5	1.[a]	0.062
0.453	453.6		7,000.	16.	1.

[a] Apothecary or troy ounce = 31.103 grams = 480 grains.

Temperature

Temperature conversion scale. To convert centigrade (°C) to Fahrenheit (°F), multiply °C by 1.8 and add 32; hence, for 10°C, 10 × 1.8 + 32 = 50°F. To convert °F to °C, subtract 32 and multiply by 0.55.

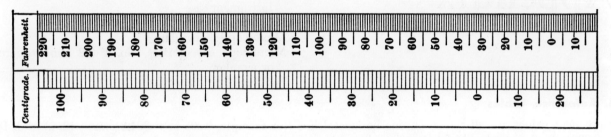

C. Formulas

Formulas are reduced to a final volume of 100 ml. All weights are given in grams (g), and volumes in milliliters (ml = cc).

1. Acetic acid

Glacial acetic acid	10	ml
Distilled water	90	ml

2. Acetocarmine

Glacial acetic acid	45	ml
Distilled water	55	ml

Bring water to boil, adding powdered carmine until no more will dissolve; filter; use cold. Should be prepared under hood to avoid inhaling of fumes.

3. Acid fuchsin

Acid fuchsin	0.5	g
Distilled water	100.	ml

4. Alcohol

Laboratory ethyl alcohol or ethanol (C_2H_5OH) is a 95% solution in water. Stock alcohol contains about 5% water; therefore, approximate dilutions can be made by using as many milliliters of 95% alcohol as the final percentage strength of the solution required and adding a sufficient volume of distilled water to make a total of 100 ml. For example, to prepare a 45% solution, use 45 ml of (95%) alcohol and 55 ml of water, etc.

5. Benedict's solution

Solution A:

Sodium citrate, $Na_3C_6H_5O_7$, $11H_2O$	17.3	g
Sodium carbonate, $NaCO_3$, anhydrous	10.0	g
Distilled water, to make	85.0	ml

Chemicals should be dissolved in 50 ml of water heated to approximately 60°C; cool, filter, and make up to volume (85 ml).

Solution B:

Copper sulfate, $CuSO_4$, $5H_2O$	1.73	g
Distilled water, to make	15.00	ml

Add A to B slowly, with constant stirring. This solution keeps well. It yields a green, yellow, or red precipitate (cuprous oxide) when heated with solutions containing reducing sugars. The color depends on the amount of sugar present.

6. Bouin's fixative

Picric acid, saturated aqueous solution (about 1 g will dissolve)	71.5	ml
Formalin, 40%	38.0	ml
Glacial acetic acid	4.7	ml

After fixation, wash in ethyl alcohol, 45% or stronger, until the yellow color disappears.

7. *Congo red stain*

Congo red	0.5	g
Distilled water	100.0	ml

8. *Copper sulfate solution*

Copper sulfate, $CuSO_4$	5.0	g
Distilled water	100.0	ml

9. *Embalming fluid for mammals*

Formalin, 40%	1.5	ml
Carbolic acid, melted crystals	2.5	g
Glycerin	10.0	ml
Water	86.0	ml

10. *Fehling's solution*

Solution A

Copper sulfate, $CuSO_4$	7.0	g
Distilled water	100.0	ml

Solution B

Sodium hydroxide, NaOH	52.0	g
Potassium sodium tartrate, $KNaC_4H_4O_6$	34.6	g
Distilled water	100.0	ml

Shortly before using, mix equal volumes of Solutions A and B. Heating this with an equal volume of a solution containing a reducing sugar yields a brick-red precipitate (cuprous oxide).

11. *10% Formalin solution* (for preserving material)

Strong formalin (40% form-aldehyde gas in water)	10	ml
Water	90	ml

Use for fixing entire specimens. Solution will decalcify invertebrates with calcium carbonate skeletons, crustaceans, and skeletons of small vertebrates. Depending on size, specimens are fixed from a few days to several weeks in formalin. Be sure to have at least 10 times as much fluid as bulk of specimen; then wash out in running tap water for at least one day. Preserve specimen in 70% alcohol.

12. *Glassware cleaning fluid*

Potassium bichromate, $K_2Cr_2O_7$, technical grade	11	g
Water	50	ml
Sulfuric acid, H_2SO_4	50	ml

Heat water to dissolve bichromate, cool, then add acid cautiously.

13. *Glycerine-carmine*

Carmine	1	g
Ammonia, NH_4OH	1	ml
Sodium chloride, NaCl	1	g
Glycerin	50	ml
Distilled water	49	ml

Dissolve carmine in ammonia by adding a little water. Dissolve NaCl in glycerin, mix in above, and add water.

14. *India ink* (for *Paramecium*)

Rub solid ink stick (used for photographic retouching) in a small volume of water to obtain a black suspension. Fluid India inks contain chemicals toxic to protozoans and therefore should not be used.

15. *Iodine-KI solution* (for starch test)

Potassium iodide, KI	0.7	g
Iodine, I_2, crystals	1.0	g
Distilled water	100.	ml

16. *Iodine solution* (for staining flagella of Spermatozoa, *Euglena*, etc.)

Prepare a strong solution of iodine crystals in 50% ethyl alcohol. Each case must be tested separately, varying the strength as necessary.

17. *Locke's solution* (physiological salt solution for mammalian tissues)

Sodium chloride, NaCl	0.900	g
Potassium chloride, KCl	0.042	g
Calcium chloride, CaCl	0.025	g
Sodium bicarbonate, $NaHCO_3$	0.020	g
Distilled water	100.	ml

Add 0.1 to 0.25 g glucose if tissue is to be kept for extended periods.

18. *Lugol's solution*

Potassium iodide, KI	10	g
Distilled water	10	ml
Iodine, I_2, crystals	1	g
Alcohol, ethyl, 95%	90	ml

19. *Methyl cellulose solution* (for slowing protozoans)

Methyl cellulose	10	g
Distilled water	90 to 100	ml

To 50 ml of boiling water add methyl cellulose and allow it to soak and stand for 45 minutes; add remaining water and stir until smooth. For use, a ring of the solution on microslide should be made. Place a drop of culture in center, add cover slip. As protozoans swim outward, they are slowed by the increasing viscosity.

20. *Methyl green*

Methyl green	1	g
Distilled water	100	ml
Glacial acetic acid	5	drops

21. *Methyl violet*

Methyl violet	0.05	g
Glacial acetic acid	0.20	ml
Distilled water	100.	ml

22. *Methylene blue solution*

Methylene blue	5.0	g
Distilled water	100.	ml

23. *Picro-acetic acid*

Glacial acetic acid	1	ml
Distilled water	99	ml

To above mixture add an excess of crystalline picric acid in order to obtain a saturated solution.

24. *Picro-carmine*

Ammonium hydroxide, NH_4OH	5	ml
Distilled water	50	ml
Carmine	1	g
Picric acid, saturated aqueous solution	50	ml

25. *Ringer's solution* (isotonic for frog tissues)

Sodium chloride, NaCl	0.650	g
Potassium chloride, KCl	0.014	g
Calcium chloride, $CaCl_2$, anhydrous	0.012	g
Sodium bicarbonate, $NaHCO_3$	0.020	g
Distilled water, to make	100.	ml

26. *Ringer's modified solution* (for amphibian tissues, Holtfreter's solution)

Sodium chloride, NaCl	0.350	g
Potassium chloride, KCl	0.005	g
Calcium chloride, $CaCl_2$	0.010	g
Sodium bicarbonate, $NaHCO_3$	0.020	g
Distilled water, to make	100.	ml

27. *Safranin stain*

Safranin	1	g
Anilin water	90	ml
Alcohol, ethyl, 95%	10	ml

Anilin water can be prepared by shaking 4 ml of anilin in 90 ml of distilled water and then filtering.

28. *Saline solution* (isotonic for frog tissues)

Sodium chloride, NaCl	0.7	g
Distilled water	100.	ml

29. *Saline solution* (isotonic for mammalian tissues)

Sodium chloride, NaCl	0.9	g
Distilled water	100.	ml

30. *Sudan IV* (Scharlach R) *solution*

Sudan IV	0.1	g
Ethyl alcohol, 95%	50.	ml
Acetone	50.	ml

Index